The Legend of the Eagle Clan

A Wake-up Call
by Cathleen M. Cramer
with Darren A. Robb

Acknowledgments

We would like to give special thanks to June Rouse, who helped with the initial editing; Pam Robb who helped with the computer programming; Larian, our cover artist; Danna Bradford, the back cover photographer; and so many others — too many to list — who gave their heartfelt support and encouragement

P.O. Box 1526
Sedona, Arizona 86339

ISBN 0-929385-68-3

Cover Art by Larian

Printed in the United States of America by

MI$$ION PO$$IBLE
Commercial Printing

Preface

As I sat on my bed talking on the phone to Derren, my co-writer, the energy changed within the room. Suddenly the Native American drum that I had designed and ceremoniously dedicated to the calling back of my People let out a loud bang.

Startled, I looked up to see a twelve-foot-tall being before me. He was magnificent! His skin was a golden bronze, his body was perfection. He wore only a loincloth. One hand held a scepter with an eternal flame upon it. One hand held a sphere.

His head had no hair but rather rays of different colors pouring straight out from his head. At that moment I realized how the Indian war bonnets had come about. The ancient Indians had tried to recreate that picture.

"Derren," I yelled hoarsely, "there is somebody in my room. He's incredible . . . ."

Derren, a gifted channel, said, "He has come to take you on a journey. This is only for you now – I have to go." Click.

As I continued to look at this perfected man, the rays of light about his head began to fold downward and become feathers. His arms stretched out, and he became an eagle!

I could hardly breathe. In my head I could hear, "You and I are one. We cannot be separated." A dove flew out of my wildly pounding chest into the eagle's chest, becoming its heart. The heart of the eagle was the dove.

With my heart pounding in the chest of the eagle, we flew out into the cosmos. During the journey we flew past a vast fleet of intergalactic star vessels. Each vessel was unique in size and shape. Some vessels were larger than planets. In my head I heard, "You see, we cannot lose. We have all of these vessels at our command, and many more throughout the universe that we can summon. We are only waiting for the proper time."

We flew past many solar systems, heading toward the Great Central Sun. The eagle began to transform; it changed into a condor, still carrying the heart of the dove.

We began to fly faster, systems whizzing past us, the Sun becoming closer. When it seemed we were at warp speed, the feathers upon the bird became singed, and the bird began to resemble a plucked chicken with the heart of a dove.

The pace quickened even more as we were pulled toward the Light of the great Sun. The bird flew directly into its force field and became engulfed by flames, emerging as the phoenix. One hour of Earth time passed, but we had transcended time and traveled millions of light years.

The Incan prophecies say that now, in this age, when the eagle of the North and the condor of the South fly together, the Earth will awaken. Now it is happening — and I was witness to it.

I am a time-walker. I travel to the future as easily as I travel to the past. Everything is here, locked into time. You only have to know how to switch the channels and change your frequency, as I did in 1987 when I first met Derren.

"I don't know why," he said upon being introduced to me, "but do you feel that we have known each other before?"

"Of course," I said matter-of-factly.

Derren still stammered before me, "I don't know why, but I have to get you to Galena."

Several weeks later, a group of us went on a journey to Galena. We were invited to stay at the geodesic home of a woman named Susana. Derren had met her during the Harmonic Convergence in August of 1987. Something told me that I would know her, even though we had never met.

Upon our arrival, a petite woman in her golden years opened the door, took one look at me and softly said, "Oh, I feel as if I know you."

I acknowledged the same to her, not yet knowing quite what it was fully about.

"Let's take a walk on the grounds," Derren said. "I'll show you the lake. There's a thumb of land with a beautiful view that juts out high above the lake. It's through that grove of trees."

It was a cool November day. The sky was gray and overcast. There were leaves on the ground crunching beneath our feet.

It was so familiar here. "That lake, it used to be a stream. They must have dammed it up to create the lake. This didn't use to be a lake." The words just flowed from my mouth without my thinking them.

"Yes, you are right. I seemed to know that too," he said as he looked at me somewhat surprised.

As we stood upon the thumb of land that hung over the lake, I said with certainty, "There are caves under here. You can't see them now because when they dammed up the stream, the water covered up the cave entrance."

"Yes, yes," he confirmed. "When I was here before, I felt that then too. How did you know that?"

Walking a few paces back from the edge, I said, "There's a sacred temple under this ground."

"You see that too? I thought I was the only one who could see it."

Puzzled, I said, "Derren, do you see tepees on that hill?"

"Yes, yes," he stammered and looked at me in bewilderment. "The chief lives there. There should be a medicine wheel down the hill, over to the left."

We continued to walk back toward the house. The day became warm. The grass was thick and wet with morning dew. Reflections of the sun glimmered off the leaves of the trees. My feet felt as though I were wearing moccasins. I felt so young and at one with nature. Spring was in the air, even though it was now November.

I heard hoofs behind me. As I turned, I saw a handsome young brave riding bareback on his paint pony. The horse had a black mane and tail and brown spots. There was a corded bit tied through the pony's mouth. The brave's black hair was loose, long and blowing. He wore only a loincloth, revealing a lean, well-muscled body.

My heart began to beat so wildly that I could hardly catch my breath, as the brave reined in his snorting, stomping pony to a side-stepping stop before me.

He put out his left foot and said, "Woman, get on my horse."

I dropped my water bucket, which I suddenly seemed to be carrying, put my left foot on top of his and put out my hand to be pulled up to the back of his mount. My buckskin dress hiked up over my knees as I strode up onto the horse.

I buried my head into his back and held on tight, feeling his heart beating as wildly as my own. Words cannot express the love I felt. My hormones were out of control. I loved this young brave with every breath I took. We rode the pony's strides as one in unison with its movement and beats, heading out of the village toward Eagle Ridge.

Suddenly my heart skipped a beat, and I found myself standing next to Derren, on a rainy day, too embarrassed to speak of what I had just encountered. Within a moment I had travelled back one hundred forty-four years and was living it as though it were now.

Derren was that brave. I was that maiden. Susana's house was home again, as she had been the young maiden's mother. Through the years that have followed I have met others from that village, many of whom share the same memories.

The time is now to retell the story of the Eagle Clan, to trigger the memories of others who share the same vision and destiny. The Eagle Clan is the same soul group that is referred to as the Anasazi, the ancient ones. Some of the ancient ones remained in spirit to guard the sacred spots and the hidden artifacts. Others of that soul group have incarnated one last time to help bring about the completion of the Medicine Wheel, for we are the ancient Medicine Wheel People.

This book is directed to the ones who need to remember who they are. This is the final gathering of the ancient ones, the return of the Eagle Clan!

CHAPTER 1

Dancing Eagle stood before the Raven, trying to control his rage. As she defiantly faced him, held fast by Tall Trees and Standing Bear, she taunted him to release her spirit.

Tall Trees stood behind her, pulling her head back by the hair, forcing her to look at Dancing Eagle. She turned her face to the left and only squinted out of one eye. The reflection of the moon was directly upon her.

The Raven tried to struggle out of the intense grips of Tall Trees and Standing Bear as each held one of her arms. Dust rose at their feet as if death were doing a dance.

Dancing Eagle took a deep breath and looked up into the night sky. Dark clouds began to swallow up a portion of the full moon. A crow cawed loudly into the night, rapidly joined by others in the trees. An owl hooted in the distance. He took all of these as warnings reminding him of his father's words: "If you kill the Raven, a curse will befall our tribe. All will perish if she dies."

Dancing Eagle stood lean and sinewy. Wearing only buckskin leggings, a breechcloth, a red arm band and two eagle feathers bound by a leather headband, his presence was a powerful force. Nature had molded him well. His piercing eyes flashed as he shook his head. His arms rose into the air as he yelled out to the spirit of his father, Tomosh, "Why did you have to bring this evil spirit into our tribe? With your greed for power you have brought a dark cloud to our village!" His words faded with the misty breath coming from his trembling lips.

Tomosh had been chief of the Eagle tribe and craved power. Through a vision he was told to go to the highest point of land in the corner of three states, where the eagle would fly. While the Eagle tribe journeyed south to the sacred land the white man called Galena, Illinois, Tomosh stole a powerful shaman's daughter. She was from the Raven Clan. Schalute, the brother of Tomosh, named her the Raven. He felt she carried the medicine of a trickster.

Tomosh waited for her to grow. When she came into her moon cycle, he took her as a wife. He told the villagers she would bring power and protection to the village because other tribes were afraid of her medicine.

Schalute knew better. "Tomosh," he pleaded, "upon your death, she shall bring death to our village. She is a moon child. We are to be gifted with a Sun child soon. Her birth is written on the great wall. I have been shown this in my visions. You must get rid of her now. She will be trouble."

Tomosh had always been jealous of Schalute, his gifted brother. Tomosh would not listen to his words. The prophet's daughter would bring him power . . . he thought.

The years passed. The Raven never produced a child for Tomosh. Tomosh eventually took another wife, Runta. He felt he needed sons to pass on his leadership. She blessed him with two sons. The first-born was Red Hawk, then came Dancing Eagle.

Even though Tomosh was a great leader and a powerful chief, he was not born with the spirit of prophecy. He believed that anyone within the power circle of a prophet could not be killed. He believed that with his marriage to a prophet's daughter, he could fight a great battle, score many a coup and be known as a great one. With his false sense of security he went to the Black Hawk War with many of the braves from the village, never to return. Red Hawk assumed the position of chief, and the Raven shared his lodge.

The Raven stood before him, struggling. Dancing Eagle walked closer to her and grabbed her by the chin. Through clenched teeth he said, "Woman, I shall cut off your hair and mark you for life if you do not tell me where Morning Glory is. After that, I'll tie you up and send you down the river. You will be an outcast of every tribe for the rest of your life." He looked into her face and screamed, "Where is she!"

Now Dancing Eagle stood before her haunting face, not knowing quite what to do with this woman who had vengefully ruined his life.

❋ ❋ ❋

Dancing Eagle had only recently experienced the happiest moments of his life. He had waited twelve years for the blue-eyed princess, the Glory of the Morning, to reach her moon cycle and become his bride. His friends used to say that she had walked in his soul since the day she came to the village.

His uncle Schalute had foretold of the blue-eyed princess from the Sun who would one day come to their village. "She will be sired from spirit!" Schalute exclaimed. He pounded his fist to his chest. "It is I who have been chosen as protector."

The Raven always felt that she would have been princess in her own tribe had she not been kidnapped. She was, after all, daughter of a prophet. She grew to hate the blue-eyed one long before she arrived at the village. Schalute knew she could control the animals and the elements. He did not take her power for granted.

Dancing Eagle remembered how the tribe had prepared a medicine wheel in the middle of the village. Each day the medicine men and medicine women would pray and wait for the arrival of the promised one.

Schalute had two wives, Rising Sun and Spring Flower. He was very proud that they were both carrying a child of his seed. Rising Sun gave birth to his first-born, a son, by the river. The moon reflected into the river, creating the effect of two moons. The boy was named Two Moons.

Running Elk, the medicine man, held the child up and said, "As I have the eye, this boy also has the eye. He is a special one!"

Schalute was proud but a little restless. He now had a son but he was anxiously awaiting the promised one. Three moons later, Spring Flower gave birth to a child without spirit. It chose not to stay.

Schalute was devastated and left the village to pray. He was confused. "What happened to the promised one?" he pleaded into the night sky.

Throughout the night he stood straight upon the highest hill, arms out to his sides, dressed in buckskin against the dampness, chanting to the Great Spirit to give him understanding. His words boomed through the hills and echoed off the valley walls. This night was cloudless. The stars appeared so close, he felt he could pluck one from the sky, as though they were dancing in front of him for that purpose.

His eyes widened as a blazing blue star shot across the sky. He knew it to be a sign, but of what? The spirits held a secret. He knew the morning to come would bring the answer.

Schalute returned to a bustling, excited village. As he rode over the hill leading to his village, fifty tepees came into view. The morning sun had not yet warmed the air. His people were whispering to each other as he rode his appaloosa pony straight to the middle of the village where the council lodge stood. He tried to pick up their words as his horse began to strut and toss its head, feeling excitement in the air.

Schalute swung his right leg across the top of his horse and jumped promptly to the ground, handing his reins to the first brave he saw. Schalute walked, as usual, with the power of a bear. His long hair flowed loosely in the wind. His presence was one of confidence and mystique. He was an honored and powerful shaman.

"The sky child has come to our village!" Running Elk proudly announced to Schalute, shuffling toward him. Running Elk's weathered face and cloudy eyes had never shown so much emotion before.

With a toothless smile and a crackling voice the old man continued, "Her smile is of the sun. Her eyes are blue as our water, with the look of purity for our land. I saw her name in the starlight. Moon shadows play with her blue-black hair. She will help our people and care for all our needs in a time of plight. She has finally come!"

"How did she come to our village?" Schalute asked the old one.

"Spring Flower, Runta and Rising Sun went to the river to wash this morn. A cry was heard near the sacred cave. They thought it was the spirit of the one who left your wife's womb. When they walked down the embankment, there was a canoe with a basket in it. In the basket was a blue-eyed child with the marking of a star on her left leg."

Running Elk was running out of breath. He was not accustomed to talking so fast but he knew he must because Schalute was growing impatient.

Spring Flower walked forward with a bundle in her arms. She was a delicate woman, taller and thinner than the rest of the women in the village. Her fringed buckskin dress was beaded about the shoulders. The braids in her hair framed her delicate face. Tears rolled from her eyes as she started to explain to Schalute and the gathering crowd the rest of the story.

"My husband," Spring Flower announced. "As I approached the

canoe fretfully, thinking that I heard the spirit of our lost child, I pulled away the blanket that covered the little one's face. Her hands shot to the air in fright. She blinked her tearful eyes open and her eyes shot to my soul. She took my breath away. In a pouch around her neck was a blue stone." Spring Flower handed it to Schalute with one hand as she embraced the child with the other against her bosom.

"Go on, woman," Schalute demanded impatiently. "Do not stop now."

"My husband," Spring Flower had to regain her composure and find the words, "there was something else. It was wrapped separately and lying in the basket next to the child."

Spring Flower motioned for Rising Sun to come forward with the package. Schalute spread the soft leather wrappings open and stood back in wonderment. Then the villagers gasped as he picked up the object and held it high.

It was a crown – one such as they had never seen before. It had feathers of different hues slanting backwards; each side, made of a metal that they had never seen before, would come down the sides of the face and forward toward the jaw line. Many colored jewels were embedded into the brow band which would come down over the forehead, dipping between the eyes to the bridge of the nose.

Schalute's hands started to shake with the power of it. He knew it would have to be hidden in the sacred cave until the child was of age to wear it.

"Schalute," Spring Flower continued, "this child started to cry, seemingly in hunger. A loud booming voice in my head clearly said, 'Feed my people with the power and the seed of my being!' Chills ran up my spine. Instinctively I put the babe to my breast. It was clear to me that was why my body had been prepared to feed a child. I am honored."

Schalute took the child from Spring Flower and held her high to the sun. As he circled around, the babe's eyes caught upon Dancing Eagle's eyes and locked.

Schalute saw that they walked in each other's souls. He smiled at Dancing Eagle, who had already seen nine winter snows, and said, "She shall be called the Glory of the Morning, as all good comes in the morning. She is the glory of our tribe."

From the day she arrived she was a part of Dancing Eagle's life. Schalute was a shaman and Dancing Eagle had been born with special gifts. Schalute was his uncle; therefore it had been proper, from the very beginning, for Schalute to take him under his wing and teach him the ways of a shaman. Schalute took Morning Glory with him often, teaching her as well as Dancing Eagle. The two children grew together and knew each other's ways. Morning Glory also had the gift of sight, so what Dancing Eagle could see, Morning Glory could also see.

Dancing Eagle was more comfortable with her than with anybody else in his life. He was wild, angry, impulsive and restless. She was in harmony and at peace. She could say more with her eyes than any man could say with his mouth. Morning Glory was the only one who could bring peace to his angry soul. She honored him with her endless love. Her touch took away his pain.

Now she was gone. The Raven was responsible. Dancing Eagle knew she had conspired with the white traders. Within days of Morning Glory's disappearance, the Raven had given birth to a male child who was obviously sired by a white man. Red Hawk banished her to live with the outcasts over the hill. She became bitter and vengeful. She always painted her face death-white with a red smile. She wore death upon her face to show that she was now dead and would never smile again.

The Raven laughed a hideous laugh and said, "I didn't want to come here. I didn't want to wear the braids of your tribe in my hair, as your women do. I didn't want to wear the skins of the doe. My people are from a northern place where it always snows. I was forced to come here, as your woman was forced to go. As I was to have been princess and was stolen from those I loved, so was she. The sins of your father are upon you."

Then Dancing Eagle dropped his hand from her chin and paced around. He whirled to face her. His voice again rose to a scream. "She never did anything to you, Raven," Dancing Eagle whispered hoarsely, enraged. "Why do you hate her so? And my brother, Red Hawk — it was you who had Red Hawk killed. Why him? He protected you after Tomosh was killed."

"Red Hawk! Red Hawk promised me for years that when he was chief he would return me to my people. He never did. He just let me rot with the outcasts. Is it my fault that a wolf spooked his horse when he foolishly rode instead of walking over the top of that slippery waterfall? You two were in such a hurry to find your precious Morning Glory. You were careless!"

Dancing Eagle spun around to face her again. "Nobody knew

about the wolf except me. I was the only one with him. You sent that wolf after us. I knew it was you. I should kill you for that. You killed my brother. Our chief."

An owl hooted into the wind. The wolves howled to the moon. The Raven laughed. "You fool! It was Morning Glory's sisters who helped me arrange for her kidnapping. Red Hawk's power was threatened by her presence. He thought the child I carried would be the next chief until he realized it was the son of a white man. I wasn't sure if the child would be the white's or Red Hawk's until I saw the face and skin of the child. I could not retain my position. And her sisters wanted to be princess. Everybody wanted something. Everybody was happier without her, except you. You always ignored me, treated me poorly, acted as if I were a fool. You did not treat me with respect."

Dancing Eagle's arms shot into the air and his hands clutched his hair. "You lie! My brother would not have taken from me the only one I had ever loved," he shouted hoarsely.

The night air was getting colder. The breath of each of them hung mistier on the air with every word. The animals in the woods became more animated with each shout. The coyotes yapped every time the Raven gave out a contemptuous laugh.

The Raven hissed, "Red Hawk was about to betray me. He became riddled with guilt when he realized how he had been used, but by then I had my revenge. He knew where she was. He was going to bring her back! He was going to betray me! No one betrays me and lives!"

Dancing Eagle started to lunge toward her, but then hung back for a moment, remembering Tomosh's warning. He lowered his knife, contemplating what to do. "If I kill her now, her evil spirit will stay among us, bringing death to our village," he said to the two braves holding her arms. "Our revenge would be as fleeting as the wind, forever whistling in our ears. To kill her would be to kill even more of the ones we love. She is the only one who can tell us where Morning Glory was taken."

"You know she will never tell you," hissed Tall Trees. "Kill her now. We will burn her body so her spirit cannot stay. She cannot be allowed to live. She already wears the face of death."

"No. I can only banish her from our village. Her evil spirit must leave this sacred place. Hold her tight while I brand her forehead with an X and a circle around it, so all will know she is an outcast. Then I will cut off her hair and send her down the river."

With burning contempt in his eyes, Dancing Eagle kneeled to put the knife into the fire for the branding.

The Raven suddenly twisted sideways, kicking Tall Trees in his manhood. Momentarily in pain, he weakened his grip on her arm. She snapped her arm free and lunged forward.

Dancing Eagle had taken his eyes off of her to heat the knife. When he heard the scuffle, he grabbed the knife and leaped to his feet – and suddenly found his knife in her chest.

Shock ran through him as he pulled the knife from her heaving chest, and he dropped it to the ground in horror. Frantically he reached for mud to put upon her wound, pressing to stop the bleeding. Her blood flowed like a stream upon the rocky ground. They all knew she was dying.

Dancing Eagle held her in his arms as she was stretched out upon the ground. He rubbed her hands, trying to bring life back. His heart began to pound like thunder. He knew this was bad medicine.

Through her painted face of death, with a hoarse whisper of a voice, she gave Dancing Eagle a final curse. "You will always mourn the Morning. You will find the shadow of death upon yourself but you shall not die. You will never find Glory in the Morning as long as you live. You will wish to die but you will be the last of your tribe to die!"

She gave out one last gurgled breath as her evil blood stained their sacred land. As her spirit left, fog rolled in across the valley as though hundreds of dark spirits were walking toward their land.

Dancing Eagle pulled away from this evil one, repulsed. She had just laid a curse upon him marked with blood. She was killed by his knife. The chill of the night became the chill of his soul.

CHAPTER 2

Morning Glory tried to open her swollen eyes. She felt her hair, wet from the cool morning dew on the grass. She could hear the stream rushing through the trees. Behind her eyelids she saw flickers of sunlight upon her brow, but every time she tried to move, she felt pain. Confused, she tried to put one hand to her face, but both came up at the same time. She was bound! She moved her feet. They too were bound!

Alarmed, she gasped, "What? Where?" Cramping, spasmodic pain racked through her midsection. Her hands clutched at her stomach as she tried to turn to her side, moaning. She tried to catch her breath. Her heart was pounding in fear, pain and confusion.

"Dancing Eagle," she moaned, as she tried to move again. She could only open her eyes partially, the swelling was so great. To her side she could hear twigs cracking and footsteps. They were the footsteps of one wearing heavy boots, not moccasins.

She jumped as she felt a cold, wet cloth being put upon her face.

"There now, lassie. That should help bring the swelling down. Sorry I had to do that but you put up such a fight, you gave me no choice."

Morning Glory whirled around onto her back to face this voice. She did not know his words. What was he saying? She could only understand his eyes. They were cold, cruel, and he was laughing. Pain again shot through her midsection. She sat up, seeing blood upon the ground where she lay. She was bleeding!

She clutched her belly and doubled over, trying to think, trying to clear her mind. Her baby – she was losing Dancing Eagle's baby. No. . . . This was to be the Son of the Sun. No. . . .

"Lassie, what is this?" The man sounded alarmed. "McVain, what have we here?"

"It appears she's having a baby, Tom. She just wedded that Dancing Eagle brave a few weeks back. You know these injuns pop them out like rabbits."

"Now what do we do?"

"Nothing," said McVain, spitting tobacco juice onto the ground. "Nature will take its course. We don't need no baby around anyways. Just another injun to feed. Might as well untie her and let her do her thing. From the looks of it, she can't go far."

Tom Shaye untied her and gave her a cup of coffee. Morning Glory eagerly took the cup. She was parched. She took a gulp and immediately spit it out. Poison! she thought. She never had anything taste like that.

Tom was shocked. "Suit yourself, lassie. Suit yourself."

Morning Glory crawled to the river's edge to wash her face and hands and get a drink of water. She looked at her soiled dress and splashed water over it, but she continued to stain it as she doubled over in pain. She was humiliated and frightened. No man had ever treated her like this before. She had always been treated with respect, with kindness by her father, brothers and husband. What kind of men were these?

Tom gave her a stick of jerky and offered her more of the black, bitter drink. She threw the cup down, letting the black liquid soil the dew-ridden ground. She pulled herself over to a tree and used it to support her back. She started to shake from the cold water and from fear and pain.

It was all starting to come back to her now, how she got to be here. The more she looked at the man called Tom, the more she remembered those eyes. He was the trader who kept coming to the village. He was the one who used to stare at her.

Now she could only stare back at him. He was quite tall. His skin was pale, like a stone. His hair was the color of straw. His eyes were cold and gray. He had a mustache. He wore buckskins that were fringed. Many weapons were at his side: a big rifle – no, two big rifles, a knife in his boot, a knife on his belt, a bow and arrows. She could not fight a man such as this. The other one, who constantly spat upon the sacred earth, was as armed as Tom was.

Morning Glory sat against the tree, holding back her pain, staring into the sky. It was turning gray. She closed her eyes as she relived the horror of the previous day.

"Morning Glory," Gentle Breeze had whispered into her lodge. "The berries are ripe for picking this morn. Grab your basket. We'll go down to the river to greet the sun, cleanse ourselves and have berries for breakfast."

Morning Glory had rolled over in her robes, already missing Dancing Eagle, and moaned, "Not now, Gentle Breeze. I do not feel very well. I don't think I can keep anything down. Besides, I had a bad dream. Dancing Eagle told me to stay in the village."

Gentle Breeze stood there with her hands on her hips. "We are only going down to the river," she said impatiently. Then, more gently, "If you get something in your belly, you will probably feel better. Besides, the berries are a good cleansing for you. We will take Ralla — that little wolf dog of yours won't let anything come your way. You know that he can knock a brave right off of his horse. No one can come near you with that dog around. You have to call him off even for Dancing Eagle."

Morning Glory sat up and said, "I guess you're right, little sister. I can't ever seem to turn down your frivolous requests. The berries will probably do me some good." Morning Glory threw back the coverings. "Come, Ralla."

Ralla whined nervously, circled about and paced. "Something is bothering him, Gentle Breeze. He senses something, I just know it."

"You heard Dancing Eagle yesterday. He said you must have been born in the night because you are always fearful. Were you?"

"Father said the moon passed before the sun the day I was born. Is that day or is that night?" Morning Glory pondered.

"Oh well, I guess Dancing Eagle was right," Morning Glory said to herself. "What could happen, if I stay close to the village?"

Morning Glory opened her eyes to stop her vision of the events of the morning and another spasm shot through her. She crawled over to the river to cleanse herself some more and to quench her thirst. Exhausted, she crawled back to the tree to support her back, trying to again relive what had happened to her yesterday, trying to regain a lost piece of her life. She closed her eyes and began to pick up fragments of her memory.

Gentle Breeze scampered about the woods, running from bush to bush, eating more than she put in her basket.

"Gentle Breeze, I want you to stay within sight of both me and the village. Do you hear me? Gentle Breeze, did you hear me?"

Morning Glory looked to the sky, as the dust of dawn had swept away. Suddenly she heard spooked horses running through the village. Indian braves were shouting and hooting!

"Huh, what is in the forest?" she breathed out loud. "What is not clear?"

Morning Glory looked up just in time to see a couple of men in buckskins coming up along the riverbank. Ralla took off like lightning toward the men and sailed through the air, right for Tom's throat. Tom's knife swiftly cut the dog's shoulder deeply. She could hear Ralla's yelp and saw the man throw her dog off to the side. She dropped her basket.

"Gentle Breeze!" she screamed in horror. "Where are you?"

She started running, not sure which way to go to find her sister. Her heart pounded like thunder.

A twig cracked behind her. Morning Glory never got a chance to look back. An arm swiftly came across her chest, binding her arms. Another hand covered her mouth. She struggled wildly, like she had never struggled before.

A hot breath whispered into her ear. "Don't make a sound or I will have to hurt you."

For a moment he relaxed his grip. She whirled around to see his cold eyes. A man Tom called Michael McVain came up beside him with a struggling Gentle Breeze. He had his hand over her mouth too but she managed to cow-kick his knee. For a moment he doubled over. As he loosened his grip on her mouth she bit him hard on the hand. He became enraged.

"You filthy little vermin," he seethed as he pulled out his knife and was about to cut out her tongue.

Morning Glory started to scream. Then darkness overtook her as she felt a merciless blow to her face.

Morning Glory groggily came to. She was being carried over this man's shoulder. Her midsection hurt unbearably as she bounced while he jogged. Off to the side she could see little Turtle Woman's brave father, Deer Slayer, with an arrow in his heart.

As Tom ran toward the river, where canoes had been waiting, the ground started to shake, the sky turned red and the river started to churn.

She struggled to free herself with all of her might but he was far too strong for her. Roughly, he bound her hands and gagged her mouth so tightly she could hardly swallow. The knot at the back of her head cut deeply into her skin.

During the night she woke up and found herself lying between these two men. She picked up a rock, ready to strike. Tom jumped up, grabbed her arm and struck her across the face. Darkness again overtook her.

Three days ago she had begged Dancing Eagle not to leave her. In her dreams she had seen a black bird come down and take her away. When she awoke, she found out that Schalute and Dancing Eagle were preparing to go on a hunt.

"Dancing Eagle, now is not the time for you to leave me," she pleaded. "The bird has told me so in my dream. I am scared!"

"Woman, I do what I have to do," Dancing Eagle replied. "I am not your father and I am not your brother."

He turned to see her in shock at being talked to this way. Dancing Eagle softened his words. "Stay close to the village. Your brother Two Moons will watch over you. You know he always does. The village is guarded. You will be all right."

The memory faded. Morning Glory tried not to show her pain to these strange men. She closed her eyes, hoping that when she again opened them, the dream would change. But nothing changed except that her pains intensified.

She started to tremble, as she had done when she saw Dancing Eagle and her father ride out of camp. She knew trouble was coming, but nobody listened to her.

Her father, Schalute, was the best tracker in the village. Dancing Eagle could see through the Eagle eye. Surely they would find her and bring her back to safety, she thought. By the time the dew dried from the spring grass, the men she loved the most would come over the horizon, she tried to convince herself.

When the sun stopped showing its shadow in the middle of the day, Dancing Eagle's baby had decided not to stay. The Eagle had taken it away.

Morning Glory fell limp into the grass, weak, too scared to dare another move. Her head was still reeling from the blows she had taken the night before.

She began to chant a mournful prayer to send her baby home.

"Stop that racket, do you hear? Stop it. I will not let you wail for all to hear. If you are strong enough to make that much noise, then you are strong enough to get on your feet. It's time to move."

Tom grabbed her by the arm and pulled her to her feet, shoving her ahead of him. As the sky started to show its last bit of red, before the sun hid behind the hills, Morning Glory sank to the earth. She could no longer go on.

"All right, lassie, we'll do it this way." He threw her over his shoulder and quickened his pace.

"We lost too much time yesterday. Can't stop now. I thought you squaws were tougher than this. But then, you are a thin one at that. Most are a little rounder than you are."

She still did not know what he was saying, only that she was beyond pain and fear. She was starting to become numb, fading in and out of the dream land.

At the end of the second day, they headed back toward the river. Tom and McVain helped themselves to a canoe banked near a small cabin and threw her in. At least she was off her feet. They headed south.

Morning Glory said nothing the entire time. These two men were skilled at handling a canoe and cut through the river at a rapid pace. She watched their every turn, into every grove of trees, hoping for a sign that her people had come for her.

Eagles flew overhead, hawks screamed in the trees, deer peeked through the brush, squirrels chattered loudly, but never did a familiar face show through.

Soon they will surprise us, she tried to comfort herself. They will be at the next bend. Dancing Eagle will be sitting upon his painted pony. Schalute will be astride his black stallion with his war bonnet. Lone Star will be among them. No one could out-fight Lone Star. They will be there for me.

Maybe it will be the next bend or beyond the next village. They were, after all, on a hunt. We probably had two days' lead, but they will find me at first light, she promised herself.

Each night her eyes barely closed, but neither did Tom's. He virtually slept with his eyes open, laughing every time she looked about for a rock to grab or a moment in which to slip away. He was too sharp. Never was he off-guard.

By the fourth night, Morning Glory dozed off. She could feel her body become heavy but then suddenly very light. She floated through the star-studded sky. She floated effortlessly right back to her village. How easy it was. She didn't have to worry. She was home, safe now.

She floated up to Two Moons. "Two Moons," she yelled with joy, "I'm back, Two Moons. Please hold me. Why didn't you come for me?"

CHAPTER 3

Two Moons woke up in the middle of the night. Sweat was pouring from his brow. He thought he heard Morning Glory's voice fade off into the cool night sky. He could feel her next to him but she was not in his lodge. He jumped from his robes and ran out into the night with a chill running up his spine. The pain he had felt in his midsection the past few days was nothing compared to the pain he was now feeling in his heart.

Two Moons had few friends in the village. The young braves of his age shunned him, saying he was not a great warrior or a great hunter, that he was more a spirit than a man.

As he stood in the night, only a small portion of the moon was left, reflecting enough light to pick out the glow of his long hair. He already had the silver of one much older than his twelve winters' time. His skin had the iridescence of the scales of a fish. His eyes changed to different hues.

He would disappear for days and weeks on end, never explaining himself to his father.

The only one who understood him was Morning Glory. Dancing Finger, the medicine man, would often say that Two Moons was the twin star of Morning Glory.

Morning Glory and Two Moons rarely conversed. They didn't have to. Each knew what the other was feeling and thinking. When one needed the other, the other was simply there. They would sit side by side, rarely talking, sometimes nodding their heads in a strange sort of answer to an unasked question, or simply a confirmation that only they knew. Two Moons always protected her, but more through spirit than through his physical being.

Two Moons remembered that for many seasons now his father,

Schalute, had talked before the council.

"The spirits of the old ones have talked to me," Schalute would boldly state. "The spirits have heard the cries of our brothers across the land, from the east, heading toward the setting sun. White man is coming in big canoes. I saw streets with trees of lights. I saw a great snake which makes much noise and smoke. It moved people across the land. We must move our people west," he pleaded.

Two Moons also would speak of his visions. He too saw the white man sweeping down upon them like a great vulture. The council would not budge.

The council would always talk and decide they were not to leave their sacred land.

"This land has openings to the other world. We must protect this land. We were guided here by our forefathers to protect this land. We cannot leave," the council would always conclude.

Traders from the Magnus Trading Company started to come to their small village. They were from St. Louis. Most of the men were trappers but some were interested in the iron ore that could be mined along the big muddy river.

Schalute did not like these men at all. Red Hawk would trade with them whenever they came to the village, but Schalute saw them in visions as a clear threat. He brought this matter before the council.

"I have seen these men in my visions. I do not trust them. They say they are here to trade but they are after more than that. They will dishonor our women. They will trick the unsuspecting few. They will change our people with their whiskey and their guns. If we trade for guns, we will have to pay them with our land in the same way our brothers, the Sacs, did."

Red Hawk was nervous. He came to their defense. "These white men bring us news of the other world. We must know of their ways to survive. They can bring us weapons to defend our people. If you are worried that they will bring us harm, then let the council decree that only the council members trade with them, and none other of the tribe."

"No!" shouted Schalute. "We do not need white men to tell us lies. The Eagle will keep us informed as to what to do. My visions are clear. The white man will delude us or betray our visions. The whiskey will make our braves go astray."

"I will forbid whiskey in our village," Red Hawk said, trying to defend his position.

The council concluded that Red Hawk could have his way. Two Moons knew that nothing would ever be the same once white man traded with the village. His visions showed him much trouble ahead. He knew his beloved Morning Glory would have to sacrifice much to protect her people and to protect this land. He could not stop her destiny, even though it would break his heart.

CHAPTER 4

The visions of Two Moons and Schalute had come to pass. Chief Red Hawk was dead. His tepee was painted blood red. Everything appeared as dead. The funeral procession carried him to the hill. The women cried for days. The dogs stayed still. The clouds didn't move in the sky. It was as if the Earth had died. Everybody wondered why.

The Raven was now dead, leaving a curse upon the land and upon Dancing Eagle. Red Hawk and the Raven took with them the knowledge of where their princess was held. Blue Dove took the Raven's son into their lodge. Schalute called him Black Wolf. He had the black hair and eyes of the Raven. He didn't want a child of the Raven's, but he would not kill a child, especially one born in his brother's lodge.

The song they sang that night at the campfire light was one of fear, one of hate. There was a giant shadow of death upon their faces. The eagle swooped and wouldn't come back. It circled the village once and bent a wing. It flew away and never would sing its tune again.

The council appointed Schalute as their next chief. Dancing Eagle would be next in line but was still young and not yet eager for the position.

Schalute rode out of the village. He ran into the woods on foot to be alone. He had to seek vision. He didn't know which way to go, where to look. The tracks were a maze. The arrows were Indian, but the tracks were of whites. The tracks came from different directions, intermingling with tracks from those of his tribe. Some tracks even looked as though they were from a young girl.

Upon the ridge of the eagle, Schalute fasted and prayed, looking for vision. For three days he sought vision, precious days in which his Morning Glory would be even farther away. It made him frantic, unfocused.

He could not understand how she had been stolen right out of the village. Where were the guards? What about her sisters and brothers? Where was everybody? How could the Creator allow this to happen to the promised one? Why?

Through the hateful words of the Raven, he now knew there was a power struggle with Red Hawk — Red Hawk, the nephew he had raised as his own son. Red Hawk sacrificed the promised one to try to find power for himself through the vengeful Raven. The Creator had taken care of that situation immediately.

How did Morning Glory get lured to the place where she would be abducted? Gentle Breeze was with her, wasn't she?

Schalute got up and paced wildly, letting out a roar into the hills. Gentle Breeze. . . . No, not his own daughter! How did she get involved with this? She was always a pouty one, always a jealous one, stomping around, trying to get attention. She was too young to be so calculating.

Schalute sat down again, calling to the Eagle to show him the truth. He closed his eyes and went into vision. Before him he could see a gentle breeze in the trees, and on a branch there landed a red hawk and a blue dove, side by side.

Blue Dove! Blue Dove had been spending an enormous amount of time with Red Hawk. She seemed to adore Red Hawk. In fact, he once had to remind her that they were cousins and her infatuation with her older cousin was inappropriate.

So that was it! Red Hawk had consulted with the traders and her sisters set it up to lure her out there. As the Raven had said, they would then be next in line to be princess.

Schalute sunk hopelessly to the ground. His own flesh and blood, seeds of his loins, had done this. Why? Was it because he gave most of his time and attention to Morning Glory? Didn't they understand that it was his duty to take care of this gift to their entire village?

Tears rolled from his eyes for the first time in his life. They were just children. They did not know what they had really done. He knew they would learn.

The village had been protected and led a fruitful life because the princess was watched over by the spirits. Now the spirits had to leave the village to follow the princess. The Eagle Tribe was now unprotected and cursed.

Morning Glory's own blood had turned on her out of jealousy and greed for power, the true curse of humankind. He didn't know if he could ever face his daughters again. His heart was split in two.

Again he prayed to the Eagle to become his eyes and show him where Morning Glory was. He had to find her. He had to bring her back to save the village. Very few truly understood what she meant to her People or why she came — not even Dancing Eagle. Perhaps Two Moons did, and the elders, but few others.

Schalute chanted through the rest of the day and into the night but could not find sight of his Glory. Exhausted, he collapsed. He knew the Eagle would not come to him because of his anger. The Eagle will only come when one is pure of heart. His heart was broken and confused. He didn't know what to do.

Schalute awoke shivering. The air smelled of winter snow. The sky was gray and the air chilled. The sun, he thought, might never shine again.

He drank from the river and cleansed his face, shivering even more from the cold. He had fasted for days and found himself a bit unsteady on his feet.

With each step he took toward his village, his anger increased. His own family had betrayed him. He couldn't tolerate that.

The village was alive with morning chores as he returned. The braves were watering the horses. The dogs were barking. The children were being bathed at the river. The women were cooking at the fires. What was missing was their splendor, their spirit. They no longer seemed alive. The heart of their village was missing a beat. Would it ever beat in rhythm again? he wondered.

He looked around at the blank, lost faces. His anger increased. His steps quickened as he headed toward his lodge in the center of the village. He had painted it himself with a large sun on one side, a buffalo, a waterfall, a tree and a deer. Each meant something special to him. His tepee was the largest in the village.

He reached for the flap of his lodge and jerked it open. Gentle Breeze quickly turned to face him and froze at his anger. He reached down and pulled her to her feet, striking her across the face.

"What have you done?" he seethed as he repeatedly struck her. She was screaming. Rising Sun rose to block his blows but he turned on her too.

"I told you to watch Morning Glory. Where were you? How could you have let this happen? Don't you know your daughters?"

"Stop! She is just a child," Rising Sun pleaded.

"Where is Blue Dove?" Schalute demanded.

"She is in the woods," Rising Sun replied tearfully.

"As soon as she reaches her moon cycle she is out of my sight. I will arrange for her to marry in another village. She is no longer my daughter."

Schalute turned to Gentle Breeze. "You are too young yet, but as soon as you are of age, you will leave this village too. I no longer claim you as daughter. You will never be a princess in the Eagle Tribe, never."

Schalute turned around and left the two crying women in his lodge. As he stepped out he realized that a crowd had gathered about his lodge and Two Moons was standing at the entrance.

Schalute glared at Two Moons. "You were supposed to have protected your sister!" he shouted. "Where were you?"

"I was in vision," he replied.

"Vision!" Schalute shouted. "That was no time to be in vision," Schalute said, outraged.

"The time to be in vision is when vision comes," Two Moons tried to explain.

Schalute ducked back down into the lodge opening and yelled to Rising Sun, "I blame you for his condition. He is more of spirit than of man. It was you who would always stop me when I wanted to take him hunting and teach him to be a brave warrior. Now all he can do is be in vision. He does not take care of his family."

Two Moons stood before him showing no emotion, for to do that would be to give away his power. He did not try to defend himself. He could see that his father was beyond words. His father was frantic at the loss of Morning Glory and did not know which way to turn. He could only vent his rage and frustration now.

Schalute turned again to Two Moons. "You will never be chief of this tribe. I will turn it over to Dancing Eagle."

Two Moons was unaffected by this attack. "I never wanted to be chief. I only want to be of spirit, Father."

Schalute brushed him aside and briskly walked by. The People of the village were standing there without a word, shocked at what they had just seen. Their chief was out of control.

Schalute searched out Dancing Eagle and grabbed him by the arm. "I must go and find my daughter."

"I will go with you," Dancing Eagle asserted.

"No! Whatever happens, if I do not return, you will rule."

Schalute took off his medallion and placed it upon Dancing Eagle's neck.

Dancing Eagle shook his head in shock. "You cannot expect me to stay behind. She is my wife. I cannot rule this tribe."

"No! You stay. This tribe has to have a leader. I don't want another life to be wasted this day."

Schalute walked toward the herd and pulled out his mount. He rode off wildly with several braves, leaving a cloud of dust behind.

CHAPTER 5

Shadow Dancer had been standing outside the lodge, hiding within the gathering crowd, as he watched his father in an uproar. He was always in trouble with his father, hiding when Schalute was in a rage. Even though only nine winters had passed, he had been brought before the council many times with his antics and was often a thorn in his father's side. But one thing he did share with his father was the rage at having lost Morning Glory. They were very close.

He often had trouble sleeping at night. She would take him then and hold him and stroke his hair and sing him to sleep. Often she would cover up for him when he was missing or something had gone awry. She would soothe their father's anger when his mischief was too outrageous. Now she was gone.

After the crowd had cleared from their lodge, Shadow Dancer walked up to Two Moons. "What will become of all this, Two Moons?" he asked.

Two Moons started to talk from spirit, as though his voice came from another source. "The whites, they come in a force that we cannot control. Like a wind that hits a tree, breaking a branch, leaving it to die. We are the branches still hanging from the tree destined to die. I tell thee, brother, things will change. Soon our lives will not remain the same. So, with thee, I take thee now and covet thy face and cry one tear. We have been disgraced. Our father's mind will rage with a fire and a hate. It will bring down our tribe."

Two Moons then simply walked away from his perplexed brother to prepare to go to the hills. He had to get away, to pray, to seek vision. Morning Glory was gone. A part of him was taken away. He was in pain.

There were few horses left in the village. Many of the braves were out looking for Morning Glory. Two Moons had little choice left but to take Schalute's black stallion.

Two Moons left the village on this dismal day for two weeks. As he rode out he looked into the dismal gray sky which bore his emotions. The air was cold, showing his breath. He wrapped a robe around his shoulders and hunched over, riding into the wind. He was to fast and pray.

When he found his spot, he laid out his robe and spread out the contents of his medicine pouch. It contained the rattle of a snake, the eye of a frog, a white and black eagle feather, a marble stone, dust from the land, a tree bark, twigs from an eagle's nest, and dried scales from a fish. He danced to the Great Spirit for the Eagle to bring her back.

CHAPTER 6

As was the custom, Dancing Eagle provided for his brother's wife and child. He did not love her as a wife. He would not even bed her as a wife. He would wait for Morning Glory to be returned.

Dancing Eagle paced in rage. He was frustrated at not being able to go out and look for her. He knew he must protect the whole tribe but he could not think of anything but Morning Glory. He did not want this position of leadership; he only wanted the love of one woman. He had waited so long for her. She was taken from him so soon.

Three summers ago he had tried to get her away from this place when the white traders came to the village. There was a tall, reddish blond lad with the traders. He stood a bit taller than Dancing Eagle, had a ruddy red complexion and blue-green eyes. He was quick with the knife and quick with the mouth, a bold one, arrogant.

This one they called Tom had walked up to Morning Glory and grabbed her by the arm. Dancing Eagle saw how she froze when she looked into Tom's eyes. She dropped the bucket she was carrying. Dancing Eagle immediately pulled an arrow from his quiver and summoned other braves to escort him out of the village.

Tom looked at Schalute and said, "I will trade you for that maiden. I have many pelts and will give you whatever you ask for, but I want that one."

Schalute went into a rage. "She is our princess. She is not for sale. The only way you could ever have her is to steal her — and if you do, you die!"

Tom was surrounded by braves and shoved roughly back to his canoe. The other traders were escorted out as well.

Dancing Eagle knew trouble was coming. He wanted to take a band of people and get out of that area but the council wouldn't listen. He wanted to leave, but not without his Glory. In desperation he went to Schalute.

Boldly he stood before Schalute and stated, "Of these People whom I do adore, this one child stands at my door. I ask you now for the right to be given to take this child to be my wife."

Schalute's eyes went ablaze. "Why would you ask for her hand now? She is but a child of nine!"

"I wish to leave now and take my band with me, but I cannot go without Morning Glory."

Schalute glared and shouted, "Not alive! You cannot leave this tribe. You are going to rule this village some day. You have to stay. Morning Glory stays with me until she is of her moon cycle. She is but a child. I must protect her."

Dancing Eagle was in despair. His father had died because of the whites who were coming across the land. He knew they should leave, but he could not leave without the one who was supposed to bring him the Son of the Sun. He was now a man of eighteen. He wanted to take a wife, but she was the only one he wanted.

On several occasions Tom was seen lurking about the village. More guards were posted, but he covered his tracks well. Dancing Eagle was uneasy about it.

Tom was not his only problem. Other braves in the village wanted her hand as well. Tall Trees wanted her because his family had been disgraced by his father's cowardice. Having the princess would give his family social position.

Schalute wanted Lone Star to wed Morning Glory. He was the strongest, biggest and hardest-working brave in the village. He felt that Lone Star was fit to protect and provide for her. Morning Glory, however, was afraid of him because he would go into rages when he got white man's whiskey.

Other braves simply loved her beauty. Dancing Eagle even got into knife fights over her. He felt very insecure because even chiefs from other tribes in the valley wanted their sons to wed her to bond the neighboring tribal issues and boundaries. Messengers from other tribes were always arriving with gifts.

Morning Glory had been gifted with the most beautifully beaded dresses, robes, feathers and things to wear in her hair. Moccasins of intricate detail were often bestowed upon her. Meat for the family was always provided.

This, of course, really upset her sisters. They were jealous that this one who wasn't even of the blood of the tribe was getting all the attention. At times they felt she was an intruder. Their father gave her more attention than he did his own children.

When Morning Glory finally came into her moon cycle, the village became even more animated. Schalute knew in his heart that Morning Glory had always favored Dancing Eagle. When she chose him, it came as no surprise. Still, a ceremony of her acceptance was proper and expected.

Dancing Eagle sat before a small fire, alone in his empty tepee. He looked around his empty lodge and temporarily lost his vision. Even though Red Hawk's wife was now considered his, he chose to be alone. His heart could not accept her as his love. She would simply cook what he provided for her and the child. He had nothing of heart to give her.

His mind went back to the preparation of their wedding. Schalute had organized a great hunt to provide a feast. The families were busy making gifts.

Dancing Eagle prepared himself through a fast and a sweat-lodge. He was preparing himself to meet spirit.

Morning Glory was not allowed to see his dance. She would have to meditate and pray that everything went well. She spent her time stringing together feathers for a headdress for Dancing Eagle. It would be her present to him at his ceremonial rite. Some day he was to be chief.

Dancing Eagle was to dance the Winged Eagle's Dance of Love. During the dance a feather would have to be dropped, signifying that love was to be given to all.

When the day came, he dressed for the dance by having eagle feathers draped across his arms, a headdress of eagle feathers, and the tail feathers of the eagle on his back to imitate the dance the eagle does on the mountain to court its mate.

Dancing Eagle could remember the excitement in the air among the villagers as he walked to the middle of the circle. The crowd became hushed as soon as they saw him enter.

He stood there for a few moments, not looking anyone in the face. He put a slight bend in his knees, and his arms stretched outward. The drum started to beat softly. He moved slowly.

The drum beats pounded louder, very rhythmic and loud. Hearts began to pound. Dancing Eagle's face was intense. His feet moved in a backward slide. His head bowed down. His arms began to glide. Rhythmically he moved with the spirit that was his guide. Around and around he soared with the current of the wind. He dipped, he soared, the sweat poured. In a frenzy, he whirled as the minutes swept by. Suddenly, the eagle's tail feather began to fly! The wind caught the feather and flipped it all about. The tribe began to scream and shout.

After the evening ceremony, Dancing Eagle came to the door of her tepee and played his flute, showing his love.

Morning Glory stayed inside the tepee, as was the custom, and reveled at the serenity of the sounds. Dancing Eagle then whistled her a beautiful song which made her heart flutter. She lay back on her rug, amazed at the love that she felt.

Dancing Eagle was caught up in the moment. He was overwhelmed with longing for this one he had waited most of his life for.

Morning Glory sat on the other side of the flap, in her lodge. She lay back, listening to the sounds of the night, the crickets, the windblown grass, the owl in the tree.

She thought, This love is for me. This man is pure. He is a gifted one. I know that he has come from the sun to gather me up and take me away. I shall pledge my love to him in the morning dew. I need him now.

She wanted to run out and grab him. It was a vibration, a feeling that she needed to feel alive. It took *him* to do that to her.

All night, Dancing Eagle stayed at her tepee expressing his love. Upon the first rays of light in the morning, he had to salute the sun. He was joined by Bear Claw, Two Moons, Red Sky and Wild Horse, who brought along his drum. They walked single file to the river.

His friends were supposed to stand behind him. A message was to be brought down to the river by a maiden to tell him whether or not he had been accepted for marriage. If he had not been accepted, then his friends were supposed to take him out and have a good time.

Except for Two Moons, the other braves were his personal warriors. The other braves shied away from Two Moons.

"What are you doing here, Two Moons?" the braves asked.

"I belong here. He is my friend," Two Moons answered matter-of-factly.

The other braves thought he was odd. He never went hunting, so he never wore the kills. He never wore the stripes for war. He never stole a horse. He never went through the rituals of his thirteenth winter. He wasn't a warrior in their eyes. The only one who would talk to him was Dancing Eagle. Two Moons spent most of his time with the old wise man.

"*Wakita*, salute the sun," Dancing Eagle said. There was a nice haze in the valley. He told Two Moons, "Today is a good day to receive good news.

"You are always of few words. Do you have anything of inspiration for me today, Two Moons?" Dancing Eagle inquired.

Two Moons just looked and said, "Know thyself as you know the eagle and the spirit of which you were born, the spirit that will fly, and everything else that comes into your eye, be true to." Then he put his head down.

Dancing Eagle just looked at him, puzzled. He was searching for words of encouragement about Two Moons' sister, not a lesson.

It was their tradition for the maiden to spread out a blanket in front of her tepee in the morning. Then she would walk out painted with a happy face and present herself to her suitor. A red dye was used, making red markings and little white circles. Symbols were painted across her forehead and down her cheeks.

If the maiden accepted, the tepee would be painted with a happy face on a big sun. If it was not right, there would be painted a half-moon with three stars by it, showing that she was not ready (moons always come in cycles).

A brilliant sun was painted: she was ready to make her union.

A maiden was sent down to the river to tell Dancing Eagle he had been accepted. When he found out, he let out a whoop. Wild Horse started to beat wildly on his drum. It was celebration time.

Lone Star was his cousin. Lone Star helped him build this tepee for his wedding night.

Dancing Eagle sat upon a black bear robe that had been given to them by his mother. Along the walls of the tepee were the most beautifully fringed and beaded dresses any woman had ever worn. Now his woman was not there to wear them.

He fingered the hollowed out buffalo bone that he always wore around his neck. Morning Glory had decorated it with shells and beads and it would chime in the wind as he wore it. She had given it to him as a wedding present. The beaded band that he wore on his arm, she had designed with her own hands. The moccasins that he wore, she had beaded especially for their wedding night.

A few weeks ago, no one could have been happier. That night the Creator had made magic in the stars. The wind stood still so that all could hear their hearts beat as one. The moon lit up the sky so that all could see the blue hue of her hair glow in the moonbeams. Chiefs from the neighboring tribes arrived with gifts to honor this woman, making Schalute proud.

It pained Dancing Eagle's heart to remember their wedding night. Drummers had called the People from their lodges for the feast of venison, wild turkey, pheasant, quail and a special feast of dove. The moon came out to rest. The firelight danced. Its sparks reflected off of Morning Glory's hair. She was unspeakably beautiful in her fringed, doeskin dress. The beading took the form of a V in front. Her heavily beaded moccasins had feathers going down the back. Her hair was braided and decorated with medallions that were engraved with eagles.

For the first time, she stood before her People wearing the plumed crown which came with her as a baby. Schalute had brought it to her from the sacred cave. She stood quietly, regally, before the People as though she were from another time, another space. She wore the symbol of her rightful heritage. In the People's minds, it awakened an ancient memory of who she really was. It would also mark a time in which her service to her People was truly about to begin.

She stood before the firelight, with the moonbeams flickering off her hair and the rainbow colors of the crowned plumes. Her eyes sparkled with the love that was so near. She took Dancing Eagle's breath away.

Dancing Eagle's heart started to pound. He couldn't take his eyes off of her. As the drumming continued, he could only hear the beat of his heart throbbing loudly in his ears.

Morning Glory started to do the Dance of Fertility. She started out slowly, rhythmically, swaying with her arms outstretched and her hair flowing along them as far as it would go. Her eyes were closed. Her spirit began to arise. Spirit took over. All hearts rose as she moved with a body message that sparked a memory of an ancient time.

Women and young girls brought her berries, fruits and nuts, all of which held the seeds of life.

Throughout the village, hearts were dancing in praise of the new days to come when they would produce a son. The People were happy now, except for the broken-hearted maidens, who wanted Dancing Eagle to have courted them, and the braves who wanted Morning Glory to be their own.

"Where is Two Moons?" Schalute asked angrily. "Gentle Breeze, go find your brother and bring him here. This is a family ceremony. No matter what he is doing, bring him back here," he ordered.

Two Moons was up by the cliffs, staring into the water at an angle from high on the peak. There was a full moon that night. He saw visions in the water about the "white creatures." White men didn't honor nature, so he didn't call them men. They were creatures.

"Two Moons," Gentle Breeze called out. Two Moons jumped surprisedly at the invasion of his vision.

"I have saved you a special place next to our father. Your place is with Father and the family now. Father wants your presence to be known."

Two Moons shook his head and mumbled, "My presence will never be known on this plane. Of this glory day, there will be dark days. Of this light, there will be dark!"

He realized then that she was only a child. She didn't understand a word he had said. He would make an appearance so that he wouldn't incur the wrath of his father, but that wouldn't make it right in his mind.

"Bring back the message to Father that I shall come back on the wing of the eagle."

"What does that mean?" Schalute roared when Gentle Breeze returned with the message. "What is he doing now?"

Morning Glory could see that Schalute was getting angry. She knew that Two Moons and Schalute had a lot to work out, but she loved them both. She wished that she could have gone and brought him back herself but she couldn't leave the ceremony.

She went to Schalute and tried to cover up for Two Moons.

"Don't ever explain him to me. I don't understand him. I understand you. I know the love that you are going through. Don't burden yourself with him."

She said, "He is my burden because he is my pain. I feel everything that he feels. I am love, as he loves. I am pain, as he is. I am everything he is. I am a reflection of him!"

"No!" Schalute blurted out. "He is not of this nature. He is not of this clan. I always thought that he was not part of my being."

Shadow Dancer, in the meantime, always wanted to play the

drum. In the circle, drums surrounded the ceremony. In the center of the circle was a special, large ceremonial drum.

While the People were feasting, the drumming was stopped. Earlier, moccasins had been taken off for the dancing. They were placed around the perimeter of the circle.

Shadow Dancer sneaked around, taking all of the moccasins, filled them with dirt and stones and hid them. Then he went racing into the middle of the circle with two large branches and began to pound on the sacred ceremonial drum.

The old man who had made the sacred drum called for the Great Spirit to swoop down and with his mighty talons pick up this boy, carry him out of the camp and take him away!

"Runta, Runta," Schalute roared, "get that wild one. If I get him, I will kill him."

Runta ran after him with a stick. Old ladies were running around trying to catch him as he darted in and out.

Those who had taken their moccasins off to dance in the soft sand of the circle of fire couldn't find them. Chaos was at hand.

Dancing Eagle was perplexed with his new little brother-in-law, but his anger was abated when he looked up to see Morning Glory's hand over her mouth to hide her laughter as the village became chaotic.

"Tie him to a tree," yelled Schalute. "Then he will be all right!"

Schalute was perplexed with both of his sons now, but then he would look over at Morning Glory and see the gentleness in her heart and the love that she felt for Dancing Eagle. That again brought him joy.

He stood proudly by as other tribal chiefs honored their ceremony and presented them with beautiful gifts. However, he was starting to lose face. Two Moons still had not arrived at his side.

Morning Glory saw this, so she went over to Schalute and asked him to do the ceremonial dance with her. She gave him a big hug, so that all now were looking at them. The ceremonial drums started to pound. The women were singing songs signifying the continuance of their union, the life span and the embodiment of their being together.

The dance was in a figure eight. They walked forward together, then walked backwards, similar to the white man's square dance. Again they took the steps, then stopped and faced each other. They took each other's hands, went around the circle twice one way, stopped, faced each other, then repeated it the other way.

When Schalute and Morning Glory got to the center again, Schalute stepped out and Dancing Eagle stepped in. They were now bonded in marriage.

Schalute stood proud with his arms crossed in front of him. He gazed side to side to see the joy in everyone's eyes. This bond would bring life to the village. This bond was a gift from the Great Spirit.

Nevertheless, Schalute was still upset that Two Moons was not by his side. What he didn't know was that Two Moons was sitting behind him at the side of a large tepee. Two Moons did not want to show his sorrow at what he saw in the waters that night, at what was in store for his beloved sister.

When the dance was over, Morning Glory caught a glimpse of Two Moons in the moonlight. His dark, silver-blue hair glowed in the moonlight. As she glanced at him, it looked as though there were two beings sitting side by side. He reflected the moonlight into another being! It was as though he had split himself into two.

Morning Glory turned to Dancing Eagle and said, "One moment please. I must speak to my brother." Dancing Eagle nodded.

Morning Glory knelt beside her brother, who could not seem to face her. With one hand she gently pulled his chin up. Two Moons' eyes looked into hers and one lone tear dropped. Morning Glory was puzzled. She would have preferred to see his joy but she knew better than to ask him what troubled him. He would never say.

Morning Glory reached to her head and removed the crown. "Two Moons, would you return this crown immediately to the sacred cave? Father is busy with all the festivities. Since no one has seen you here, you can easily slip out and return the crown to its place of safety until it is time to use it again."

Two Moons took the crown into his hands and nodded. He could not speak to her. His heart was in his throat. He wished he could wish her a happy future but he knew that she had much ahead of her.

Morning Glory rose to her feet and slowly walked toward Dancing Eagle. She looked back at Two Moons to wave goodbye but he seemed to have disappeared. She was not surprised. He seemed to do that frequently.

What no one realized was that hidden among the trees was a pair of white eyes!

The villagers continued in their festivities. Many presents were bestowed upon them. Morning Glory's favorite was from Runta. Runta had spent many moons making a magnificient cloak from a white-tanned hide; it was hooded and trimmed with the fur of a white fox. On the back was a beaded symbol of an encircled Y, signifying upholding the world.

Dancing Eagle kept glancing at his Morning Glory, marveling at her strange beauty. He was becoming distracted beyond belief. People were talking to him but he heard not a word.

Dancing Eagle took Glory of the Morning gently by the hand and pulled her off toward the trees. He wrapped his arms around her and pulled her tightly to his body, pressing her body against his yearning loins.

Then with a quick swoop of his strong arms, he easily scooped up her slender body and carried her toward the wedding tepee Lone Star had helped him construct. As he carried her, she buried her face into his pounding chest.

Inside the tepee, he laid her gently down upon a black bear robe. Dancing Eagle lit a fire and spread herbs into the flame to purify their tepee.

He looked over to her and saw her shyly standing there, waiting for him to guide her through their first night together. He caressed her hair and gently lifted her chin so their eyes could once again meet.

His arms wrapped around her as he pulled her tightly to his desirous body. Ever so gently, he kissed her eyes, her ears, her nose, her throat, and then her long, slender neck. His breathing became rapid, as did hers.

He removed his fringed buckskin shirt, revealing his tightly bound muscles and his lean waist. He then removed his moccasins and leggings and left on only his breechcloth.

Morning Glory watched him, admiring his well-detailed body. He reached forward and helped her remove her dress, letting it fall to the ground. She quivered with anticipation.

Dancing Eagle caressed her body with oil so no unwanted spirits could attach themselves. Morning Glory then massaged his body with the oil. She rubbed him ever so slowly, feeling every muscle, every detail, reveling in the feel of a man's body.

Dancing Eagle shivered with desire as they stood there face to face, their skin glistening in the firelight. Their shadows reflected upon the walls of the tepee.

Both of them could feel the presence of a spirit that wanted to be born through them. With a penetrating tone, Dancing Eagle sang a song calling to the spirit to come to them on their wedding night. Morning Glory replied with a whispering voice – her plea to the spirit to join them through the act of love. Back and forth they sang, separately, then together, with a haunting chant.

With a swift pull of the string, he let his breechcloth drop to the ground of their tepee. He kissed her deeply. At first she thought she wouldn't be able to breathe, her heart beat so wildly. He kissed her mouth and her throat and gently laid her down beside him, but oh, so slowly, so as not to frighten her. He had waited this long. He would take the whole night to revel in it.

Dancing Eagle had lain with many a maiden while he waited for his Glory to grow. Now he was with her, and he would show her his love and how gentle love could be.

She quivered with excitement as he slowly caressed her body. Her breathing became labored. Her body arched toward him. He knew she was ready.

Gently and deeply he planted his seeds in her receptive body. His body couldn't believe the pleasure he held in his arms. For the first time he felt satisfied and whole. Contentment filled his fiery soul as he lay next to the Glory of his life.

The memory faded. Now she was gone! She was taken from his life by a white-eye! No! This cannot be so! How could he go on? She was what he lived for. She was what he had waited for. No other could possibly replace her. There was no other like her.

CHAPTER 7

Tom Shaye and Michael McVain brought Morning Glory to a secluded one-room cabin in the woods. Morning Glory's hands were still bound as they shoved her inside. She whirled around in fright as she heard them close the door behind her. Tom walked in and put his rifle up on the wall. McVain spit into a pot in the corner. She had never been in a structure such as this before. She looked around the dark room.

The only light came from a single opening in a wall. She walked up to the opening and touched something that she could see the sky through, but it would not let her hand through. She was puzzled.

In the middle of the room were a table and three chairs. The table was of a rough-sawn wood, with stains of round rings on it. Bugs crawled over it, eating crumbs of food.

One wall had stones on it, and in the middle of the wall was a place for fire. She saw black-colored pots to the side of it. There was a slab of bacon hanging from a hook in the corner.

The other wall had a place in which she thought he must sleep. It had robes over straw, but it stood upon legs.

Roughly, he dragged her to this sleeping place, pushed her down on it and bound each hand over her head to a rough-hewn wooden headboard.

He removed her gag and laughed. He spoke a bit of her tongue, enough for her to understand his intent.

"You can scream all you want now, lassie. Nobody is going to hear you. You ain't going no place ever again without me."

McVain again crudely spit his juice into a bowl in the corner of the cabin. It made her skin crawl.

"Well, Tom, we did it," McVain said between stuffing his jaws with tobacco and starting a small fire. "Taking this princess ought to do the trick. You can be dang sure that this will start an Indian war. When those injuns start to rile up, the army will have to come in and disperse them. Then we can just move in and get that iron ore they was sittin' on.

"Those injuns up the river are always wantin' more rifles and ammunition. The Sacs have been givin' up some of their land because they wanted more rifles and ammunition than their pelts could buy.

"Never could get that little Eagle tribe to trade for guns. Schalute was too powerful in the council. Said, 'No trading with white man.' Couldn't get 'em to budge, outside of Red Hawk once in a while. Seemed the council listened to Schalute more than Red Hawk.

"But now we have their prize possession. Schalute won't stand for that. He's gonna want to fight for that little filly over there. Army'll have to get involved and will move them. All we have to do is move right in after them."

Tom took a bottle off the shelf, blew the dust off of it, and plunked it down on the table. He took two metal cups off the shelf, wiped them out with the inside of his shirt and started to pour whiskey into them. He picked one cup up and handed it to McVain, sloshing some liquid over the edge.

"Let's make a toast to our new venture. This is gonna make us rich men, Michael."

Morning Glory strained to understand what these men were saying, but she couldn't make out a word. Her wrists were raw and bleeding from the leather bounds that held them. Her hands were becoming numb. Her belly hurt. Her head hurt. More than anything, her heart hurt.

The two men drank for hours. McVain passed out with his head lying on the table. Tom got up, swaggered over to Morning Glory and took out a knife.

Morning Glory closed her eyes to welcome death. Instead, she felt a tugging at her wrists. She opened one eye. Tom was cutting her loose. As her hands dropped, she tried to rub the blood back into them. Her wrists were raw.

He offered her his cup. She shook her head.

"Have it your way, lassie. You can drink what you want, but you are mine now."

Morning Glory lunged for the door. In two quick strides, Tom tackled her to the floor. He crawled over her and turned her around to face his foul breath. She struggled, but in vain. He was much too big for her.

Tom laughed. "I'm too tired now and too drunk to fight ya. Besides, ya just lost a baby. I'm a Christian man, no heathen, ya know. But you'll not be getting away from me, ya hear?" He looked at her hard. "Since I can't close my eyes for a minute without you takin' off, I'll just have to keep you tied until I get you tamed."

Again he dragged her to the bedpost and bound her. She would have rather died by his knife.

Tom threw his saddle down in front of the fire and unwound his bed roll, falling asleep as soon as he hit the floor.

CHAPTER 8

Schalute was frantic. He wildly drove his band of braves from tribe to neighboring tribe, trying to get support to fight against the whites and regain the princess.

Since the Black Hawk War, most of the tribes had been moved west of the Mississippi River. The small bands that were left behind did not have any braves to spare for a war that was not their own. He understood their position.

None of his trackers could pick up the tracks of the abductors. A heavy rainstorm had followed the abduction and wiped out all tracks.

Schalute returned to the village with his band of braves, his head hanging in shame. Again he fasted and sought out solitude, going to the hills to pray.

"Creator," he called out, "why have you not let me find my daughter? She was to protect our People. I saw it written on the great wall. How can she protect us if she is taken from us?"

Five times the sun rose and set behind the hills, yet no answer came to Schalute. He returned to the village with no answers.

Upon returning to his lodge he faced his two daughters, Gentle Breeze and Blue Dove. He could never forgive them, he thought, scowling. They must leave and let him live with his disgrace.

Shadow Dancer felt lost. It was no longer fun to tease his sisters, and Morning Glory was no longer there to get him out of trouble. Two Moons was sullen and uncommunicative.

Rising Sun was ill. Even though she was not Morning Glory's birth mother, or the one who held her to her breast, she had raised Morning Glory for most of her life. Adding to her sadness, she missed Spring Flower, who had died trying to bring another child to Schalute, two summers after Morning Glory's arrival.

Now Morning Glory was gone. It would be a long time before Schalute would forgive his two daughters – if he ever did. He never did understand Two Moons. Shadow Dancer with his antics was forever a thorn in his side. As the season changed, Rising Sun began to lose her will to live. Her lodge was no longer a place to call home. Her spirit stayed less and less in her body, until one day it never came back. They buried her on the hill next to Spring Flower and her stillborn child.

CHAPTER 9

"It's time for me to report to the fort, Michael," Tom said as he cleaned up a fish for dinner. "Trouble is, I can't bring that princess with me, or the colonel will have my ass. I can't leave her behind, because if she ain't tied, she'll run and if she is tied, she'll starve."

"I've been gone too long. If I don't get back, Commander Worthington will have me replaced as head scout. With all the tribes being relocated west of the river, he needs me now."

Michael spit toward the spittoon, missing it by a long shot but not really caring. He wiped the spittle from his mouth. "You leave her here with me, Tom. I'll feed her until you come back. One of us should stay behind, because the trappers from the Magnus Company will be coming up soon. I want to make arrangements with them about setting up business on that Indian land. She won't be much trouble. I'll just throw some food her way once in a while. She won't be much company, though. She ain't said one word since we got her."

Tom became defensive. "With those eyes, she don't have to say nothin'. It's all in them eyes. One day she's gonna bring me sons, and they will have them eyes too."

McVain spit more wildly, wiping the drool off his chin. "What you talkin' about? She's just an injun, a squaw."

Tom grabbed him by the throat. "She's my squaw, you hear? You don't talk about her like that in front of me. Understand?"

McVain pulled Tom's hands off his throat and choked on his tobacco. "No need to get so all-fired upset with me. We're all in on this deal, you know."

Tom threw the fish onto the fire. "There's one thing your

forgettin', McVain. I wanted the girl, first and foremost. You're the one who concocted this scheme about getting the Indian land by starting a war. You might win this war. You might die. But I'm the one who's got the girl. You best remember that."

Tom stuck a knife into the fish and flipped it over. "I'll leave first thing in the morning. If you harm one hair on her head, you're a dead man. You can't fight no Indian war without me and my men. They only take orders from me."

"Don't get all riled, there, Tom. You just get back here as soon as you can. I've got some trappin' to do before we're snowed in."

Tom cut the fish in three, untied Morning Glory and brought her to the table.

She bowed her head, put her hands over the fish and chanted a few words before she ate.

"First time I heard a word from that one," McVain said in disgust. "I guess she's got a tongue after all."

"Injuns pray over everything. Don't let it bother you, McVain. You ain't even a Christian man. Little prayin' wouldn't hurt you none."

McVain almost choked laughing. "Comin' from you, that's pretty funny, much as you hate injuns."

"It's a cruel world that we is born into. Man can only survive by being the strongest. If white man is strongest, then he is the one to win. That's the way I intend it to be. Simple as that."

CHAPTER 10

Schalute and Dancing Eagle took turns going off with a band of braves to scour the land, looking for Morning Glory. Two Moons had to take the role of father for Shadow Dancer. The time was at hand for Shadow Dancer to go on his first hunt.

Schalute faced Two Moons and sternly said, "Shadow Dancer is not to come back without a kill. You can go into spirit, but you still have to provide for the People and yourself."

Schalute started to walk away, but quickly spun around to again face Two Moons. "You can't be of my lineage – the Great Spirit has possessed your body. I want my son back."

Two Moons glared back at him. "I was never really your son because you never were really of spirit."

Schalute was enraged. "If you think you can rule this clan better than I, I will give you my knife and the opportunity to kill me right now."

Two Moons took the knife and winged it at a tree. "That is where the knife belongs – out there, not here."

It was time to show Shadow Dancer the art of survival through the hunt. Shadow Dancer wanted Schalute, not Two Moons, to take him out for this ritual. Even though he went to Two Moons all the time, he had always thought Two Moons was very weak in body.

Two Moons changed the rules. He would not hunt as his father did. He led Shadow Dancer through a four-day fast and a sweatlodge. They were to have four days of communication with spirit. They danced and prepared for the art of knowing nature, to bring spirit in.

Two Moons wanted only to teach Shadow Dancer about spirit and not to hunt and kill. Shadow Dancer said that he didn't care about spirit.

"When spirit strikes your eyes, what are you going to say to spirit?" Two Moons asked.

Shadow Dancer loved a challenge, an exercise in manhood, so he replied, "I will confront him, like I confront everything else in my life. I will spit fire and fire will spit at me. I will wrestle spirit to the ground."

Two Moons shook his head. "If you are going to go out and make this kill, I will only let you use a knife, and you will have to make it of your own being."

Shadow Dancer already had a nice knife, given to him for his birthday by Schalute. "I'll use the knife I already have. I'll use my bow."

Two Moons took all of these items away from him and took him down to the riverbank to collect shells and flint. He showed him how to make his own shell knife.

Two Moons tried to explain to him that it was best to use the cunning of one's own mind, not weapons. Then Two Moons showed him the call of the animal. He showed him how to bring the animal to him, how to live with the animal, how to sleep with the animal, how to walk with the animal and how to talk with the animal. He showed him how to be part of the animal, so the animal would be one with him.

Two Moons spent two weeks in the wilderness with Shadow Dancer, living on instinct, showing him pure spirit. The hunt was successful. Shadow Dancer did it with his own knife. He blessed the animal and thanked its spirit for supplying him with needed food.

Upon their return, Schalute was proud that Shadow Dancer had brought back his first hunt.

"Now, my son, it is time for you to do a ceremonial job. The Tepee of Hope, in which we perform special ceremonies, must be taken down. First you must dry it out with herbs and fold it in a sacred manner to be put into storage. It must be done before the sun sets," Schalute added as he walked away.

Shadow Dancer was to take the tepee down in the morning and dry it out in strong sunlight. He did not want to do such a boring job. He had other plans in mind and wanted to speed it up. He fooled around the whole day, teasing Turtle Woman and putting honey into her hair. Suddenly he realized the sun was starting to set — and the tepee had not been dried out yet.

"I'll have to make a nice warm fire in it. That will dry it out quickly. I'll put it away later," Shadow Dancer announced to himself. He built a fire and put a lot of sticks into it to make it good and hot, but there was some sappy wood among the sticks. It spit a lot and sent out sparks that lodged in the walls of the tepee. Shadow Dancer was not around to watch the fire, and the walls smoked, then blazed. The tepee burned to the ground.

He was in the woods playing tricks on Turtle Woman when he heard the sound of the drums. He ran to the village to see the tepee ablaze and the medicine men standing around it with their arms crossed over their chests.

Now he was really in trouble again. He would be called before the council with this one. Schalute had already raised a tepee for him in the village of the outcasts over the hill, in which he'd been sent to stay many a time. He spent the night there.

"You will be chief of the outcasts," Schalute would always say to him.

Shadow Dancer was worried about what action his father might take. He knew that Schalute would surely punish him severely for this act. He would have to explain himself to the council soon. Then he had an idea.

"I will go and prove to my father that I am worthy of my strength. I will seek out and kill the great cat that stalks our horses at night. When I bring back the carcass of this great beast, my father will forgive me and forget the trouble I have caused him. I must find Short Leg and Fast Walker."

Shadow Dancer found Short Leg down by the Grove of Plenty, a place by the river where berries were picked in their season. It was the place where Morning Glory was last seen.

"Short Leg, I have exciting news. We are to hunt and kill Marona!"

"Marona, the great cat?" Short Leg almost choked. "Shadow Dancer, are you crazy? Our best warriors can't capture and kill Marona. It is like a spirit that appears and bares its teeth and then hides at night to sleep, only to scare our people."

"That is why we must find and kill Marona," said Shadow Dancer. "We must raise its spirit and let it find a new home."

"No!" shouted Short Leg in panic. "I cannot go. I have no quarrel with Marona. I don't want my spirit to tangle with hers."

"Are you afraid, my friend?" Shadow Dancer inquired, to put him on the spot.

"Now, don't say that, Shadow Dancer. I just don't want to hunt such a great demon spirit."

"I will tell you what we must do," said Shadow Dancer plottingly. "We must find Fast Walker. Then we will all go and seek advice from my brother Two Moons."

Short Leg seemed relieved. "I will agree to go if Two Moons agrees to give us protection. He is a wise one. If he sanctions this mission, then I will go with you. If he doesn't, I am here to stay."

While Shadow Dancer and Short Leg were looking for Fast Walker, Two Moons had been in vision in the cave. As always, he was watching over his brother. He felt an uneasiness about his brother's plans. He contemplated what he had heard.

He thought to himself, "Shadow Dancer has found the wrong way to please our father. Marona is not to be taken by so young a brave. Marona is a great spirit brought back only to frighten and stay in our memory so that we will always remember that we are still part of nature. One boy is no match for a mighty demon. It is true that Marona must be stopped, but Shadow Dancer is not the one. I will see that no one is hurt."

As Two Moons finished his vision, Shadow Dancer and his friends found him.

"Two Moons, my brother, I carry a heart of two minds. One is of guilt, one is of joy. The first one is to release the guilt of my actions toward Father and the council. The second one is joy, which I find in my heart if I can redeem myself in everyone's eyes. I am to find and kill the great Marona!"

"I know," Two Moons said. "I don't agree with what you want to do but I will sanction your rite of manhood to seek and kill the beast."

"Will you bless the three of us and ask the Great Eagle to watch over and protect us?"

"I will if I am given a sign. I will let you know."

That day, Two Moons saw a sun dog. The sun was covered by clouds, and rings like halos formed in many colors around the sun. It was a good sign. It was a blessing for the hunter sent by the Great Wolf to his children. It signified a great hunt.

Blue Dove had seen eleven winters and would soon be in her first moon. Since she was the oldest female in the lodge, she now made the meals for the family. Since she no longer had a mother or an older sister to help her, Gentle Breeze was her assistant.

At the family meal that night, after they had given the blessing of the food, Two Moons spoke to Shadow Dancer.

"I will bless and protect this hunt. Promise me this – you will follow my every word."

Shadow Dancer was fidgeting with excitement. "We shall, my brother. We shall."

Two Moons continued, "Your success will be the success of the spirit, of the tribe."

The next day the three boys celebrated and waited for the Great Eagle to appear in the western sky. At high sun, Short Leg spotted the eagle above the trees.

The three, not telling a soul, went off to the valley far below. They hunted all day trying to pick up the tracks of the great cat.

By nightfall, Short Leg was willing to give up the hunt.

"I want to go back to the village. This is a useless waste of my time. I will be missed tomorrow. My father looks to me to tend the horses," he tried to explain.

Shadow Dancer cavalierly replied, "Don't worry, by tomorrow we will have found and killed Marona. We will be heroes. You won't have to tend horses anymore."

Short Leg said doubtfully, "I hope you are right, Shadow Dancer. I will be in much trouble if we come back empty-handed."

What Shadow Dancer and the other young braves didn't know was that Two Moons had followed them. He had to make sure that they weren't hurt.

Two Moons had asked the Great Eagle to give him the Great Eagle eye so that he could see Marona ahead of time. By secretly leaving signs, he could direct the boys into Marona's lair.

The Great Eagle responded positively. Two Moons went ahead of the boys and left trackings of the great cougar. The boys followed the tracks and made plans to end the cat's days.

Shadow Dancer said, "This is what we are going to do. The cat is hiding in a cave upon the ridge. All the signs lead to this. We are going to fan out and surround the ridge. With arrow ready, I am going to make a call of the bird. The cat will come out and Marona will be heard. Have arrow and spear ready."

The three boys thought this was a great idea. They crept up farther onto the ridge, waiting for the cat's signs to say that it smelled their presence. As they continued farther, they sent out their signals to see that everyone was all right and everything was in its proper place.

What they failed to realize was that the cat was not in its den. It had picked up their scent when they were in the valley, going up the ridge. Marona had circled around and was behind them, stalking them.

The boys were very cautious. They took off their moccasins and walked barefooted. They didn't want to wake the cat in its lair.

Two Moons was perched high in a nearby tree. He saw Marona behind his brother, not more than one hundred yards! The cat was gaining.

Two Moons was afraid that someone was going to get hurt. Holding a cut blade that was a gift from his father, he prepared himself for battle with the great beast.

The three boys surrounded the cave and made calls of the bird and the wild. They didn't hear anything in return. They listened into the stillness of the cave. Nothing appeared. It was then they realized the cat was on its own hunt!

Shadow Dancer paled as he said, "The air is clear. I don't hear anything except our own voices. This is a bad sign. Fast Walker, stay to the right. Don't veer. Stay to the right. Short Leg, watch the trees. Watch the trees. Make sure nothing is in the breeze. The cat is near us. I feel its presence!"

Short Leg was scared. "Let's go back to the village now. We will get the elders. We will get the braves. I don't like this."

"No! Hush! He is here. I feel his presence."

Slowly, behind the boulder, Marona crept up directly behind Shadow Dancer.

Suddenly, Two Moons jumped out of a tree as if an eagle had taken him by his neck and dropped him right onto the cat's back. With his blade he swung around and pierced the cat beneath its chin and cut her within, ripping her from head to toe.

The cat's fangs grew and there was blood all around. At the sound of a roar, the boys all turned. Eyes wide, they watched Two Moons fight this magnificent creature.

Shadow Dancer's heart beat fast. His tongue wouldn't move. His eyes bulged like great peaks. He was in a state of despair.

"What do I do now?" He pulled his hair. "How do I help my brother?"

The three ran toward Two Moons. The cat lay to rest at Two Moons' hands.

Two Moons lay there panting and holding the cat. He had claw marks up his back. A piece of his neck was missing, and part of an ear. The feathers in his headband were all disarrayed. His hair was full of blood. He had saved the day.

Two Moons pulled himself to his feet and picked up the cat, handing it to Shadow Dancer. "This is a gift to my brother."

Shadow Dancer shook his head and backed away. "I can't take it. That mighty cat is yours. Marona is now part of the Great Eagle."

Two Moons continued to walk forward and dropped the cat at Shadow Dancer's feet.

"I have done this for your judgment and right. You want to be forgiven in Father's eyes. You have to do what is in my mind. You take this now. Say not a word. You three boys have killed Marona. I will go on and follow the great stream. I will take care of myself. I won't be seen for three days." Two Moons disappeared into the woods.

The three boys couldn't believe their eyes. The great Marona was before them. They would be heroes this day. They walked a fine path home, singing songs of the glorious sun and how the Eagle had helped them win this battle. They would always remember in their hearts the one brother who had helped them all, Two Moons, and how he had fallen from the sky.

Upon their return, a whoop went up from the village. The women scampered. The men came running.

"What is this? The great Marona slain by three young braves! Oh, the spirits are alive this day."

Schalute, hearing all of the commotion, ran out of his lodge. "What brave has done this?"

Shadow Dancer stood up strong, his two friends alongside him.

"We did, father. Killed him to the last breath. All three of us feared the death. But it was all right, because of the Eagle eye."

Schalute looked about in wonderment. "I am pleased. We shall celebrate. The great Marona is dead."

The drums started. The horses were gathered. The tribal chief would celebrate a new victory, new warriors that day.

The one, who for three days was not found, lay bleeding from head to foot. He knew that what he had done was right, because the Great Spirit came to him that night and thanked him for the mighty deed.

For three days, he lay as if he were half-dead. Then the spirit took him over and gave him new life. His wounds healed fast. He would walk again. The visions would begin. Everything was all right once more.

CHAPTER 11

Tom Shaye rode back to the fort. He had been gone too long. The villages surrounding the Mississippi River were all being moved west. There were skirmishes all about. He knew the Indian tongues. He knew the land. Most of the men followed his command. The commander would be upset at his prolonged absence.

Tom approached the fort and was about to holler for the gate to be opened but before he could, it suddenly swung open before him and a brigade of men rode forth.

Commander Worthington loped toward him on his horse, sitting back as he reined the horse to a sliding halt in front of Tom. Tom had to bring his own horse down from rearing up when the commander's horse slid into his.

"Damnation, Tom, where in thunder have you been? The whole territory is in upheaval. We needed you. Seems some fool took a princess over by Eagle Ridge. Damned Indians are in an uproar. You know anything about that?"

Before Tom could answer, the troop's horn was blown and the brigade galloped out.

"Well, turn that horse around, Tom. You're goin' with us. Got to get things tamed down out there before it gets out of hand. There was enough ruckus goin' on just trying to get them all to move. Now with this princess thing, I just don't know what's goin' to happen."

Tom had to do some quick thinking here. The commander was obviously upset with the new Indian uprising. Worthington didn't seem to care about the iron ore land or the Magnus Trading Company or some blue-eyed squaw. All he wanted was for the Indians to settle down.

The squadron rode upriver. Tom could feel eyes in the trees watching him, yet no arrows penetrated their ranks. The hair on his arms rose. Overhead, a raven swooped down. The birds stopped chattering in the trees. There was no breeze. All the men knew they were being watched and they didn't know why they weren't being attacked.

Schalute was no fool. He was hiding in the woods with his loyal braves. He knew if he killed Tom now, they would not be led to Morning Glory. Instead he would stalk him until his dying day, if necessary.

For days the squadron traveled, camped, scouted. They all knew they were continually being watched. Fear was in their throats. They couldn't sleep at night. Most would rather have had a battle than have to go through this waiting. The not knowing was making them jittery.

Tom walked through the campsite with his hand always half touching his knife. When he went to the river to wash his face, he looked carefully in all directions before he dared put his head down into his wet hands. He listened carefully, but the Indians stalked craftily. They were trained by Schalute to crack not even a twig.

The nights were getting cold. Frost covered the hardened land. The men sat around the fire to keep warm and drink coffee.

Tom dumped out the grounds from his coffee cup and said, "Commander, we are just playing cat-and-mouse out here. Schalute is never going to come out of those trees. His game is to watch us. He's looking for his daughter, not trouble. What do you say we just head on back?"

Commander Worthington stood up, dusted off his pants, kicked the dirt with his boots and picked up his roll to turn in. "I think you're right, Tom. In the morning we will saddle up and ride back."

Tom was anxious to get back to his cabin. He didn't fully trust McVain with Morning Glory. Besides, that woman haunted his soul. He wanted to be with her, but he didn't know quite why. Women were few and far between in this part of the country. Many of the men took squaws but none had one like this one. She was beautiful beyond compare.

The morning was gray, damp and hazy. The chill went right to the bone. Most of the men were glad to be heading back to the fort, especially Tom.

Tom knew that he couldn't leave the fort right away. Schalute and his braves would be hot on his trail. It was not his intent to lead them right to his cabin. He was going to have to devise a plan. Also, he couldn't have them trailing him for the rest of his life. Even as well as he covered his tracks, it was too much to keep that up forever.

By the time the brigade arrived back at the fort, the sun had already set. Behind the rolling clouds, there was no moon. Lightning and thunder rocked the land. The wind howled. It was easy for him to sneak out the back of the fort into the woods during the storm. He wouldn't be seen.

By morning a thick fog had rolled in, making an even better cover for him to ride through. When he arrived back at his cabin, he peeked through the window and saw that Morning Glory was still tied to her bed. She was even thinner and more drawn than the last time he saw her. Her dress was dirty, her hair unkempt. Upon opening the door, he found the cabin cold, the fire untended. Morning Glory never even looked his way when he walked in. In her mind, she was already dead, a no-thing. In her mind, he was a no-thing.

Tom brought wood in from the porch and stoked the fire. He felt a gush of cold air upon his back as the door opened behind him. Knife in hand, he whirled around to see Michael McVain standing there with pelts over his shoulder.

McVain dropped the pelts to the floor and kicked the door shut behind him. "Glad you're finally back, Tom. I wanted to tend my traps farther north before the snows come. I couldn't go far because the squaw kept getting loose. She didn't care what she did to her wrists, cut them to shreds to get out of her bonds. No matter how tight I'd make them, she would manage to pull her hands through, like she had the bones of a cat."

"Couldn't get her to eat, neither. My guess is she's trying to starve herself. Indian women will do that when they lose their man. You're gonna have your hands full with this one, Tom. She's gonna be nothin' but trouble. Get rid of her."

Tom took his knife and stabbed it into the middle of the table. He pulled out two cups and brought down his bottle of whiskey, pouring for each of them.

He handed McVain one. "Here, warm up your cranky old bones with this and mind your own business. This one is gonna bring me sons, do you hear? Don't want to hear none of your lip."

McVain swallowed the liquor down in one gulp and put the cup down on the table. He made one last attempt to spit into the spittoon, as he wiped his mouth with his shirt.

"Suit yourself, Tom." McVain swooped up his pelts, threw them over his shoulder and hunched from the weight. "I'm headin' north now to collect my traps. I'll see you in a few weeks at the fort."

Tom shook his free hand. "Thanks for watchin' my lassie."

McVain nodded as Tom gave him one last slap on the shoulder and closed the door behind him.

The fire was now hot. He put the black iron pan over the fire and cut several pieces of bacon off the slab hanging on the hook. The pan sizzled and spat. He opened up a can, took out a fistful of coffee, threw it into a pot with water and put that over the fire too. Tom took another swig of liquor and with his knife flipped the bacon over.

With two strides he walked to the bed and untied Morning Glory. Without any effort whatsoever, he pulled her up by the arm, dragged her to the table and roughly seated her.

He pulled two blue-speckled plates from the shelf, shined them up with his elbow and slammed them down on the table. Morning Glory didn't flinch. She didn't care what was going to happen to her. She already felt dead.

Reaching over to the spattering pan, Tom stuck in his knife and pulled out chunks of dripping bacon, dividing them between the two plates. He finished what whiskey was left in his cup and refilled it with coffee. He filled Morning Glory's cup as well.

He sat down opposite her, stuck his knife into the greasy bacon and bit off a hunk, grease trickling from the side of his mouth. He wiped it with his shirt sleeve. Morning Glory never moved a finger.

After a quick swig of coffee that burned his mouth, Tom commanded her, "Eat."

Morning Glory was unresponsive.

Tom jerked to his feet. The chair fell backwards onto the floor with a clatter. Grabbing her by the hair, he pulled her head back and forced a chunk of bacon into her mouth. She immediately spit it out.

With a swift backhand across her face, he knocked her to the ground. With another swift move, he grabbed her by the arm and threw her back in the chair.

"Eat," he again hoarsely commanded.

Nothing had changed. Without respect and pride and freedom, Morning Glory considered herself dead. Frustrated, Tom went into a rage. Any white man or woman would have struggled to stay alive. He could have tormented them with fear of death. Her fear was to stay alive. He could see that. True to his Irish nature, he was not afraid to verbalize.

Pacing back and forth in front of the table, frenzied, he yelled, "I am Thomas Joshua Shaye, from the noble House of Shaye in Ireland. My family is from wealth and power. I went to the third grade. I can read and write. How many people do you know who can do that? I can outhunt, outshoot, outfight any man or brave alive. I am a prize to any woman. You will be my woman."

Morning Glory was unimpressed by the sounds of his words. She judged a man by his actions, not his words.

Again he pulled her head backwards and forced another piece of meat into her mouth. She would not chew or swallow, so he poured hot coffee down her throat. She gagged and vomited.

He could see he was getting nowhere. With any other person, he would have slit her throat in one mighty sweep. This one he wanted alive.

The cabin was getting cold again. The wood supply had dwindled in his absence. He took the ax off the wall, grabbed his deerskin jacket and marched out the door.

The moment he stepped out, the cabin door slammed behind him. He heard the bolt go down across it from the inside. He ran to the window and the shutters slammed shut in his face.

Wildly he pounded on the door. "Open this door now or I'll chop it down and beat you bloody."

She did not.

He chopped through the door with several good swings of the ax and kicked it open. Morning Glory stood back against the far wall. With a roar he thrust the ax straight at her. It embedded into the wall right above her head. She never flinched. He knew she would have preferred the ax to cut her in two.

Never before had he been so frustrated or felt so helpless. Because he was so strong and forceful, others always bent to his wishes. This slight woman with piercing, sorrowful eyes wouldn't budge.

Her wrists were too raw to bind, so he picked her up and threw her onto the bed. He turned to the fire to stoke it once more with what little wood remained. He closed what was left of the door and pulled a chair in front of it, tilting it back so that he could recline in it. That is where he slept the night, guarding the broken door.

* * *

The sun poked through the broken gaps in the door. Morning Glory awoke to her worst fear: she was still alive.

Tom got up from his chair, tried to stretch out his back and strode to the fire. He stoked it to a flame, put the iron frying pan over the fire and cut more pieces of bacon. The pan came alive with sizzling grease.

He reached to the shelf and pulled down a tin can. With his fist he pulled out a handful of coffee and threw it into a pot with water. That too went over the fire. Seeing that the plates and cups were still dirty from the night before, he threw them to the side and took down the last two from the shelf.

When the bacon was done and the coffee boiled, he put them on the table and signaled for Morning Glory to join him. She did not. He dragged her to the chair and forced her down.

He lit his pipe and waited for her to eat. She did not. He quickly inhaled his bacon and chugged down his coffee, then put his feet up on the table, tilting back the chair to accommodate him.

"Well, lassie, I figured as much," he said, looking at her closely. Then in her dialect he said to her, "Now, you listen to me well. Your village should have moved west while the moving was good. Now they are in danger. Schalute has been raiding every campsite he comes across, looking for you.

"My chief is in a bind. The town's people are demanding that all villages east of the big river be dispersed. As you know, he already moved out most of the Sacs and the Fox. He never bothered much with your little village because they kept to themselves and kept out of sight.

"Things are different now. Schalute is out there making an awful fuss. He's stopped every wagon on Stagecoach Road, scaring the whites half to death.

"If Schalute is told to move, you know he won't leave without you. That leaves my chief no choice but to go in shooting. You know as well as I do that your village is too small to fight the cavalry. There's hardly a rifle in the village. Bows and arrows are no match for rifles. They will all be killed."

Morning Glory stiffened at what he was saying. She was becoming horrified at the reality of it.

"Part of the reason that the fort never bothered much with them is because I have always told them how unarmed your village was. But now that Schalute and his braves are becoming a threat, he won't blink twice at taking action, especially with the town's people on his butt.

"I want you to be my wife. I want sons."

Morning Glory was shocked. She shook her head no. "I am married to Dancing Eagle, no other."

"I don't think you understand. Dancing Eagle has gone off half-cocked too. He will probably be among the first to die. The only way to save your people from sure annihilation is to marry me. I have to convince Schalute and Dancing Eagle that you stayed with me willingly, that you agreed to be my wife. The council has to receive word that they will have peace if you stay with me.

"If you marry me, I can tell my chief that you are the insurance he needs so that the fort will not be attacked by Schalute. I am the head scout. The fort is mostly run by scouts and volunteer militia. They are under my command. I can protect your people. The commander is influenced by my words and actions."

Morning Glory's heart pounded like thunder. His words whirled past her ears. She could see no way out. She had known since she was a little girl that her purpose was to protect her People.

She would be among the walking dead. If her People believed she had run off with a white man, she would be dead in their eyes. Dancing Eagle's heart would be broken. Schalute would be disgraced. She would never be able to see the ones she loved. Two Moons – oh, how could she never see Two Moons again? Yet what choice did she have?

She also knew that her People needed to be on that sacred point of land. They were there to protect it. It was the land of the ancients, a window to the inner world. They could not leave. If forced to, they would have to die and protect it with their spirits. But they couldn't leave.

"Lassie, you are beautiful beyond compare. I will never let you go anyway. You might as well stop fighting me and help your people. If you don't, I promise you they will all die. What is your answer? Will you be my woman?"

Numbly she nodded her head yes as one lone tear rolled down her cheek.

Tom shot out of his chair, leaving it to tumble noisily to the floor. He picked her up out of the chair and held her high, dancing a jig around the cabin. She simply hung like a rag doll, not having the strength to do much else. Her spirit was gone. Only the shell of her body was left.

Finally putting her down, he picked up his ax and reached for a saw. "I'll fix this door for you, chop some firewood and fetch some water from the river, then I'll go to the fort to make arrangements. Have to talk to the preacher. I have to get you some proper clothes too. Can't get married in those rags. Has to be a proper Christian weddin'."

CHAPTER 12

Commander Worthington believed the way to control the Indians was to Christianize them. He wanted to become a territorial governor. His political speeches spouted the notion that the savages had to be Christianized to bring peace between the whites and the Indians.

Preacher Louis Wisner had heard Commander Worthington's speeches and offered his services. The preacher had a different gain in mind. If he could establish a Christian community, the community would have to supply him with land and tithes. And this area was a great spot for fur trading. It was right on the Mississippi River, between St. Louis and Canada, a growing, thriving region. The only thing stopping growth was the Indians.

Thomas Shaye was a powerful and fearless leader of men. He knew the land and many of the Indian tongues. He had traded for years with many villages, making friends with them. The only village that wouldn't accept him was the Eagle tribe. Schalute had an intense dislike for him.

Three summers before, Tom had spotted Morning Glory walking through the village. He tried to trade with Schalute for the girl. Schalute had gone wild. "She is our princess and will produce sons of a chief. She is not to marry a white!" he shouted hoarsely. During the argument, Dancing Eagle strode up with his arrow drawn from his quiver and stood intently by Schalute's side.

Tom would not back off. "I will give you ten horses for that maiden and all the furs you require. I want her for my wife."

Dancing Eagle signalled to his band of braves. Shaye was surrounded in a moment. Dancing Eagle and another brave each grabbed him by an arm and shoved him roughly toward his canoe.

In their canoes, they escorted Shaye down the river for half a day. Dancing Eagle shot an arrow into the center of Shaye's canoe before he and his braves silently turned back toward the village.

Since that time, Shaye had never been welcomed into the village. Jim McMellows and Gene Baptiste had to do his trading. He had sworn from that day on to have that girl. Now he had her and he would do anything to keep her.

On the way to the fort, Tom stopped at Stalley's saloon. The sign had been shot down the middle, splitting the name.

A French fur trader came in with a supply of buckskin dresses from Indian villages he traded with. The wives of the white officers bought them to keep as souvenirs or to give to their servants at the fort.

The Frenchman had one very special dress with him this time. It was a white one with fringe and intricately designed beading, a ceremonial dress.

Tom wanted that dress for Morning Glory. "I have pelts I'll trade you for that dress, Frenchman."

The Frenchman walked up to the bar and ordered a shot of whiskey. "I have plenty of pelts of my own. What can you give me that I don't already have?"

Tom stood with his feet wide. "I can spare your life!"

The Frenchman put down his drink and slowly turned to face him. His hand was over the knife he carried in a shield. The hardened trappers in the bar jumped up and started cheering the Frenchman on. The man was famous for his knife fights. Pelts were thrown into the corner for wagers. Whoever won the fight would get all the pelts, plus the dress.

The usual procedure for a fight such as this was that the men sat across from each other at a table. A knife was held in one hand. The other hand was tied to the leg of a chair. Their feet were also tied to the chairs. There was one knife to the table, and each man stretched his arm across the table, trying to cut the other one. The first one to draw blood was the winner. They rotated and locked arms to wrestle. The knife would come back and forth across the table, toward each other's faces.

As the Frenchman lost his grip, Tom swiftly cut his wrist. The Frenchman came around and slammed his arm down. Tom suddenly reached down with his free arm, took a knife out of his boot and lunged across the table, stabbing the Frenchman right below the jugular.

The other men were shocked. Tom had broken the basic trust of this game. He cut his bindings and got up. "Now, is anybody else going to go against me? They will die right here!"

The rest backed off and left. Tom picked up all the pelts and the dress, and went on. Morning Glory would be forced to wear his sin.

Tom went straight to the commander's office when he arrived at the fort.

"Commander Worthington, I have the solution to your problems. I am going to marry Schalute's princess. That will bring a bond between the Indians and the whites. It will bring a forced peace."

Commander Worthington shot up. "Tarnation, Tom, how'd you pull that off? Schalute would never let his princess marry a white man!"

Tom gave a wry smile. "I gave her a proposition she couldn't refuse. Believe me, Commander, this will work. That princess has great power over the village. If we can get her Christianized, the whole village will follow. Peace will again reign upon this land. You'll be elected territorial governor for sure. Will you and your lovely wife be witnesses, Commander?"

Commander Worthington stuck out his hand to shake Tom's. "It would be my honor. I've heard a lot about that princess. Be interested to see her."

"I have to find the preacher and set things up with him." Tom bolted out the door, excited.

Now the problem he had to face was the preacher. The preacher was always trying to make him a Christian. Hated that man, he did. When Tom was roaring drunk, he was nasty. Since the preacher wouldn't preach to him when he was liquored up, he headed to the saloon first.

Having his fill, he swaggered out the saloon door. "There you are," Tom said as the beady-eyed preacher from New York happened to be walking by. Tom reached out and roughly grabbed him by the shoulder to stop him.

"I'm fixin' to be wed, preacher. You're gonna marry me to that blue-eyed princess of Schalute's."

The preacher seemed thunderstruck. "You're gonna marry a heathen? Why, I've been to that village. I've seen that girl there. During their heathen ceremonies, that girl wears a crown of feathers and stones and talks to the spirits. Works with the devil, she does."

Tom seized the preacher by the throat. "You watch what you're sayin' about my woman, do you hear?"

The preacher gasped and nodded. He straightened out the lapel on his dark suit and dusted off his jacket, trying to regain his composure.

"Come to think of it, Tom, this might just be the best thing for those savages. If we can keep that girl out of that village, then maybe we can Christianize them."

Two days later Tom and Morning Glory rode their horses through the gate of the fort. Morning Glory was dressed in a white dress he had bought for her at the trading post. Her hair was combed. She wore an eagle feather in her braided hair and a medicine bag around her neck.

Heads turned as they rode into the wide, dusty yard of the fort. They dismounted and stopped by the water trough to let the horses drink before they tied them to the post.

Jim McMellows, a tall, bearded Scotsman, walked up to Tom's sorrel horse. He rested his hand on its haunches, crossed one leg in front of the other and said, "So this is the woman everyone is all fired up about. I guess she is worth fighting a war over, huh, Tom?"

Tom didn't like this remark. "Aye, Jim, she is. Got anything more to say about it?"

Jim shook his head. "No, Tom. That's about it." Jim turned his head around again to take another look as he walked away. This one haunted him. He didn't know why.

Tom helped her down from her bay mare. Unlike Tom, she preferred to ride bareback. She stood straight as she looked quickly around at the inside of the fort, something she had never seen before. As people began to gawk at her, she lowered her eyes so that they could not see into her heart and soul.

Tom led her by the hand to the commander's quarters. The first person she saw was a shifty-eyed man dressed in black, holding a black book. He had round spectacles that hung low on his nose. To keep them up, he squinted his eyes.

"Commander and Mrs. Worthington," said Tom to the other two people in the room, "this is Morning Glory. She is to be my wife."

Commander Worthington walked toward Tom, reaching around to pat him on the back. "She is beautiful for an Indian. Not as round as most. But where did she get those blue eyes?"

"That's why they are fighting over her, Commander. She's a

prize in any man's eyes."

Morning Glory didn't know what the two men were saying to each other. Tom was not translating any of this conversation for her, but she knew she didn't like it.

Mary Worthington was a well-fed woman, with streaks of gray in her tied-up hair. She wore a blue bonnet on her head to match her dress with its high, white lace collar. She looked quite proper.

"Why, she is just a girl!" Mary whispered to her husband.

Commander Worthington simply shrugged his shoulders. "They marry them young, those injuns do."

Mary walked in front of Morning Glory and extended her hand in greeting. Morning Glory was not used to this exchange and didn't know what to do. As she looked up into Mary's eyes, Mary melted. There was an instant bond. Mary put her arms around Morning Glory's shoulders and hugged her gently.

Morning Glory took a deep breath. This was the first decent treatment she'd received since she was abducted, but at this point it was of little comfort. She was about to embark upon a life that she truly dreaded. She didn't know how she was going to bear it, being with a man she found repulsive. Had it not been for her People, she would have surely killed herself.

While the formalities of introduction were going on, Morning Glory was watching the preacher out of the corner of her eye. He had been practicing the ceremony to himself, pacing back and forth, hands waving in the air, periodically thumping a black book that he was carrying around. She didn't know what he was saying but she thought he was truly mad.

"Well, Tom, let's get started here," said the commander. "Preacher, you stand right in front of these two. My wife and I will stand to the side."

The squinty-faced preacher mumbled under his breath, "Don't usually bother to marry no heathens."

Tom grabbed him by the throat. "What did you say, preacher?"

The preacher's spectacles slipped down to the edge of his nose and one hand flew in the air, as if to wave a truce.

"I said, she's a pretty injun, sure enough, Tom."

"I thought that's what you said. I'm a Christian man. We are going to do this proper."

"Sure thing, Tom. Sure thing." The preacher opened his black book and started reciting words that had no meaning to Morning Glory. He would say a few words to Tom and then look over his spectacles for a reply. Tom would answer, "I do."

Whenever he would pause and look over his spectacles toward Morning Glory, Tom would say, "She does."

"I now pronounce you man and wife!"

Tom grabbed Morning Glory and kissed her harshly. She closed her eyes and turned her head away, repulsed. Mary Worthington was shocked. Until this point, she hadn't realized that Morning Glory had been kidnapped and forced into this marriage. Had she known, she would not have witnessed it.

CHAPTER 13

Morning Glory knew that unless Dancing Eagle truly believed she had betrayed him and wanted to stay with this white man, he would continue to search for her and lead raiding parties. She had to find a way to make him believe this lie, but it would tear both his heart and hers. If her People were to survive, she had to make this sacrifice.

Tom knew Indian ways. He prepared two canoes full of gifts to send to Schalute in exchange for his bride. The canoe contained rifles, ammunition, pots, beads, blankets — all things that the People needed badly. He sent word that the tribe would be untouched and safe because of the union between himself and the princess.

Tom had political ambitions. He knew this would look good on his record and raise him in the ranks of the cavalry. His goal was to be governor one day.

Even though Schalute dedicated his life to the safety of Glory of the Morning, he knew without question that her destiny was to protect the People. She knew that despite his love for her, he would have to accept the decision of the council. This arrangement would be exactly what the council was looking for.

Dancing Eagle, on the other hand, would be torn from his heart right to his soul. This was unbearable for her. She had to figure out a way to keep him from continuing to look for her; otherwise he might get killed. The council wouldn't back Dancing Eagle in his search, and one lone man would surely get killed. She couldn't bear that. In order to keep him alive, she would end up breaking his heart. It was her hope that he could eventually forget and find another love, for many sought after him.

Gene Baptiste and Jim McMellows, traders from the Magnus

Trading Company whom Tom had known for years, were selected to go to the village with the presents and the message to be presented to the council, Schalute and Dancing Eagle.

Baptiste and McMellows arrived at the village on a cold, windy afternoon. The sky was overcast and the air was heavy with pending snow. As they approached the bank, they turned to find ten braves aiming arrows at them. Both of them immediately raised their hands above their heads and in the Indian tongue asked for Schalute.

"We bring news of the princess," they immediately said to keep themselves from becoming riddled with holes.

Dancing Eagle had just returned from a hunt and was tanning a hide with a rock. He was solemn and surly. He showed no interest in life. Most of the People avoided him because he became unapproachable.

The council decided not to alert Dancing Eagle about the message, because they didn't know if they could control him long enough for the members of the council to get all the information they needed. Schalute had the two men quietly brought into the council lodge where the other council members had gathered.

Baptiste chose to speak. Schalute had traded with him before. Baptiste was a Frenchman with a heavy, dark beard, who wore fringed buckskin garb and carried a knife. He was slight of build but wiry. He knew the land. He knew the People.

"I bring you news. Your princess is alive and well."

Schalute and the council members glanced at each other with relief, but they knew all was not clear.

"Your princess is an honored one, a woman of beauty. She has chosen to stay with one of our leaders who will treat her like a princess. He carries much wealth and position."

Schalute could not be contained. He shouted, "No! She is already married to one of us. She was already honored by us. She would not willingly do this! She would not disgrace herself by staying with white man. Her place is among the People."

The council looked at each other and agreed.

Baptiste had to talk slowly, measuring each word. This was indeed a touchy situation.

"The princess has acknowledged that her destiny is to protect your people. She can best do this by a communion of white man and red man. She is now married to a leader in the white man's army. He promised your village would be safe as long as she stays with him. Their union will protect your people."

"Who is this man?" Schalute demanded.

Baptiste looked down and tried to think how best to put this. "We cannot identify this man. He knows she left a husband behind, and he would look for her if he knew where to go. He acknowledges that any man would look for such a beautiful woman. Therefore we can only tell you she is being cared for. As long as your village keeps to itself and does not cause trouble among the whites, you will not be forced to leave. The other tribes are being forced to move west of the big river. You can stay as long as there is union between this man and your princess."

Schalute knew they were cornered. The white men were removed before the council spoke together.

Dancing Finger spoke, his voice barely more audible than a whisper. "Twelve winters ago, our princess was brought to us as a gift. Now she is presenting us with a gift of life for our People. I feel we must honor her gift, as we know it is being given with great sacrifice. She is leaving behind a loved one. She is leaving her family and People. For her, this is the greatest sacrifice of all. I honor her."

Old Wise Owl spoke. His eyes were clouded with age but his mind was full of wisdom. "Our princess carries our heartbeat. We live because she carries us in her heart. We will always know that her heart is here with us. As long as we live, we will know she lives. With every breath we take, we will know she has provided that breath for us. We are too small a village to fight the white army. Black Hawk fought the white man with hundreds of brave warriors, only to lose his home and the battle. She has won the battle for us with her heart. We cannot dishonor her by refusing such a gift of life."

All of the council agreed. Schalute knew in his heart they were right, but he was torn. He had raised her by his side. He didn't know how he was going to convince Dancing Eagle to let her go.

The two white men were called back to the council lodge.

Schalute spoke. "We will agree to such an arrangement, but only under the condition that my daughter be honored and treated with respect for the rest of her life. She is from the Sun. If she is not taken care of, the sun shall no longer shine."

McMellows spoke. "I have seen your princess. She has the sky in her eyes. Right here and now, I shall vow to protect her myself. I don't know why, but I too carry her in my heart."

Baptiste took something from his pouch and handed it to Schalute. "This was given to me to be returned to the one known as Dancing Eagle. I am told to deliver this message:

The butterfly now lands in a different bush.

Schalute looked into his hand. It was the necklace Dancing Eagle had given to Morning Glory as a wedding present. Schalute shivered. He knew this would destroy Dancing Eagle.

Baptiste added, "In addition, Dancing Eagle is to know she will be given riches far greater than she could ever receive here. Her new man has wealth and can buy her anything her heart desires."

Two Moons quietly slipped out of the village and followed the two scouts to their canoes, carrying a small bundle wrapped in a blanket. When they reached their canoes, he startled them. He appeared through the trees as though walking out of thin air.

Two Moons handed McMellows the bundle. "I know you carry Morning Glory in your heart. Give this to her as my wedding present. It will bring her comfort and safety." McMellows nodded in agreement.

Two Moons had given McMellows the crown. He knew that with the crown she would always be able to send and receive messages across the land. He would always know through this device if she were safe.

Schalute waited until the canoes were unloaded and the men left before he approached Dancing Eagle.

Dancing Eagle was still absent-mindedly tanning his hide. He seemed unaware of what was going on around him. In fact, he didn't care about much anymore. His spirit had left so it wouldn't feel his pain. No one could seem to get his spirit to come back.

Schalute stood before him, holding something in his hand.

"Dancing Eagle, I have something for you."

Schalute handed him the necklace.

Dancing Eagle shot up. "Where is she?" he asked with the first look of spirit he had shown in weeks.

Schalute put his arm across Dancing Eagle's shoulder and said, "Come with me. We shall walk. We shall talk. I don't want to talk to you with others around here."

Dancing Eagle knew this was not good. He could tell that something was terribly wrong. His heart began to pound. His mind began to dance around in his head. His heart was in his throat. He could not speak.

They walked until the sun was about to set.

"Sit down, Dancing Eagle. We must talk. Morning Glory is not here. She sent this to you. She must now stay with another man."

Dancing Eagle shot up and paced wildly. "What are you saying? She is alive? I will go and get her."

Schalute proceeded to explain about the new arrangement.

Dancing Eagle went wild. "What are you saying to me? You are not her husband. I am! You had no right to make such a decision. You had no right at all!"

"It was Morning Glory's decision. You have to accept that."

"No! She is being forced into this. Can't you see that? I have waited for her most of my life! She would not choose another man so easily."

"Dancing Eagle, you cannot see beyond your own heart. This is not about you and her. This is about her destiny, her People. She had to choose her love for her People over her own desires. This is not a decision she made easily. This is not a decision the council made easily. My heart is broken too. I am chief. My People have to come before my own desires. She is of that nature too."

Dancing Eagle wouldn't hear anything more of what Schalute had to explain. His heart thundered in his ears. He kept pacing. The only thing he could remember hearing before Schalute finally walked away was, "The butterfly now lands in another bush."

Nothing could have torn him apart more than that sentence. The little songs they'd sung back and forth to each other during their youth were very private, very special. For her to deliver that message was more than he could bear.

Days passed. Dancing Eagle never returned to the village. He was shamed. His woman had left him for another. Her message cut him to the core. In his mourning, he began to hate the Morning. It was the only way he could deal with his loss. Before, he had hope that he might find her. Now his hope was shattered through humiliation.

"She left me for white man's riches," he told himself. "Well, he can have her. And to think that she was to have my son. Through her I would have a son to carry on my blood, my purpose for being. Now she will have a white-eye's son. I don't ever want to see her again, not after what she has done to me."

As the moons came and went, Dancing Eagle became a recluse. He talked to no one. He barely provided food for his brother's wife and child. His mother chastised him for not taking care of his horse. He didn't care. His spirit was gone. He was more dead than alive. He walked in shame, anger and loneliness. The only one who could make his spirit alive was taken from him.

CHAPTER 14

Commander Worthington insisted that all Indians who worked within the fort be Christians. Therefore, the preacher set out to Christianize Morning Glory.

The first thing he tried to do was to get the crown from her, insisting that it was being used for Satan's work. The preacher knew Tom had given Morning Glory the crown. Tom had talked too much one night after he got all liquored up.

Morning Glory vehemently refused. The preacher then complained to Tom, insisting, finally, that he had to have it. He told Tom she refused to be anything but a heathen.

Tom didn't know what to do. He tried to talk Morning Glory into giving the preacher the crown. She knew it was sacred. She would rather die than give it to him. Every time the preacher complained, Tom beat her, trying to get her to become Christian. If Morning Glory could become convinced that the crown was the work of Satan, she might give up the crown.

Morning Glory steadfastly tried to explain the oneness of all to him. She was as stubborn as he was.

"Woman, in the morning I am riding to the fort with that damned crown of yours and giving it to the preacher, once and for all. Then maybe he will leave both you and me alone."

Morning Glory panicked. The preacher could not have this crown. In her mind, he was evil. During the night, she sneaked out of bed, wrapped the crown in a blanket and ran. She ran until she thought her heart would burst, then, just before sunrise, she dug a hole and buried it, praying to the spirits to protect it. When the time was right, she would come back and reclaim this sacred object.

As the sun rose, she created false tracks to lead trackers away from her hiding spot. She followed the river back, only to meet a very angry Tom on horseback.

"What did you do with it, woman?" he yelled as he leaped from his sidestepping horse and grabbed her by the hair.

She would not respond. He threw her to the ground and kicked her in the ribs. Pain shot through her, taking her breath away. To breathe caused intense pain. He had cracked her ribs. She still would not tell. Tom knew he could kill her before she would tell. The crown was gone. The preacher would be furious. Commander Worthington would not be happy.

Morning Glory fulfilled her promise to stay with Thomas Shaye. They stayed in his cabin outside of Kaskaskia, near the Mississippi River. Since Kaskaskia was the seat of the Illinois government and Tom had political ambitions, it was perfect for him. He could travel down the Mississippi River to get to St. Louis on business whenever he needed to.

She cooked, although Tom hated Indian cooking. She mechanically fulfilled her wifely duties, but her spirit was gone. Morning Glory never gave Thomas Shaye any passion, though it was what he wanted the most. He wanted her to love and respect him but she couldn't. Nevertheless, he lusted for her all the time.

Morning Glory was driving him wild. "I feel like a bear chained to a tree," Tom would yell. Everything he did, she would turn against him. He would beat her up, then he would leave because he couldn't handle the fact that he had beaten her up. There was a brothel nearby. Tom had a woman there because he wasn't getting consensual sex from Morning Glory. He would go off to his "lowering time," as he called it, his time to release.

He would finish off with the woman at the brothel, then go back to Morning Glory wanting more. Tom kept waiting for her to submit to his passions, but she never did. He had his way nevertheless. He would bring her presents from the fort or from his raids. She just put them in a corner and never touched them again.

He wanted her to wear the kind of clothes the white women from the fort wore. She would only wear her buckskins. Since he was a trapper, she always had an ample supply of skins and was skilled at making beautiful beading on all of her clothes. He didn't want her to look Indian. She did anyway, with elegance.

Tom tried to teach Morning Glory a Scottish dance. It was called the Dance of the Three Rocks, and through it he could express himself. Three rocks were put into an oblong area. After he got liquored up, he would clap his hands and jig around the rocks. At the last rock, he would grab her and hold her against him tightly. She would always fight it.

"Someday you will love me, lassie, because I am all you've got," he said to her time and again.

She would just stare off, looking blankly into the air. She knew that if she showed any emotion, he could take it from her. She went within to hide. That way he couldn't reach her spirit, only her body, which didn't matter. This enraged him. He wanted her spirit to lash out at him: then he could snatch it. She wouldn't do it.

Tom started to teach her to speak English. She learned quickly, picking up his Irish accent. He wanted her to wear a cross around her neck.

"Thomas, I do not understand. How can the whites think that everything is not one? How could they think that the land is not connected to the heartbeat of every man? How can they think the sky is not connected to the water, and that all man is not connected to everything they see? Do they not see through their eyes that everything depends upon everything?"

Thomas took out his black book and pointed to the cross. "Jesus Christ is the only thing that matters. You have to go by the good book," he said impatiently.

"I am trying to understand what you told me. A man many generations ago called Jesus Christ ruled the Earth. Correct?"

"Aye, lassie. He was a god!"

"If he was a god, why did your people not worship him? Why did they kill him, and why do you worship the cross they hung him on?"

Walking toward the fire on which she had a pot of stew simmering, she stopped and turned back to look at Tom. "Why do your people not honor what their God taught them? Mary has read many things to me from your black book. I do not remember him saying it was right to kill anything. I remember something in that book that said, 'Though shalt not kill.' But you do, Tom. You kill my People all of the time. You trap animals and leave them tearing themselves apart trying to escape the pain. You don't pray over them to send their spirits on their way when you take from them."

Morning Glory looked at him, waiting for a sensible answer. Impatient that he did not satisfy her question, she went on. "My People believe there is a Creator, and He created everything. That is why we honor everything. You only honor the cross that killed

Him and a black book with words I do not understand."

"I understand the book, lassie. It says that we should destroy heathens, and that I do," Tom said with some pride.

Morning Glory stood up with indignant defiance. "Who are the heathens, Thomas? I think the heathens are the ones who do not honor creation. I think the heathens are the ones who think they own creation. I think the heathens are the ones who kill to try to steal creation!"

Thomas slammed his whiskey cup down on the table. "Damned fool woman! I am tired of talking nonsense with you. The heathens are the ones who don't wear the cross. Do you hear me? Now, you wear this cross like the rest of the women at the fort."

Morning Glory flung it across the room. "I will not wear the symbol of death. I will only wear life. She pointed to the eagle feather in her headband. I am of the Eagle. My spirit flies to the highest Source. You cannot take that away from me."

Tom would have slugged her, but he was too drunk to move fast enough and she ran into the woods. By the time she got back from collecting herbs and spring flowers, he had passed out cold.

Whenever Tom was scouting for the cavalry, he would bring Morning Glory to the fort. Morning Glory and Mary Worthington became close friends. Mary, in her late thirties, had never had children. Morning Glory was like a daughter to her.

Mary spent time teaching Morning Glory to read and write. That pleased Morning Glory. It gave her a sense of worth and knowledge. She never turned down knowledge that made sense to her. In turn, Morning Glory taught her about herbs and healing.

Mary thought it proper to try to convert Morning Glory to Christianity. She often read to her from the Bible.

Morning Glory explained how her People would ask the spirits of the animals they hunted for permission to send their spirits on. She explained how they had ceremonies to honor the sun, the moon, the seasons and the hunts. She explained that they thanked everything they ate. They thanked the sun for rising in the east.

Mary countered by saying that was blasphemous. She should only honor Jesus Christ and the cross. Morning Glory could make no sense of honoring a cross and not the sun. Although they had many discussions, she never understood how this could be preferable.

Mary Worthington would say, "I love you anyway, even though you have simple ways."

Morning Glory showed her how to tan a hide and how to bead moccasins and headbands. Mary didn't have much use for such things, but she found it interesting.

There were many Frenchmen at the fort, so Morning Glory picked up a bit of a French accent too. Mary Worthington used to love watching Morning Glory in action. This beautiful young Indian girl walked among the men in the fort when the doctor was not there, healing whatever wounded were brought to her.

The men were enchanted with her blue eyes and blue-black hair. She always walked proudly and could converse with most people at the fort with her curious mix of Indian, Irish and Scotch tongues with a French accent. Now she could even read and write a bit, which most men in the fort couldn't do at all.

The mornings were again becoming hard on Morning Glory. She was carrying his child. She did not want a child sired by a white man, but the spirit came to her anyway.

Tom hauled her around with him and the other trappers on his trips. Morning Glory hated it. She despised trapping animals, taking them without asking their spirits first. She would always pray over the trapped ones, enraging Tom.

Michael McVain was always with them. He constantly spat upon the sacred earth, dishonoring it. McVain disliked all Indians, especially her. He wanted the land her people were on for the iron ore. Because of her, Tom had made a deal to allow her people to stay. Tom and Michael got into a huge fight over it. McVain took quite a beating from Tom, and never forgave Morning Glory for her part in it.

Samuel White worked for the Magnus Trading Company, based in St. Louis. He was the territorial representative from the company and would head north each season to check on the traders from the company and exchange supplies. He also brought the payroll. He had a wife and daughter in St. Louis and would write to them and send them money.

Sam was a large, square-built man with dark hair and a beard. Often he wore a plaid shirt, fringed leggings and a fringed buckskin jacket. He was proud of his name. "Samuel is straight from the Bible," he would say.

Jim McMellows and Gene Baptiste were always with Tom and Morning Glory on their trapping trips. They treated Morning Glory with respect. Often, when Tom was drunk and got violent and demanding with her, Jim fended him off, distracting him onto another subject. Jim did not want to fight with Tom, because few men had ever gotten the best of him. When they did, a mysterious death befell them later.

Houser Woolin was another one with the group. They called him Hank. Hank was a short old German man with a bulbous red nose. He tanned all of the pelts that they trapped. Hank always wore an old army cap, a plaid flannel shirt and suspenders that held up brown pants that were too big. When he didn't have his mouth full of chewing tobacco, he chewed the stub of a cigar. Sometimes he would do both – chew tobacco and spit out of one side of his mouth with the cigar stub in the other. Morning Glory couldn't take his manners either. He had a foul mouth and hated women in general, thought they were all a thorn in his side. To Morning Glory, he smelled more vile than all of them put together. He worked with dead carcasses without respect, and that repulsed her even more.

Hank had a string of mules to haul all of the pelts and gear. He was as harsh with his animals as he was with her. He had a gimpy leg because a while back one of his mules had kicked him. She felt he probably deserved it. Arthritis had set in and he hobbled most of the time. He often would have to reach into the cold streams to pull out the traps and then clean the skins, so his hands were curled with arthritis too. It made it difficult for him to pull open the metal traps.

Gene Baptiste was a loner. He didn't care much for working with a group such as this. He didn't want to admit it to himself or anyone around him, but he found himself drawn to Morning Glory. Women were scarce in these parts, especially ones like her. She would cook for the group. He would quietly watch as she searched daily for herbs for the food. He wondered at what she was doing when she would kneel and talk to the plant before taking only part of it, never all of it. He watched her as she turned away every time a trap was brought in.

"Damn it, Tom," Baptiste said one day. "Why don't you let that girl go back to her people where she belongs? She will never be happy with the likes of us."

Tom whirled on his feet, drawing his knife in the same motion. Startled, Baptiste lifted his hands and said, "I don't want to fight you, Tom. I'm just telling you, if you love her, let her go. She's not one of us. This way of life is sucking the life out of her. I know Schalute and respect him. He wants her back bad."

Through clenched teeth Tom said, "If I can't have her, nobody can. Now prepare to die."

Morning Glory screamed, then pleaded, something she never did for herself. "Tom, please, spare him. He meant no harm."

"Hank, get her out of here, now," Tom commanded.

Morning Glory was repulsed as Hank came near her. She tried to run and she could smell him as he grabbed her. He clamped one hand over her mouth and the other around her waist as he dragged her away.

Jim and Sam were out setting traps this quiet spring day. McVain made no attempt to help Baptiste. He didn't care for Frenchmen or Indians.

"I've seen your eyes following my woman, Gene. You knew she belongs to me. If you think you are a better man, prove it, or prepare to die."

Baptiste knew this was it. He was a good man with a knife, but Tom was relentless, ruthless and much stronger. It was over in a second — Tom plunged the knife into his heart before Baptiste could even get one swing in.

Morning Glory was sickened. She fainted as she felt Baptiste die. She didn't care what happened to her, but she had never wanted another person to die because of her. It was more than she could bear.

Jim came back from his traps to find Morning Glory passed out, with Hank standing over her. He thought Hank had harmed her. With one quick slug, he knocked Hank out cold and scooped Morning Glory up, carrying her back to camp.

When Jim and Sam arrived with Morning Glory, they saw Tom and McVain hauling off Baptiste.

Standing there, holding an unconscious Morning Glory, Jim yelled out, "What in thunder is going on here?"

"Baptiste got out of line, Jim. No concern of yours," McVain added.

Morning Glory began to come to. She turned her head to see the bottoms of Baptiste's boots as they dragged him away.

Tom looked wild with fury. "Put her down, Jim, or you'll be next."

"Please put me down before someone else gets hurt," she pleaded.

Tom looked unsympathetically at Morning Glory. "Now you see what I mean when I tell you that you're mine. Remember that. If I can't have you, nobody can. If another man ever looks at you, he is dead."

Morning Glory began to vomit. Her head began to whirl. She couldn't believe this horror. The child she was carrying belonged to a murderer, a man of no soul.

Sam stood there in shock. Since he only traveled through seasonally, he didn't know Tom as well as Jim did.

"I'm going to have to report this to the company, Tom. You can't go around killing company men like that," he said.

"A man's got a right to defend what is his. When a man has a woman, he defends her and guards her. Baptiste was out of line. That is what you're going to tell the company." He drew his knife. "I have a right to defend myself. Ain't that right, Michael?"

McVain spit into the newly budding bushes. "Sure the hell is, Tom. Man's got a right to do that. He sure enough would have killed Tom, had Tom not got him first. That's a fact." He finished his statement by wiping his chin with his sleeve and putting more tobacco into his mouth.

Sam was puzzled. He looked to Jim for more confirmation. Jim knew better. He said nothing.

"That man got any family that needs to be contacted?" Sam inquired.

"Nay. He's just a drifter, like all Frenchmen. Frenchmen are always after other men's wives," Tom said.

"Well, let's give the man a proper burial," Sam insisted.

"I'll read over him with the good book."

A shallow grave was dug into the muddy ground. The rain had just subsided that morning. Everything was wet, as though it carried Morning's tears.

Morning Glory chanted a song to send his spirit home. Her chant haunted Samuel and angered Michael and Tom. They couldn't stand her chants and cut her short.

Samuel could see she was upset, so he offered to read another prayer from the Bible. She knew he meant well, but she insisted that his spirit could not find its way home unless the death song was sung. None of the men there understood what she was talking about.

CHAPTER 15

After Morning Glory's disappearance, Rising Sun had weakened considerably. The family had been disrupted. Schalute was always in a rage. The girls were all but outcasts. Shadow Dancer had gone wild. Shortly after Morning Glory left, Rising Sun became one of the first in the village to die from smallpox. Red Hawk's wife was also stricken and was now dead, leaving behind a girl child, who was taken in by an aunt.

Many in the village perished with this white man's disease. The village no longer had the protection of the spirits. Some of the villagers said that when Morning Glory left, the spirits had to go with her to protect her. That left the village unprotected. Some even began to blame her for that.

Blue Dove had come into her moon cycle — none too soon, as far as Schalute was concerned. He had already made arrangements for her to wed Wonka, the son of a chief from one of the clans of the Sac tribe. Since the Black Hawk War, this particular clan had moved west of the Mississippi.

This marriage suited Schalute well. He no longer wanted her in the village after what happened with Morning Glory; it also helped to bond territorial hunting rights between the two tribes.

Blue Dove was sent off without much ceremony. She took little Black Wolf with her; Schalute despised him too. Since she was the oldest girl in the lodge, she was the one who had done most of the cooking. Now it would be up to Gentle Breeze.

Gentle Breeze was terribly unhappy. Her mother was gone. Blue Dove was gone. She thought maybe she could get Dancing Eagle interested in her. She could be a princess too. Her father was chief.

Dancing Eagle would go out on hunts with the braves and half the time come home without the group. He often rode off to be by himself. His smiles were forced and few. He sought no women. He was short-tempered with the band of braves that had previously followed him. One by one they left him too.

Schalute shared his sorrow but had a tribe to run. He tried to get Dancing Eagle involved in council matters but without success. Dancing Eagle simply existed as an empty shell.

"Dancing Eagle," Gentle Breeze called out, as she saw him sitting by the river's edge. "I made you a new pair of moccasins."

Dancing Eagle politely thanked her and continued to look at the river. This infuriated her.

"It's about time you stop mooning about. Morning Glory gave you up for another man, a richer, white man. She even told me someday she would have riches far beyond what she could get in this village. I could make a good wife for you!"

Dancing Eagle became enraged. "You little fool. The riches she talked of were of another place, another time. She didn't mean what came from a white man's mine. You could never replace her. Now leave me alone."

Gentle Breeze hated him for that. She was insulted and lonely. She had no one to turn to. Even Two Moons was upset with what she had done, although he still tried to counsel her.

"You are of the stars, not of this land," she shouted at Two Moons when he tried to talk to her. "I need a man of this world."

Gentle Breeze took to running away. She would be gone for weeks at a time. Sometimes she would visit her sister Blue Dove, who was now with child. Blue Dove liked her sister to stay with her. She was a stranger in her new village. Few of the women talked to her.

CHAPTER 16

Two Moons often spent time with the old wise men of the village. He was always eager to learn the ways of the medicine man. Each medicine man had certain aspects to offer. Old Wise Owl talked to the birds. Deer Runner talked to the animals. Broken Limb talked to the plants.

The medicine men would teach through stories. This night Old Wise Owl spoke. His voice was barely above a whisper, which made one lean toward him to catch his words. His gray hair was wispy. His body was bent with age.

> Our village once had a young brave named Red Leather. He was born on a high-vibrated day in which two suns appeared in the sky. This meant that two embodiments came into one being.
>
> Red Leather would always be of two people, two sides of himself. He had a dark side and a light side. He lived in two polarities. He was very unpredictable.
>
> By the time he'd seen seven winters, he was already committing crimes against his own body and against his own people. They brought him to a shaman to see what had taken over Red Leather.
>
> The shaman was very wise. He told Red Leather not to speak. Red Leather's eyes were of fire. Red Leather felt he had a mission to destroy himself because, as the fire burns, the fire dies.

Old Wise Owl looked toward Two Moons. "Do you understand what I am talking about?"

Two Moons nodded. Old Wise Owl went on.

The shaman said, "You have to keep the fire alive. Keep feeding the fire."

"Now sit and listen," he said. The shaman set him on a rock while he walked around him teaching him about the elements of the wind, air, water and fire, for Red Leather was born of four conditional elements.

We all live in a sea of emotion. All energy thought is brought up by emotion. Red Leather was very in tune with spirit. Whenever there was a thought in the village, he would pick up the thoughts and vibrations. He carried them in a pouch of emotion. He felt, saw and sensed things he couldn't control. Because he couldn't separate information that was being received, his emotions got out of control. He was going crazy at a young age. He felt things he didn't know he was feeling.

Red Leather became animalistic, because he was of the animal sense. He had opened up every vibration in his body. He could sense everything at a high-pitched level. He saw things other men couldn't see. He knew things other men didn't know. This bothered other men. It bothered him, because he didn't know where his awareness was coming from.

The shaman had to reprogram his emotional state of mind so he could live and be part of Earth. He had to be walked through every frame of emotional level. The shaman used the elements to do that.

The shaman brought Red Leather down to the river. They swam together. He said, "Feel every stretch of your arm length in the water, not just the way it drops and the wetness of the water. Feel the vibration of the water. Start learning to use vibration properly."

The shaman took the boy's hand and drew it near the fire. Red Leather pulled his hand back. He didn't burn his hand, but he wanted him to sense the vibration and feeling of fire. Once he learned how fire operated, he taught Red Leather how to put his hand in fire and never be burned, because he had become fire. His hand would become the element of fire, the manifestation of fire. He became blue flame!

The shaman then took Red Leather to the mountain.

He buried Red Leather's whole body in the ground, leaving an opening for his face. A leather mask was placed upon his face.

The shaman walked around him, chanting and talking. "I want you to tell me what you feel in the ground, the vibrations and senses that you feel."

Red Leather told him of the sensations of the land. He felt the land breathe, sweat and tremor. Red Leather then realized he was the effect of the Earth. Now he could disseminate, dissect and disintegrate all the information that he was receiving and feeling.

Red Leather was born gifted, but he turned his mind off. Too much was coming in too quickly. His mechanism of mind could not operate on the sensory devices of the material that he was receiving.

Old Wise Owl looked at Two Moons. "Do you realize why I have told you this story? A shaman believes that all illnesses can be cured if you can get in tune with the elements and find out what information – which you don't even suspect – is being dissected in the physical, mental and spiritual forms. It is discernment of information. It is finding yourself. The shaman taught him to go into himself and find out what causes effect."

Two Moons thanked him with a present of tobacco for the lesson of the day.

CHAPTER 17

The townspeople were up in arms. Because of the forced westward migration of the Indian tribes, there were many skirmishes between the whites and the reds. Tom was called in by the fort to look for renegades with his band of scouts. Most of them consisted of off-season trappers from the Magnus Trading Company.

It was late fall now. The golden leaves had nearly all fallen. The air was damp and chilly and the nights were nearly too bitter for camping out. The horses already had much of their winter coats.

Morning Glory was heavy with child. It was not easy for her to get around. Tom did not want to leave her unattended. In her condition she could not hunt for meat or chop wood, and if she were to go into labor when she was alone at the cabin, she wouldn't be able to get help.

Sam White was not a scout, so he volunteered to provide for Morning Glory in Tom's absence. Sam was the only one Tom trusted with Morning Glory. He was a devoted husband to his wife back home, as well as a Bible thumper. Most of the men at the fort were wild and woman-hungry.

The first thing Sam did was hunt for a buck to supply meat to jerk for the winter. When the weather turned he stayed in the cabin and made a rocking cradle for the soon-to-arrive baby.

Morning Glory watched him carve out this cradle. She had never seen one that rocked so well. She liked the way Sam hummed and sang songs while he worked.

He treated her gently, with respect. He showed her how to cook the white man's way. He got her to start drinking coffee. He told her it was "powerful medicine."

Sam loved her quiet ways. He just liked being around her, being in the same room with her. He couldn't believe how crudely Tom treated a woman of such delicacy.

He began to call her Little Deer. He said, "You are just like a little fawn in a big forest, and you are my dear." He would pat her on the head all the time.

Morning Glory called Sam "the Wood Chopper" because he always carried his ax. He continually made things out of wood for her.

Together they worked on tanning the deer hide. He showed her a different method than she was used to.

When Sam made a trip to the fort for supplies, he got flower seeds for the next season to surprise her. While he was there, an old trader passed through the fort. He had a heart-shaped turquoise ring with him. Sam bought it. Something for Morning Glory, he thought.

When he got back to the cabin, Morning Glory was standing over the fire, stirring venison stew with squash and corn.

"Close your eyes, Glory, and hold out your hand," Sam softly requested.

He placed the ring upon her finger.

When she opened her eyes, her mouth dropped open. The stone carried the heart, a very special sign. In her eyes, it was a very special gift.

"Samuel," Morning Glory softly said, "things of the heart never fade. It is something your spirit always remembers, and your spirit is forever. This is a forever gift."

A moon had come and gone. Sam and Morning Glory were sitting at the table eating their evening meal when suddenly the door blew open. It was Tom. He saw them sitting across from each other, looking into each other's eyes. Morning Glory had been smiling and laughing, something he had never seen her do. When he walked in, she jumped up from her chair and tensed up.

Sam sat for a moment, his hands gripped around his cup of coffee. Tom thought he looked like one caught in the act of something. Sam finally got up and stuck out his hand toward Tom to shake.

"Well, Tom, glad to see you are back safe and sound. Did you succeed in your travels?"

"Aye, that I did, lad. That I did. But what is it that I see over there in the corner? Bring it out into the light now."

Morning Glory nervously pulled out and showed off the cradle, rocking it back and forth as she held her protruding belly.

Tom started to grow a bit tense. "Good work man. Good work. From the looks of it, my lass will be needing it soon."

"Now that you are home, Tom, I'll be going back to St. Louis. My family is waiting," Sam said nervously.

"I'll walk you out to the canoe, Sam. I have a supply of furs for you, like I promised. I'll help put them in your canoe."

Sam nodded to Morning Glory, saying goodbye.

Her heart quickened as she nodded back. She wished he didn't have to go. He was a good man, better than the others Tom hung around with. He showed her respect and kindness. He was gentle with her.

Tom was about to walk out the door when he saw Morning Glory's hand.

"What's on your hand, woman? Let me see," Tom said suspiciously.

Morning Glory looked down, now sorry that she had not hidden it somewhere. He grabbed her hand.

"Where did you get something as fine as this?" Tom demanded.

Sam tried to explain. "I gave it to her, Tom. It's just a little trinket I picked up from old Bob the trader when he passed through the fort. It's nothing. He gave it to me for a pelt. It was a good deal —I couldn't pass it by. It was just a token of my appreciation for all the cooking and sewing she did for me. It ain't nothin', Tom."

"Sure, Sam. Sure," Tom said, as he walked out the cabin door patting Sam on the back.

They walked through the trees toward the river. The air was damp and cool. The wet leaves stuck to the bottoms of their boots as they walked.

"My canoe is banked over here, Sam. Why don't you just look into there and pick out the best pelts, all that you want. They're yours for taking care of my lass."

As Sam leaned over the canoe, he felt a sudden tearing pain rip through his back. Tom had flung his knife into him.

Sam reached behind him and tried to pull it out. It was too high. With a puzzled look on his face he turned toward Tom. He tried to hold himself up by holding on to the rocking canoe.

No remorse showed on Tom's face as he coolly said, "You have stolen Morning Glory's eyes from me!"

Sam crumbled to the ground, still frantically trying to pull the knife out. With his last breath he said, "The wrath of God will be put upon your head. When you caused my death, you caused your own."

Blood flowed out of Sam's mouth as he gave out his last sigh.

Tom pulled the knife out, rinsed it off in the river and wiped it dry on Sam's shirt. He buried him in a shallow grave near the riverbank. The ground was muddy so it was easy digging.

Tom cut Sam's canoe loose, shot an arrow into it and sent it down the river. Without a moment of remorse, he went back to the cabin.

Morning Glory looked up at Tom when he came back in. She didn't like the feel of things. Something was wrong.

Tom simply said, "Sam's headin' back to his family now. He's been away too long. His wife will be waitin'. Don't know when he'll be back. He said his wife doesn't want him travelin' so much anymore. He expects to look for a job that will keep him in St. Louis."

Morning Glory didn't know why she felt like she did but her heart pained her. She would surely miss Sam.

CHAPTER 18

Morning Glory had been up half the night in labor. Tom went out at the crack of dawn to bring Mary Worthington back to the cabin.

"Tom, you stay at Stalley's until I send for you. This is a woman's work. I don't want you underfoot, do you hear?" Mary insisted.

Tom tipped his hat at her. "Yes'm," he said. Normally he wouldn't have been so polite to a woman but she was the commander's wife. He had to watch his manners.

Mary was afraid there might be a problem. She had attended several births in her time, but never one by a girl who was yet to see her thirteenth winter. Tom was a large man and Morning Glory was very thin. She wasn't sure if she could safely deliver a big baby.

A cold rain howled. The cabin door rattled noisily from the wind. Morning Glory said, "The spirits are pounding on the door to see what kind of spirit I will bear from a man such as Tom."

"Hush now, child," Mary insisted. "This child will be of your heart and your eyes."

Morning Glory thought highly of Mary, but at a time like this she wanted the assistance of a medicine man. She wanted her mother and sisters. Mary was white: What did she know of bringing in a spirit? Did Mary know what herbs to use for her and the baby? Not likely, she thought.

"When a child is brought to the land," Morning Glory said, "there must be a proper naming ceremony so the child will know its direction and purpose. There is no medicine man here to bring in that ceremony. How will this child find direction without it?"

"I'm sure Tom will name him Thomas," Mary said. "All white men name their sons after themselves."

Morning Glory became alarmed. "That means he will have the same direction as Tom. I do not want that. I will have to name him myself."

Mary simply shrugged as she held Morning Glory's hand through another contraction. She got up to rinse a cloth so she could mop Morning Glory's brow.

Morning Glory was soaked with sweat even though the cold wind howled in around the door. Mary kept the fire stoked and water boiling.

Throughout the day the contractions came at short intervals, but the baby did not come. Morning Glory was exhausted. She prayed to the Creator for help to free her from this pain.

As the sun set, the child finally came forth. A blond head emerged with a mighty wail to let the spirits know it had arrived. The wind died down. The rain slacked off. The door stopped rattling.

Morning Glory put the child to her bosom and stroked its hair, which was the color of straw.

"Kachant," Morning Glory said.

"What did you say, Morning Glory?" Mary asked as she watched her staring blankly into the fire.

"Kachant, meaning Fair Hair. He is Kachant."

A lone tear ran down her eye as she thought to herself. "I was to have the son of a chief. He was to become a mighty chief and rule our People. He was to be born of the love in my heart for Dancing Eagle. Will the pain ever leave my heart?"

Morning Glory kissed the head of this child and wondered what the Creator had in mind. The boy was the image of Tom — large, loud, strong. He carried some of his mother's blood, being blue-eyed with copper skin. He would be a handsome child, but of two bloods.

Mary cleaned up the child, wrapped him in a bundling and handed him to an exhausted Morning Glory. Morning Glory held the child in her arms as she drifted into vision, something she often did.

In her vision she saw large boats, endless waters, special gifts from the Great Spirit being carried to the boats, and a young man walking toward a boat. The boat had a picture of an Indian woman painted on it. Below it was written, "Morning Star." The young man turned around. He had blue eyes and blond hair and was big and strong. Two Moons was by his side!

She did not fully understand but only knew that this child was to be. He was part of her destiny.

CHAPTER 19

Schalute was a wise and powerful leader. In his council were seven members: three elders, three younger men and himself. Schalute was the deciding vote in any three-to-three tie.

At council meetings, all braves had a voice. If Crow Feather had a problem with his wife, Doe Eye, he would come in and say what the problem was.

At times the braves would not talk the truth. Women were not allowed to talk. When it was a brave against a brave, they would bring in witnesses to testify. Women weren't allowed to testify.

The old wise ones would usually go with the brave, because being brave, you were to be of truth. But Schalute knew that there were times when the braves weren't of truth.

Schalute couldn't counsel the women but he had to feel and see of the woman eye. He had to know of the woman and her being. Schalute knew all in the village well. He would routinely talk to all of the women because he had to know the other side of things. He had to know their personality. If a situation arose, he would judge them on their personality.

He was very shrewd. He would trick a brave into telling the truth. The braves knew that he was shrewd and they would try to hide behind outrageous stories. Schalute knew how to trick them into telling the truth.

Of all things, lying to Schalute was the gravest act one could perform. He could always catch a person in a lie. He gained a great deal of respect among his villagers because of his power and wisdom. He treated all fairly, even the women.

While he was chief, he only ran one brave out of the village. This brave had stolen a totem pole from a neighboring tribe. He had thought the totem made this tribe powerful. Since he wanted to be more powerful, he took the other tribe's totem for its power.

This brave thought that by stealing a totem he could become chief. The tribe came looking for him. He thought Schalute would protect him.

The totem belonged to the Sacs, a powerful Indian nation. The Sacs certainly would not tolerate the theft of their image, and a painted Sac war party boldly rode to the center of the village. Their heads were partly shaved and they wore paint to show their fierceness. At least fifty braves stood before a fearless Schalute on that sultry, hot day.

"Why do our friends ride into my village wearing the paint of war? Do we not have a bond through the marriage of my daughter Blue Dove? Are we not allies of the same blood?"

"How can we be allies if you try to steal our power?" a brave asked as he leaped down from his appaloosa pony.

"I do not steal power! One cannot steal power!" Schalute said with certainty.

There was a struggle from behind the gathering crowd, as Lone Star pushed the guilty brave forward and onto to his knees in front of Schalute.

"This one took their totem," Lone Star informed his uncle. "He hid it within the woods along the riverbank. I found it yesterday as I was hunting. I saw him sneaking back into the village."

Schalute glared at Gray Hawk, took a swift stride toward him and grabbed him by the arm, shoving him toward the Sac war braves.

"You can never take power that way. You inherit power through your blood and you earn power through your efforts. Theft never gains power. You will be a lesson for all.

"Take him and deal with him as your council sees fit," he said to the head Sac brave. "I will not have a spirit such as this in my village."

"Tell your chief I regret that one of my village would commit such an act. To further bond our alliance, inform him that I have another daughter who has come of age for marriage. By the next moon, my braves and I will accompany her to your village. I know his second son is waiting for her."

Schalute walked away. The Sacs had retribution. The village obtained a lesson. Gray Hawk would never be seen again. Schalute would send his final daughter away from his lodge. It was finished and all would remember, especially his daughters.

Schalute was fair but stern.

CHAPTER 20

Five more winters passed. The spring rains had ceased. The trees and bushes were in full bloom. Morning Glory dutifully tended a garden in back of the cabin.

She now had two sons in tow and another on the way. Watna (meaning Awakened) had arrived during the spring rains three years ago. Tom named him after his older brother James.

Morning Glory had kept her part of the bargain. She was Tom's wife. She did not run away, but her heart was never free of pain. Not a day passed that she didn't think of her family and Dancing Eagle.

Giving up Dancing Eagle was the hardest thing she could ever imagine having to do. It tore her heart out that she had had to make that decision.

She would go to bed at night and see him in her dreams and visions. She would call out to him. He would turn to hear his name. What she always saw was an empty shell of a man. His spirit had left him. She knew that she had done that to him. If it weren't for the bargain, that she could protect her People by marrying Tom, nothing could have torn her from his arms. She was also an empty shell but she did have sons to love. Dancing Eagle had none. She could feel that. Her heart cried out to him every morning and every night.

She wondered what became of her family. Oh, how she missed Two Moons, although it was different with him. A part of her was a part of him, so she carried him with her always. They could never be parted in spirit, only in body. They could talk to each other through their thoughts. He was not torn of spirit as was Dancing Eagle.

She missed Schalute. Schalute had taught her everything he knew, something a shaman rarely does for a girl. Their relationship was very special. She knew that had caused rivalry in the family, and that was why she always tried to cater to her younger sisters. She understood why they often disliked her but she couldn't change that.

She could no longer feel the presence of Rising Sun. She worried about Shadow Dancer and his antics. Shadow Dancer always sought attention by disrupting Schalute's well laid plans. She was not there to patch things up. She missed his carefree ways. He used to make her laugh. She rarely laughed now. She barely cried now. She simply worked.

It was an unusually hot day for early summer. Morning Glory toiled in the garden, cooked for the boys, hauled water, prepared fresh meat and washed clothes in the river. By the time the sun centered in the sky, she was doubled over in pain. Tom went to the fort to get Mary Worthington.

The day passed, the night passed, the sun rose again. Morning Glory was still in labor. Her strength was all but gone. She could hardly stifle her screams. The child appeared breech first, and large. Morning Glory was narrow in the hips.

Mary tried to turn the child but she could only turn it part of the way, leaving it in a worse position than before. Morning Glory started to bleed profusely and was too weak to continue to push. Her eyes started to roll to the back of her head. Her hand dropped limply to her side. Her skin turned ashen gray and cold. The child inside of her stopped stirring, as though it were dead.

Mary Worthington kneeled at her side and prayed to Jesus to save the girl. A rush of energy passed through the room and a chill went up and down Mary's spine.

Morning Glory gasped and sat up. She asked for water. Her throat was dry. Mary stared in wonderment as the color started to come back to Morning Glory's tender face. Within an hour the child came forth with a cry: another blond-haired, blue-eyed one.

Mary cleaned the child and handed the wrapped little boy to Morning Glory.

"Oh, Chata. You see, he has special Bright Eyes. His eyes carry a spirit similar to his uncle Two Moons."

With a weak voice, barely audible, Morning Glory used the last of her strength to whisper. "You know, Mary, a little while ago my spirit flew with the Eagle's eyes. I was flying high above in the stars, so high. I saw the bright light of a spirit fly by. I followed it and it seemed to go right into my body, with my spirit following behind it. That spirit entered this little baby's body. It came from the skies! It came from the Sun!"

Mary did not know what Morning Glory was talking about. She only knew that the Lord had spared her.

"Child, you will never have another baby. You are so torn up inside that you would not survive it. You are too narrow of the hips. It will take you a long time to heal and regain your strength from this one." She paused, then said, "Do not worry. You are like the daughter I never had. I shall take care of you and your boys."

Moments later, Morning Glory slipped into an exhausted stupor. She had lost much blood.

Mary busied herself sweeping out the cabin, making food for the boys, stoking the fire to bake bread and rocking the baby in the cradle that Sam had made years before.

Nightfall came. Tom burst in, roaring drunk. "Ah, 'tis another fine lad we have here. This one we shall name Nathanael, after the good book," Tom said as he held the startled infant up over his head.

Mary wagged her finger at Tom as he swaggered around the room. "Morning Glory will never survive another child. You leave her be and go to your brothel or you will have no mother for your children next time. Do you hear me?"

"Mary, Mary, she is an Indian. They produce children like rabbits. Don't you worry now, lassie. What's for dinner?"

Mary slammed the Bible down on the table in front of him. "Read this for your dinner. It is what saved your wife and child!"

Tom just laughed, patted her on the shoulder, picked up a bottle and headed for the door. "I'm goin' to the fort to celebrate my new son," he said as he swaggered out the door.

CHAPTER 21

It was late fall. The trees had already shed their leaves. Little Chata was in his bed by the fireside. The sun rested behind the trees. Sheets of cold, blowing rain brushed the sides of the cabin. The shutters rattled against the walls in the wind.

Tom had been out collecting the last of his traps. He had taken Kachant and Watna with him. Morning Glory pleaded with him to leave them behind. They were too young to be out on a cold, wet night.

Mostly (though she didn't dare say), she was trying to keep Tom from taking Kachant. Tom was always trying to beat him into being a man, but he was just a young boy. Every time Kachant would make a mistake in setting a trap or following a track, Tom would clout him with the back of his hand.

Kachant never cried, or even said a word. He would show no expression on his face, just like Morning Glory. He would not for a moment show a lack of power.

It was well into the night. Morning Glory had expected them back yesterday. There was no moon. She thought it too late for them to find their way in this storm. She hoped they were in a warm, dry place.

She heard footsteps, or so she thought, through the wind. She was about to open the door and look about, when the door flew open. In the rain stood one large man and two wet, frozen young boys.

Morning Glory reached out and grabbed Watna by the arm. He looked unable to move any farther. Kachant slowly followed him in. She tipped Watna's face up to hers and wanted to cry. His beautiful eyes were glazed and drooped. His head was burning up and his body was shaking. He could hardly talk because his throat was swollen shut. Kachant was not in much better shape.

Morning Glory was torn between rage with Tom and panic for her boys. She pulled off their wet clothes, wrapped them in a blanket and sat them before the fire.

She turned toward Tom and between clenched teeth started to hiss at him in her native tongue. This made him furious, because he didn't know what she was saying, but he knew it wasn't good.

He took three long strides across the room toward her and slapped her across the face with the back of his hand.

"I'm going to the fort to get drunk. I was only trying to make them into men." The door slammed behind him as he strode out like a wild man.

Morning Glory briskly turned to put water over the fire. She needed to make them an herbal brew. It would take time for them to get well. Until then, it would be hell.

Watna could hardly swallow any of the tea. She put him to bed and hoped that sleep would help heal him. He could only toss and whimper.

She wrapped a blanket around him and took him closer to the fire. He cuddled his head against her as he sat on one side of her lap. Kachant sat close but was not fond of being touched because of Tom's constant beatings.

Morning Glory was about to tell them a story by the fire that night, like Schalute had done with her so many times. Little Chata awoke and toddled over, taking up the other side of her lap. She reached around and covered him up snuggly, too.

The fire spit and hissed loudly as drops of rain fell through the chimney hole. She checked to see if they were all warm. Satisfied, she began her story.

> When I was a young girl in my tenth winter, I was in my lodge sleeping. The whites have a special day. They call it Christmas. Presents are exchanged. Your father does that with you.
>
> Our People did not have it that way. I heard about it from the traders that came to our village. For me, though, the day before Christmas was special too. It was a day of preparation and anticipation and the predawn of an awakening. For some reason, I had that in my mind. Well, this was the day of predawn awakening.

> Everyone in our lodge was sound asleep, making the noises that come from their breaths as their spirits start out to talk to all the rest. I was not completely asleep. My spirit would come. My spirit would go.
>
> I did not know why, but I was compelled to go out in the snow. I wrapped a warm robe about me and stepped out into the night. Oh, the sky was such a sight!
>
> The air was crisp. The snow was deep but soft, not full of sleet. There was no wind spirit about that night. It was so quiet, the only thing you could hear were the horses moving about in the far field. Their sound carried so near.

Little Chata stared at her with his big, bright eyes. He just loved to have her hold him warmly in her lap. Watna was so weak that he could only lean his head against her and listen with closed eyes. Kachant had his head down but listened intently. She went on:

> I thought I heard a voice from afar calling out my name — "Glory of the Morning, come this way."
>
> I felt compelled to walk to the river's edge. My feet crunched through the crisp snow. On the hillside was a long, flat rock outcropping that looked east over the river. I sat upon that rock and looked into a spectacular sky. What an incredibly clear night, I thought. I felt as though I could reach out and touch the stars.
>
> I kept staring into the sky but then I had to blink my eyes. A star was twinkling so brightly that it lit up the whole night. My mouth dropped in wonderment. Was that star growing or was it coming closer? I kept staring. For a while, it would stop. It would move to the right, to the left and then once again come down closer! Was my mind playing tricks? I kept staring. It started to blink red, then blue and then shoot out streaks of light! Oh, what a sight!
>
> The night seemed to come to no time. The light from the star grew brighter and brighter. Closer and closer it came, and shined so bright upon the river that night! I sat upon that rock and couldn't move. Soon, lights of all different hues came swirling down. The lights were so bright, I could hardly keep my eyes open. I had to hold my hand in front of my face. I was not afraid, but I started

to shake. I didn't know why, but I shook at an alarming rate. My heart pounded so.

"Glory of the Morning," a voice announced in my head, "we come to you on this special day. Your light was so bright, we could not fail to see it in the night. Each ray of light has in it a different hue, but all are part of the one. In your world is much anger. Never does anger bring joy. Joy should be for every girl and boy."

I was looking around to see where these voices were coming from. Could it be from that star? But these voices sounded from afar, voices of a hundred people all sounding as one! The voice had music in it and was pleasant to my ear. All I wanted to do was just hear!

The voice of many went on through the night. I could not remember all. It was almost like a dream, but it was not.

"Glory of the Morning," they again said to bring me awake in my head, "you shall have special sons! They will help all in the world to remember to become one. You must remind them to find their path. Only then will your People be saved. Remember what you came for. Remember. Remember. . . ."

It was not quite sunrise yet. There was just a flicker from behind the hill across the river. I opened my eyes to see Schalute's moccasins by my side. He quietly put my hand in his and said, "Glory, what has brought you here?" Before I could answer him, he reached down and scooped me up easily in his strong arms and carried me toward our lodge.

"Father," I told him, "a star came to me this night and told me that all would be right. My sons would help make it that way! Oh, Father, a star really did come to me that way! Do you believe me?"

"Of course I do, Morning Glory. You are from that star! You are a princess from afar. That is why you look like no other. The spirits have told me about you. They said I was to care for you. I always will. Our People have waited for you a long, long time. Yes, your sons will be special some day. We are awaiting."

Schalute gently laid me down on my robe by the fire in our lodge. I slept until the light of day.

The dogs woke me with a start. I wondered if the night was a dream or if it really happened that way.

With the wind's blusterous opening of the cabin door, Morning Glory's attention was brought back to the fact that she was in Tom's cabin and not with Schalute anymore. Oh, how she missed that great man. What would he say if he knew her sons had golden hair?

CHAPTER 22

Over the years Thomas Shaye had become a valued scout. He was given the title Major Shaye, even though he was officially a scout.

Whenever he was going to an Indian village that might prove to be hostile, he would take Morning Glory with him. Most of the tribes in that area were aware of her status and honored her presence to some extent. When she was with him, the council would be forced to at least listen to what he had to say. She hated being dragged around like that, being used as a pawn for the white man.

She did not honor his intentions or the army's purpose. In her travels she could see the loss of spirit in the People's villages. The white man's disease had overtaken many of them. Smallpox killed off many of the People. There was little she could do to stop it except to bring them a helping hand.

Often the People looked on her scornfully because she rode with a white man. That broke her heart. When she entered a village, she kept her head down, talking only when approached. She felt their shame. She rode in shame. She was no more free than they were.

She saw more and more of the People turn to the white man's liquor. She saw them lose their senses, lose their land, lose their power and spirit. Everything was being taken from them.

Often Tom and his men would ride into a village to tell them that they had to keep moving west. He would tell them that if they did not listen, they would be destroyed. The People were sick, hungry and tired. They had nothing left to fight with. Their tribes were divided both in numbers and in policies. The People no longer thought in unison.

Morning Glory traveled often with Tom. Many times she left the boys with Mary. They were too young, she felt, to travel so much. Mary didn't mind. She loved them as her own and they gave her a sense of purpose, a reason to be.

Jim McMellows always seemed to be with them when they traveled. Morning Glory never realized that he was there because he loved her. He always volunteered to come with Tom to protect her. He only pretended to be Tom's friend.

Morning Glory still dressed and lived as an Indian woman, something Tom always tried to change. She insisted on wearing only a buckskin dress with heavy beading. In her own way she always looked elegant. Her blue-black hair was always neatly braided. She always wore a beaded headband with an eagle feather. She stood and rode straight, yet she would rarely let someone look directly into her eyes. She did not want them to see into her soul, for she was shamed and heartbroken.

Word had gotten back to the Eagle tribe long ago about the travels of the blue-eyed princess with the white man. This cut into Dancing Eagle's heart. He became embittered and vengeful. His hate for white men grew with each passing of the moon.

Anger ruled his emotions. The hurt he suffered over Morning Glory having left him made him scorn women in general. He would never let another woman get close to his heart. He tolerated his mother and occasionally slept with a willing maiden, but he never opened up his heart again.

He still provided for Red Hawk's daughter, Shalita. Shalita had been a close friend of Morning Glory's, although three winters younger. White traders were coming to the village with regularity now. Dancing Eagle would often catch Shalita conversing with one of them, a man named Bill, and would go into a rage when he saw them together. Bill was tall and blond and had a mustache like Tom Shaye. He even talked with the same Irish accent.

"Shalita," Dancing Eagle roared, not caring whether anyone else heard him, "I will kill that white-eye the next time I see you with him! I forbid you to be with him. Now go. Get out of my sight."

Two Moons saw this happen and walked away, shaking his head. Dancing Eagle was out of control. Two Moons knew the day was at hand when red man and white man would mix. There would be resistance to it, but it was coming just the same.

"Dancing Eagle," Two Moons called out, jogging to catch up

with him.

Dancing Eagle continued to walk on. The day was overcast and dismal, as was his temper. He did not want to hear any lectures from Two Moons now or ever again.

Dancing Eagle's hair was often unkempt. He seldom bothered to braid it or to wear his feathers. His leggings were worn thin. His moccasins did not bear any decorations. He no longer took pride in his appearance. His mood was mostly surly. No one wanted to bother with his bad disposition, and his friends all but disappeared. They were tired of his self-pity. Schalute barely talked to him anymore. The only time Two Moons spoke was to reprimand him. He didn't want to hear that now.

Two Moons caught up with him and grabbed him by the shoulder. Dancing Eagle spun on his heels and lashed out, "What is it this time, Two Moons? Are you going to tell me the Great Eagle is going to swoop down and make everything right?"

"I'm going to tell you this," Two Moons said sternly. "It is time you change your ways before it is too late. It is time you think of what you can do for our People and stop thinking only of yourself. If you do not, you will end up a man alone. You will be left behind."

Dancing Eagle put his hands on his hips and laughed into the sky. "It is already too late. I am already a man standing alone. White man has seen to that. I don't need anybody else to mess up my life. The People don't need me. I don't need them. I walk alone."

Two Moons said, "Then you will die alone."

CHAPTER 23

Morning Glory always wore around her neck a turquoise stone that Schalute had given her as a child. There was always a medicine pouch on her. She proudly wore the eagle feather in an upright position at the back of her head. She would not give up that way of life.

Her hair was quite long now and always worn neatly in two braids. She always wore a beaded headband to hold her feather. She wore doeskin dresses, which she worked into soft leather. She always took pride in her appearance.

Her boys had a white father. Morning Glory did not accept his ways of teaching the boys. In her tribe it was tradition that the uncle taught the boys. Two Moons was no longer at her side to do this so she tried to teach them the Indian way of being a young brave with honor. As she prepared meals, she always showed them how she honored the animal that gave up its life to feed her family. She honored the leather that came from its hide. She never took anything for granted.

Tom didn't honor anything but brute strength. He never honored her request not to drink. He never even considered it. As far as he was concerned, it gave him power. It made him feel like a man. In her eyes it made him appear like a fool.

Tom was usually out of control when he drank. After he sobered up, he often regretted things he'd done in a rage, but by then the damage was done. Morning Glory usually tried to keep the boys away from him when he drank but it was not always possible, especially in the winter months.

She never forgot how Tom had flung Chata against a pot in the fireplace. The boiling liquid splashed out onto his legs. She had to tend to him day and night for three days. Tom regretted it when he sobered up; but Chata carried the scars the rest of his life.

Tom taught the boys in his own way. He taught them how to hunt, trap and live off the land. He taught them how to use a knife. He taught them about boats. He taught the boys all he knew.

When Tom wasn't around, Morning Glory would teach them the natural way to transcend the lands. She taught them to call in the vision of a tree and the sky they would seek. They knew of the Eagle ways. They knew where to go and what was right. She taught them to honor the Great Spirit in their hunts. She taught them to walk silently through the fall leaves and be part of the breeze.

When they were old enough to learn to ride, she taught them to ride as one with the animal. They moved as the animal moved. The animal moved as they moved. She demanded that they treat their pony with respect so the pony would not sway at their sight. If the animal was to serve them right, it had to be treated with respect.

Morning Glory taught them to call the birds through their own skill. Each one of the boys mastered a birdcall of his own, one by which they could identify each other. She would take them to the forest and blend them with the trees. She taught them never to go to bed without talking to Spirit and not to rise without Spirit.

Tom was often impatient with these methods. He wanted things when he wanted them, not when they came to him. When he was drunk, he became even more demanding and impatient.

"Woman, I want something else to eat this night. I am tired of venison stew," Tom bellowed, pounding on the table with his knife.

Tom looked around. Morning Glory simply continued to stir what was already cooked in the pot. She did not even look his way.

Tom became crazed. As usual, Morning Glory paid him no mind. "If I have to go out, I'll cut the head off a deer and drink its blood," he yelled to impress the boys.

"Do not talk without respect in this lodge, Tom Shaye," Morning Glory said, turning to face him. "I'll not have that kind of talk around the boys. You are trying to scare them. That is not impressive," Morning Glory said with her hands on her hips.

Tom noticed the boys staring at him.

"What are you lads looking at?" he growled with exasperation.

The boys pointed numbly at his billowing shirt. He was wearing a three-eyelet, buckskin shirt. The shirt was moving in and out off of his chest!

"Oh," he remembered. "It was a surprise I had for you. I totally forgot in my wildness. I found this down by the creek."

Tom reached into his shirt and whipped out a snake, flopping it down on the table.

"This was to be your pet. Now it will be my dinner!"

With one clean sweep of his knife, Tom cut off its head.

"Prepare this, woman, and make it a feast. Goddamned thing ate the hair off of my chest!" he said.

Tom poured a few more drinks into his metal cup and passed out onto the table.

Morning Glory fed the three boys the venison stew. They all went to bed, leaving Tom, as usual, passed out on the table.

CHAPTER 24

At the height of the summer, the government in Washington sent a Colonel Clemens to the fort. There were many Indian uprisings occuring along the river. The government officials wanted the Indians moved even farther west. If they would not move willingly, this would of course mean more wars.

Colonel Clemens and a contingent of soldiers arrived carrying many government-issued gifts such as blankets and food. They were to be used to bribe the Indians to leave their land.

Tom Shaye was called to the fort to speak with the colonel.

Colonel Clemens was a round-faced, short-statured man. He had blond hair and a mustache and walked stiffly, routinely snapping the side of his boot with a riding crop. He smoked a good brand of cigars and puffed on one laboriously as he talked.

"Major Shaye," Colonel Clemens said with authority, "I hear there is still a band of Indians east of the Mississippi. How in tarnation did that happen? They should have been moved out of here a decade ago. I hear that you had something to do with that. You had better explain yourself, sir."

Tom was caught by surprise. Morning Glory's small village was known but the People kept to themselves. They bothered nobody, except for the sighting of an occasional drunk. Schalute kept his villagers in tow. The village was so far off the big river that few white men ever stumbled across it.

"Why, Colonel," Tom sputtered, "how did you even hear about that insignificant village?"

Colonel Clemens snuffed out his cigar and turned to face Tom squarely. "I saw that blue-eyed squaw of yours. There is quite a legend surrounding her. You apparently overlooked an entire tribe just so you could have that woman. That's what I hear. I know women are scarce around these parts, but that is pushing it a bit far, don't you think, Major?"

Tom was becoming unglued. He could see trouble brewing and he didn't like it. He had done his part in keeping the Indians at bay. He had killed quite a few redskins in his day. Now here was this pencil-pushing colonel from Washington walking in and wanting to take away his thunder.

Tom looked him straight in the eye. "With all due respect, Colonel, there's really no need to worry about that village. We made a bargain with them a long time ago. They kept their bargain so we left them alone. No need for bloodshed there. Now, my lassie, that's another story. She's the mother of my boys. She is not a squaw, do you understand me?"

Colonel Clemens' face reddened. "Excuse me, Major. That sounded rather like insubordination. I see a woman with braids, an eagle feather and a buckskin dress walking around the fort in moccasins. She looks like a squaw to me!"

Colonel Clemens began to pace back and forth across the room. He stopped to look out the window in back of his desk for a minute. He locked both hands in back of him while he contemplated his next move. It was clear that these two men did not like each other.

Colonel Clemens opened a drawer in his desk and pulled out a fresh cigar, offering one to Tom. Tom shook his head to decline.

With a quick sweep of his match across the top of the desk, Clemens lit his cigar and inhaled three deep puffs, blowing the smoke into the center of the room. Again he paced.

"Now, you listen here, Major Shaye. There is no way in hell I can wire Washington and tell them that this land is ready for mining iron ore and they can send all the river boats they want up from St. Louis, when you still have an entire tribe east of the Mississippi. I can't exactly explain to Washington that this is so because of your squaw!"

Tom had long ago given up trying to get Morning Glory to look like a white woman. He thought he might pull it off because of her thin build and blue eyes, and he would buy white women's dresses for her. But she steadfastly refused to touch them. In time, everyone at the fort seemed to accept her. Commander Worthington was happy enough all these years because the Eagle tribe was peaceful and out of sight. Now an outsider from Washington had laid eyes on her and decided to upset his entire world. Tom knew that if the Eagle tribe were forced to move, Morning Glory would never stay with him. She'd never learned to love him. All of these years she'd only stayed to protect her People.

Tom was wild with passion for her. She was the only thing he had never been able to conquer. She was a constant challenge for him, and it made his blood boil to constantly pursue her. She was also the mother of his sons. He had long ago forgotten that she was considered a squaw.

Colonel Clemens continued to puff vigorously on his half-finished cigar. He stood behind a shroud of smoke as he continued. "I'm sorry to have to tell you this, Major Shaye, but before the summer is over, that tribe has to move west. I will give you supplies to take to them as bribes, but quite simply, it has to be done. You can use the bribes to try to get them to move peacefully. If they won't move, the army will disperse them. That is all. You are dismissed." Colonel Clemens swiftly left the room, leaving Tom there in a quandary.

Tom mounted his sorrel gelding and trotted it back to the cabin. It was a hot day. The sweat poured down his face, droplets following the scar, received years back in a knife fight, down the left side of his face.

He took a swig from his whiskey bottle every few minutes, all the way home. He would drift to the left and his horse would steer left. Tom would sharply snap the reins to the right too far. The horse would go in circles. By the time the gelding found its way home, Tom could hardly sit on the animal.

When Tom's horse stopped at the watering trough, he slid off the animal to the ground, pulling himself back onto his feet by holding the stirrup.

Morning Glory stepped out, shaking her head at the condition of the animal in front of her. Its mouth was bleeding from Tom's holding on to the reins too tightly to support himself. The poor animal was hot and lathered and appeared ready to indulge itself by drinking the entire trough of water. She knew that would kill it.

"Kachant," she called out. "Take this poor beast to the barn. Unsaddle him and walk him down until he is cool. Then you can take him to the river for a cool drink of water. Let him drink only a little at first, then walk him some more before you let him drink his fill. If you do otherwise, it could kill him. Take your brothers with you. They can help you curry him down. Put a little saddle soap on that tack while you are at it. The leather has become stiff and sweaty and the girth will crack if it isn't softened up soon."

"I understand, Mother. You always told us never to bring a horse back in this condition," Kachant said out loud in defiance of his father, who could hardly stand.

Morning Glory spun on her heels and slammed the cabin door behind her, leaving Tom swaggering about the porch.

In the heat, Tom's temper grew. Morning Glory had made a fool of him in front of his sons. He wouldn't let that slide.

Tom kicked the door open and it slammed back against the log wall. Morning Glory looked up from sweeping the floor to see his eyes afire.

"You ungrateful squaw," Tom seethed as he held himself upright on the doorjamb. "All these years I protected your people. What did I ever get for it but your defiance? Well, it's out of my hands now, anyway. It's all over, do you hear?"

Morning Glory started to tremble. "What do you mean, Tom? What is over for my People?" she asked, barely able to speak above a whisper.

Tom laughed, pulling up a chair, barely able to get to it without falling first. "That fancy new colonel at the fort. He saw you in your buckskins and feathers. Knew you were a squaw. You wouldn't dress as a white woman, as I asked. No, you had to dress Indian. Well, he spotted you right off. He found out about your people. I can't protect them no more. They've got to move west like every other redskin now."

"They bother nobody," Morning Glory sputtered.

"Don't make no never mind. This colonel is from Washington. They don't care about you or your people. They just want that land for the ore. Your people are sittin' right on it. They want it now. It's all over."

Morning Glory dropped the broom and started frantically pulling her things together.

Tom leaped off the chair. It fell backwards onto the floor as he grabbed her wrist. "Just where do you think you be goin' now, lassie?" Tom said as he gripped her wrist even tighter.

Morning Glory tried to pull free, but he just laughed at her even attempting such a thing.

"Let me go, Tom. I promised to stay with you if you protected my People. My People have been betrayed. I must warn them. I must protect them. It is my destiny."

Tom pushed her down into the chair. "You're not goin' anywhere, lassie. You are my woman."

Morning Glory bolted for the door. Tom lunged right after her, tackling her to the ground. He then dragged her to the hitching post, binding her hands to the ring hanging from it.

In a rage he pulled out his bowie knife and ran into the cabin to heat it in the fire. When the blade turned blue, he pulled it from the fire and staggered out the door. He cut the top of her dress open and through clenched teeth said, "You will always be my woman. You will do as I say. You will wear my initials so every man will know you are mine."

Morning Glory screamed in pain, clutching on to the hitching post as he carved his initials over her right shoulder blade.

Tom staggered back, shocked that he could do such a thing to Morning Glory. He dropped the knife into the dust. He knew that honor and pride were a part of her being. She stayed with him because she gave her word for her People.

She was the mother of his sons. She was the most beautiful woman he had ever known, yet he had just branded her as though she were a steer.

The boys came running from the barn at the sound of her screams. Tom couldn't face them after what he had just done. He grabbed his half-empty bottle that lay on the ground and ran off into the woods.

Morning Glory hid her face in her hands, humiliated. She did not want the boys to see her like this. Kachant unbound her and supported her while she stumbled back into the cabin.

Morning Glory faced the fire and took a few moments to pull herself together. Slowly, she turned and held her head high.

"I am going to be all right. Watna, please go outside and bring me that knife. Kachant, take your brothers back to the barn and finish tending to the gelding. We can't afford to lose such a fine animal. Shut the door on your way out. Before you come back into the cabin, I want you to chop wood and haul water – lots of it."

Watna ran out and fetched the knife. The boys looked back on their mother's tear-stained face, as she shushed them out the door. She shut the door behind them.

Morning Glory picked the knife up from the table and walked to the fire. She put the knife into the fire until the blade was again blue. She took a deep breath, braced herself against the chair and put the knife over her shoulder to burn out Tom's initials.

"I am not his woman. I will never be branded that way," Morning Glory told herself with indignant defiance.

Morning Glory awoke from the floor. She had apparently fainted, pulling the chair down on top of her. The side of her face was swollen from the fall.

By the time the boys came back from the barn, she had packed their things and loaded them into the canoe. She was going to take them to Mary Worthington for a while.

Morning Glory knew she had to warn her People. She was going to have to travel fast. Her boys were too young and the trip was too dangerous. Besides, they were white. Bringing them into her village might not be smart right now. She didn't know if her People would accept them.

Mary saw the four of them enter the fort. She had heard from her husband, Commander Worthington, that Morning Glory's tribe was going to be forced to leave their land. She knew Morning Glory would be leaving.

Mary embraced Morning Glory on this hot summer day. Even though it was humid and sultry, Morning Glory's hands were freezing-cold from stress. Her eyes seemed glazed, but Mary thought it was from worry. She didn't know about the burns on her shoulder.

Morning Glory gathered her boys about her. She stood stoically in front of Mary as she cleared her throat and tried to stall for time to give her the courage to do what she had to do.

"Mary," Morning Glory said with a lump in her throat, "would you kindly look after my boys until I return. I have to warn my People of the impending danger. I am afraid the cavalry might just charge into my village and not give them a chance. I cannot take the boys with me yet. A way has to be paved for them first."

Mary knew how torn Morning Glory must be to have to try to save her People and leave her boys behind.

"Of course I will. I brought these boys into the world. They are sons to me. I am worried about you, a woman traveling alone. And what about Tom?" Mary asked with great concern as she mopped her sweaty brow and pushed back ringlets of hair.

Morning Glory's voice began to quiver as she looked at her sons' faces. They didn't understand her loyalty to her People. They felt as though they were being deserted by their mother.

Morning Glory cleared her throat to try to get the words out. "Tom is on a drunken spree. I expect he will stay that way for days.

I must travel fast, before he decides to follow me. He must not stop me. I must go now."

Morning Glory turned to her boys and bravely fought back the tears. She wanted to give them words of wisdom but if she did, the tears would flood and she would never be able to leave. The boys were still in shock after seeing what Tom had done to her. With her words that she was leaving them, they were confused and angry.

"My sons, I can only tell you that you are always in my heart. I will come for you as soon as I can. I don't know when that will be. You are in good hands with Mary. I pray that you will be honorable."

Morning Glory hugged them all quickly and ran out of the fort while she still had the courage to go. She only had a few hours of daylight left, so she had to paddle with a fury.

It was not good for a woman to travel alone, but she had no choice. She prayed to the Creator to allow her to find a way to return to her People in time.

The sun beat down on her, draining what little energy she had left. Her heart beat out-of-sync. She feared for the future of her People. She feared what Tom would do when he found out she was gone. The faces of her confused sons haunted her.

Morning Glory didn't take the time to eat or rest because she wanted to get as much distance between her and the fort as she could. After a few hours she could hardly lift the paddle anymore. Even though the evening air had started to cool, she was sweating profusely. Her right shoulder was becoming inflamed and burned intensely every time her paddle cut through the water. She was beginning to run a fever.

When the last rays of the sun set behind the trees in the west, she banked her canoe, almost too weak to pull it ashore. Her shoulder throbbed. Her head ached. Her body was weak beyond belief. She reached into the muddy shore and scooped up a fistful of mud, putting it on her wound to draw out the infection. It was too dark to look for the proper herbs to use. Morning Glory was too tired to even eat what little food she'd brought with her. She pulled out her blanket and slumped beneath a tree, too exhausted to even think.

Sleep proved to be fitful. Faces from the past came to her, haunting her. Ten winters had come and gone.

Jim McMellows and his friend Bill traded with her village from time to time, but they had never told Schalute where she was; they knew it would bring trouble. They kept her informed of what they had heard or seen at her village. She knew that Schalute was now chief and that her sisters were now married.

Whenever she asked of Dancing Eagle, not much was said. Shalita, Red Hawk's daughter, had been good friends with Morning Glory. Bill, a tall Irishman who typically wore buckskin leggings and a fringed jacket, took a liking to Shalita. He had a handlebar mustache that he kept neatly waxed. Shalita would sneak off with Bill from time to time.

Bill told Morning Glory that Dancing Eagle would probably kill him if he knew Shalita spent time with him. Shalita had told him that Dancing Eagle had grown to hate all whites. If it weren't for Schalute holding him at bay, he probably would have gone to war.

In a few days she would again lay eyes on Dancing Eagle. She didn't know what was going to happen. Not once in all those years had she ever gotten him out of her mind.

Her throbbing shoulder wouldn't let her sleep, so Morning Glory rose before the sun's rays stroked the sky. She climbed back into the canoe and started paddling north again.

Her mind raced with many questions. What would happen to her People? Would they leave, if given time to decide? Would they foolishly try to fight the white man's army with their limited supply of weapons and manpower? Did they hate her for abandoning them? Did anybody understand why she couldn't return? Did anybody at all know how much she loved them?

Two Moons was the one she had always felt was with her. She missed him terribly, but they were never really apart. It was something she could explain to no one. She knew he understood what she had had to do.

By the time the sun rose high in the sky, she had to pull over into the shallow water near the bank. Her body alternated between shivering from the cold and sweating from the fever. Every move of her arm sent pulses of pain across her shoulders, up her neck and into her throbbing head.

Periodically, she would put on a fresh poultice from the riverbank. When she first put it on, the coolness of it took the fire out of her shoulder but the respite was short-lived. Morning Glory had to bank the canoe before the sun set into the west. She couldn't move her arm anymore. She was weak beyond belief. She had to get some rest.

She also noticed that the river ahead had white man's boats on it. White men were becoming numerous on the waterways. She didn't want them to see her. It was time to pull off the water and travel inland. Besides, she couldn't paddle one more stroke with her arm.

Morning Glory forced herself to eat what little food she had left. She was too weak to carry anything but a gut bag of water. She found shelter from a thunderous storm that night under a hollowed-out log. The rain soaked her blanket, making it too wet and cumbersome to carry in her weakened condition. She was simply too weary to pick it up.

She did not want to be seen, but at this point Morning Glory wasn't worried about leaving tracks behind. Tom would know she had headed back to her People; she only hoped she could get there first. Morning Glory continued her journey through the woods. Journeying on foot would take longer, but she had no choice at this point.

This land was not familiar to her. She prayed to the Creator to have the Eagle show her the way. Periodically during the day, she would hear a shrill call. It was the Eagle showing her to continue north. At night she followed the star from the north. Always she headed north.

Her moccasins were wearing thin and holes were torn in the soles. She would pad them with leaves during the day, but they didn't offer much protection. Her feet became torn.

The water bag slowly emptied. Her burning body became parched. Her lips began to blister from lack of water. Her shoulder ached beyond belief.

Often she would stumble, barely having the strength to get up again. Had she not needed to reach her People first, she would have prayed for death.

Morning Glory's food ran out after three days. Her fever raged so high that she would not have been able to eat anyway. Her travel consisted of dragging steps, stumbling, falling, resting, pulling herself up against a tree and praying for strength. With each prayer she found a little more strength to go on. After a while, she didn't notice her shoulder or her feet anymore. Her body moved mechanically. She became numb from head to toe.

Occasionally she would find a stream and quench her raw throat and soothe her blistered lips. Whenever she could find mud, she applied it to her shoulder.

She lost track of the days and the nights. She only knew to go on. When the land finally became hilly and she found it harder to climb, she knew she was almost home. Among these beautiful hills, valleys and cliffs, she once rode on the back of Dancing Eagle's pony. They used to share the song of the Eagle and revel in the pony's motion as she wrapped her arms around him while they rode.

These beautiful hills were soon becoming impossible for her to climb. Her strength was gone.

"O Great Spirit," she pleaded, "help me to go a little bit farther. I can walk no more. My feet cannot carry me. I must reach my People. I am so close, but I might as well be far."

Morning Glory tried to grab a branch as her world began to spin. For a moment she thought the earth would blend with her head. As she passed out, she fell upon a rock and blood gushed from her brow. She crumpled beneath the trees, bringing sweet relief from her tormented body.

CHAPTER 25

"Has anyone seen Lone Star?" Schalute inquired around the village. "He's been gone for days. When he doesn't return from his drunk after the sun has risen for the third day, I wonder what trouble he has gotten into.

"Tomorrow we will go on a hunt. We'll track him down and take him with us if he is fit to ride," he announced to Dancing Eagle.

Dancing Eagle shrugged his shoulders. He couldn't care less about Lone Star or anything else. To him, one day was the same as the next. At least Lone Star could lose himself for days. Dancing Eagle couldn't even manage to do that. He knew that nothing he did could ever make him forget or forgive.

Lone Star had had to leave the village, as usual, because Schalute wouldn't let him drink within the village limits. All too often he had lost control with his drunken rages. Dancing Eagle and his braves had had to bind him down with leather ties so many times that finally Schalute forbade him to drink around the People.

Lone Star respected Schalute, but yet he couldn't face life without the white man's liquid spirit. His spirit had left a long time ago when the princess went away. Dancing Eagle didn't know it, but Lone Star had loved her too. Lone Star knew he never had a chance with her – she had always favored Dancing Eagle – but nonetheless, he had always wanted her.

The village had never been the same. When she left, the spirit of the whole village seemed to leave. Sickness overtook many of the tribe. They lost many to smallpox. White man left them that curse, too.

They had to stay away from the big river because that was white man's territory. They couldn't travel where they wanted to anymore. Game was becoming scarce. Their village lost pride. The People lost spirit.

Lone Star's uncle Schalute had become chief of a dying village. Two Moons, his cousin, was hardly there. Blue Dove had come back to the village to live with her daughter and Black Wolf. Lone Star often brought her meat.

Gentle Breeze, who had married Standing Bear a while back, had recently had a baby. She would often leave the village for weeks at a time. Schalute never paid her much attention since Morning Glory left, and she never quite forgot what had happened so many years ago.

Lone Star had been gone for three days. He had ridden out from the village on his appaloosa pony and headed for the woods. He painted a circle around the pony's right eye to give it sight and attached feathers to its brown mane. He was ready for war, if need be.

He favored a spot that had a good view of Eagle's Ridge. There by the stream he could let out his wild rages. He would shout and roar to the heavens and wait for an answer back. He saw what he wanted to see. He could escape reality – or at least he tried to.

This was one of those times. He had all but polished off an entire gallon jug of whiskey. The ground swirled beneath his feet. Every so often he would crawl to his pony and hobble him near fresh grass by the stream, often passing out beneath its hooves. He was used to talking to old Diablo for hours, telling him all his woes. Diablo would listen silently as he munched away for hours. They were a team.

Many winters ago, Diablo had been gifted to him by Schalute. Schalute figured this horse had to go to Lone Star because it was the biggest horse he had ever seen and Lone Star was the biggest brave in the village. They were perfect for each other. Many braves couldn't even mount such a big animal.

Lone Star's head pounded so heavily that he could not think. He liked it that way. Whenever he thought, only frustration came his way.

The rays of morning light poured upon his eyes, waking him to the pounding in his head. He swatted at the insects buzzing around his face and looked around to find his pony. It had wandered off. Strange, he thought, the grass was still good here by the stream. That old gelding of his rarely wandered off.

Lone Star finished off the last drop from his jug and flung it into the woods. He steadied himself against a tree to stand. His feet didn't seem connected to the rest of him; his body went one way, but his feet didn't seem to move at all.

From deep in the woods behind him, he heard movement within the trees. Squatting down, he pulled an arrow from his quiver and slowly walked into the trees. He figured it was probably his gelding, but one didn't take chances these days. The whites would shoot at anything wearing a feather, whether it had two feet or two wings.

Now he wished he had his full wits about him. He was wobbly on his feet and could not walk as quietly as he should have. He heard a horse snort through the trees. Was it his horse or another's?

His gelding nickered upon his approach, but its head was down, nuzzling something on the ground. Lone Star started. It was a woman! She was face-down upon a rock. There was blood on the ground. Her dress was torn and her moccasins were worn out. As he approached her, his scalp tingled. Something was all too familiar about her slender build. Her hair was soiled but almost blue. She wore an eagle feather.

"Woman," he called out, "who are you?" There was no reply. The body crumpled on the ground didn't move.

He knelt down beside her and shook her. There was no response. Gently, he pulled her over and held her in his arms.

A shock ran through him. His heart beat wildly. Was he still too full of liquor, even after sleeping all night long, to be seeing clearly?

"Morning Glory!" he whispered. He gently shook her, trying to wake her up. Her face was ashen gray. Her pulse hardly beat. Near the temple of one eye, a gaping wound was crusted with dried blood. Her body was on fire. She was barely alive!

Oh, why did he have to be drunk now? Even though his legs were wobbly and he could not walk a straight line, he still had the strength to pick her up and carry her to the river. She was as light as a feather to him.

Quickly, he took the shirt off his back and wet it in the river water. Tenderly, he wiped the blood off her face. He mopped her brow, her neck, her arms and her legs, trying to calm her fever.

He ran into the woods, stumbling a few times, to find the jug he had flung. When he found it, he filled it with water and tried to get her to drink. He could not wake her so he put a few drops into her mouth, hoping it would help. There was no response. She was completely limp.

Lone Star's head was spinning. He couldn't think. He leaped into the river and submerged his head, trying to clear it. It barely helped.

He pulled his dripping head from the water and tilted it back. "O Creator, help me now! Our princess has returned. If I cannot get her back alive, all hope will be lost," he prayed out loud, yelling to the sky.

Lone Star jumped as he felt something on his back. It was Diablo nuzzling him. Diablo, even though still hobbled, had followed him back to the river's edge.

Lone Star stroked Diablo's muzzle. "That's a good fellow. Now, you just stand there. Don't go away." Lone Star removed the rope hobble.

He picked Morning Glory up and laid her on her stomach over the middle of Diablo's back. Holding on to the reins, he tried to leap onto the horse's back, but with its uneven load it kept circling. Lone Star was having a hard time, in his condition, getting up onto the big horse without jumping right on top of Morning Glory.

Finally, he led Diablo to a large, flat-topped rock. Lone Star pulled Morning Glory off Diablo's back and held her limply against him across her waist. He climbed onto Diablo's back from the top of the rock and sat Morning Glory upright in front of him, holding her against his chest with one arm and holding the reins with the other.

Lone Star could hardly sit the horse straight. Every time he would veer to one side, Diablo would circle in that direction. It was not a straight trip home.

All those years that Lone Star had watched Morning Glory grow, he had a hard time communicating to her. He was quiet; words did not come easily to him as they did to Dancing Eagle. There were so many things he had wanted to tell her. And now she might die! Liquor loosened his tongue. She couldn't hear him, so he had the courage to talk.

"Oh Morning Star, from the moment I first saw you, I knew I had to protect you. I had always wanted to hold you in my arms, but it was never to be. Now I have you in my arms. I promise you, I will protect you from this moment on, with my life. I failed you before. But if need be, I will die protecting you. It is the only way I can show you my love."

Morning Glory stirred a little in his arms and opened her eyes for just a moment. She was confused and frightened and started to shake. Moments later her eyes rolled to the back of her head and she slumped against his chest again.

In that short time, he was able to see her incredible blue eyes again. They were glazed with fever, but in their depths he saw that her soul was filled with pain and sorrow. If he could do anything to change that, he promised, he would.

Diablo climbed the last hill before coming in sight of the village. Smoke curled toward the sky from the cooking fires. The dogs barked at his entrance.

He steered Diablo gently toward Schalute's lodge and called out to whoever was behind the flap.

Runta pulled the flap back and stepped out. She put her hands over her mouth and fought back the tears that rapidly welled in her eyes.

"Woman, where is Schalute?" Lone Star abruptly asked.

Runta stammered, trying to think. "Uh, he and Dancing Eagle went on a hunt with Shadow Dancer and a few of the braves."

Runta started to walk closer to Diablo. Her hand reached out in disbelief. "What have you here? Can this be? Is that our Glory?"

"It is, woman, but she is barely alive. Don't just stand there," Lone Star said in exasperation.

Gentle Breeze came out of a tepee and ran up to them. "Give her to me," she demanded tearfully.

Lone Star lowered the sagging form of Morning Glory into the arms of Runta and Gentle Breeze. As they lowered her down, she simply crumpled onto the ground.

Lone Star leaped off his horse and picked her up in his arms. He kicked the flap aside and carried her into the lodge for the women. His job was done and the women were to take over now. He jumped onto Diablo to leave the village. He did not want anyone, especially Morning Glory, to see him until he had sobered up completely.

Gentle Breeze picked up a bucket and ran to the river for fresh water. A crowd of People started to form outside of their lodge. Whispers went back and forth. "Who did they bring into their lodge?" they asked among themselves.

"It was a woman," one of them volunteered. "She wore the feather of our People."

Gentle Breeze hurried back, brushing through the crowd without an explanation. She turned before entering through the flap.

"Go back to your lodges. Leave us alone, now," she demanded.

Runta was in the process of removing Morning Glory's moccasins and torn dress. When they slipped the dress past her shoulders, they gasped at the oozing burn wound that showed inflammation all around it.

"This is where her fever is coming from," Runta said with concern. "The infection has taken over her body." The wound on her head was again bleeding. "She has lost much blood from this wound, too. She is so very weak," Runta said, shaking her head.

"Look at her feet," Gentle Breeze pointed. She has cuts down to the bone. She has traveled for many days.

The women bathed her with clean water. Runta applied a salve to her shoulder and wrapped it with a clean cloth. She applied herbs to her feet and wrapped them, too. The gash on her head stopped bleeding, but it was apparent that she had lost much blood.

Gentle Breeze put her arms around Glory to sit her up while Runta attempted to get an herbal brew into her mouth, but she was unconscious. They could not get her to swallow.

"The best we can do now is to get the fever down. When it breaks, she will awake and we can get her to drink," Runta said.

Throughout the day, they bathed her body constantly. Gentle Breeze made several trips to the river for fresh water. People still gathered about the tepee. She kept chasing them away without explanation.

Morning Glory's body still lay completely limp. She did not utter a sound. Runta knew that her spirit was not there. Her body was in too much pain for her spirit to stay.

When the sun began to rest behind the village, the dogs started to bark at the braves returning from the hunt. Schalute rode into the village with a strange feeling in his gut. Instead of bringing his horse to the herd, he rode straight to his lodge. People were standing about, but why?

Schalute leaped to the ground and dropped the reins, ground-tying his horse. He pushed through the crowd and jerked back the flap on his tepee.

On the ground was the lifeless form of a young woman. Schalute had not yet figured out who she was.

"My sister has returned to us," Gentle Breeze tried to explain. She was fearful because she was in Schalute's lodge, from which she had been banned years ago.

Schalute wavered on his feet for a moment. Her words rushed

past him like thunder.

"It is Glory," Runta acknowledged. "She is very, very ill."

Schalute quickly turned to Gentle Breeze and his words lashed out. "Go now. Leave my lodge. Tell the People outside to go back to their own lodges. I will talk to them when the sun rises over the river, not before."

Gentle Breeze left tearfully, turning back to Schalute one more time. "I want to stay with my sister."

"Go now," he demanded.

Schalute dropped to his knees and stroked Morning Glory's hair. She was so flaccid, so pale. She hardly breathed.

"How did she get here?" he whispered out of respect, looking up at Runta.

"Lone Star brought her back from the forest. He could hardly sit his horse but he held her gently in his arms," Runta explained with compassion.

He knelt even closer to get a good look at her in the firelight. She still looked like a little girl to him. Her face was so sweet. She was a little taller now, but still very slim.

Runta gently turned Morning Glory on her side and showed Schalute her burn. She unwrapped Morning Glory's feet to show him the miles she had carried. She took the poultice off her head to show him that she had shared her blood with the earth.

Schalute was horrified. "I must find Dancing Eagle, Two Moons and Shadow Dancer. They must be told, but they cannot see her tonight. First the medicine man must bring her spirit back. I will work with him to remove the white man's spirit from her or she will not survive again among her People."

Two Moons was not immediately about, as usual. Schalute could not find him. Shadow Dancer was already on his way to bring meat to the outcasts who lived over the hill. He had been given the position of leader to rule over these People. He liked it and they respected him. A runner was sent to inform him of his sister's return.

The hard part was having to tell Dancing Eagle. Schalute didn't know how he would respond after all of these years. Dancing Eagle was not the same man Morning Glory had left behind.

Schalute went to Dancing Eagle's lodge. Dancing Eagle hadn't even hung around like the others to see what the commotion was in the village. He didn't care anymore.

Schalute called out to Dancing Eagle. "It is I, Schalute. May I enter your lodge?"

"If you must," Dancing Eagle replied.

Schalute pulled back the flap, stepped inside and sat within the lodge. He looked at Dancing Eagle for a while before he spoke, trying to find the proper words.

Over the last ten winters, Dancing Eagle had gained some streaks of silver hair. He was not quite as lean as he used to be but he was still strong. The spark was gone from his eyes, from his soul.

"Dancing Eagle, sit before me. I have something very important to tell you."

Dancing Eagle shrugged his shoulders and sat. He couldn't imagine anything being important anymore.

"So. I am sitting. What is so important?" Dancing Eagle said with aloofness.

"Morning Glory is back!"

Dancing Eagle shot to his feet and started to pace. His clenched and unclenched his hands. He couldn't look Schalute in the eyes. He didn't know what to think. After she left him for the white man, he had never wanted to see her again, yet his heart had always ached.

Schalute continued. "She is in my lodge, barely alive. She is not even awake. Lone Star found her in the forest. She is in pretty bad shape. Her spirit is gone. We have to bring it back. We do not know what happened, for she still has yet to speak."

"I know this is a shock for you. I know in my heart that she came back to protect our People. I also know in my heart that she still loves you. She always did. She always will. She did what she had to do. Try to remember that." Schalute paused, then added, "By the way, if you can find Two Moons, inform him that she is here."

Schalute rose, stood up and abruptly left. He felt the need to get back to Morning Glory.

Dancing Eagle sat down, motionless. Every emotion from joy to anger raced through him. He wanted to run and hold her in his arms but he hated her for tearing out his heart. He wondered what she looked like after all of these winters. Had she thought of him, as he thought of her? Had she tried to block him from her mind, as he tried to block her from his? Had she found happiness with the white man all of these years?

Schalute went to find Deer Runner, the medicine man, to help heal Morning Glory. Deer Runner was the son of old Wise Owl, skilled with the drum and the ways of spirit and healing. He was about the same age as Dancing Eagle and a bit shorter in stature.

Deer Runner joined Schalute in his tepee to do a cleansing of Glory with the beat of the drums. He purified the lodge with sage and sprinkled special herbs into the fire. He beat a drum back and forth over her body to cleanse her being, to strengthen her heartbeat. They chanted through the night to call her spirit back to be with her People once again.

The spirit of the white man was chased out of her body so she could be of the People again. The spirits that protected her were called to bring her back to them.

Throughout the night, Morning Glory lay motionless. The ways of the shaman were brought back to her being. Runta worked to heal her body so that her spirit could be brought back in.

Dancing Eagle fingered the hollowed-out bone that he had never taken off, the one Morning Glory had given him on their wedding night. He listened to the drumming throughout the night. Part of him wanted to be there, to work alongside him as he had done so many times before. He knew that Schalute would never allow it because of his mixed emotions. His emotions would keep her from coming back.

Two Moons was in vision in the cave all night. No one had reached him to inform him of her return. They didn't need to. Part of him knew. He knew that part of his heartbeat was near. He too drummed, from the cave, simultaneously with his father.

Over the years, Two Moons' hair had turned completely silver, even though he had only seen twenty-one winters. His eyes turned different colors, picking up the hues of what was around him. He seldom talked. When he did, it was with a rhythm and rhyme, which drove Schalute wild. Schalute never understood him. Two Moons didn't care. He needed no one. He could see whatever he wanted to see. He could call to the Eagle and get whatever answer he needed. What he would not do was change anyone's destiny, even that of Morning Glory.

He knew what she had been through while she was gone. He felt all of her emotions. He knew that her heart had been ripped in two. He had felt her love and loss for Dancing Eagle and her People. He also knew that this was her destiny.

Now she was back. He knew this was only the beginning of many other events. He was glad she was back but he knew that nothing was going to be easy.

Throughout the night, as though in a trance, he pounded the drum and chanted. His voice echoed through the cave, entered the Earth, went to the Central Sun and came back renewed. The Glory of the Morning had returned!

CHAPTER 26

As the dawn of the day rose into the sky, Morning Glory opened her eyes. Before her stood Schalute.

She had to think. Was she in a dream? Her heart skipped a beat. Tears welled in her eyes.

Schalute stared in wonder for a minute, crossed his legs and sat directly in front of her. He took her hands and pulled her up to a sitting position. As he held her hands, he started to shake. Words did not immediately come. As he shook, she cried. Tears then welled in his eyes.

"Father, I am so happy to be back!" She could hardly whisper.

"All will be well, now that you are here. The spirit of our village left when you left. You were the wealth and glory of our tribe. This time I will do a better job of protecting you. Forgive me for letting you down."

"I have forgiven all. It was what had to be. I only hope that I will be forgiven. What of the others? It has been so long since I have seen the ones I love."

Schalute stood up. "I will get them and let you visit with them for a short while. You are still weak. You must rest." He turned to Runta. "Feed this child. She must regain her strength."

Schalute stepped out of the lodge, only to find that a crowd had again gathered about. "Our Blue Star has returned," Schalute announced to the People. "She is here for the People of our village," he beamed.

"Look," he said, pointing into the southern sky. "There is the sign that needed to be. The Eagle is back with us. We now are a tribe again. We shall prepare a celebration. Go, now. Gather the seeds of the earth. Prepare a great hunt," Schalute ordered. "With the rising of two suns, we shall honor her return."

The People nodded in agreement. The Eagle had shown itself. Things would change.

Two Moons watched from behind the crowd of People. As they dispersed, he continued to watch the Eagle. It was he alone who saw the Eagle proceed to do the Dance of Death. He wanted to see Morning Glory but he retreated into the hills. He must first contemplate what this meant. Was there to be a celebration of life because she'd returned, or was there to be death?

Schalute brought back Gentle Breeze and Blue Dove to see Morning Glory. Morning Glory had never known how they had joined forces with the Raven in arranging her kidnapping. At this point she only knew they were her sisters.

With a tearful embrace Morning Glory asked about their lives. Blue Dove explained that she had only been married to Wonka one winter before he was killed, but that they had a daughter. Gentle Breeze had come in carrying an infant son she had just borne with a brave called Standing Bear.

Schalute only let them stay a short while, then Shadow Dancer was brought in. Shadow Dancer was now a young man, not a little boy.

"Oh, how handsome you have grown, my brother. Are you still full of tricks?"

Shadow Dancer nodded in affirmation while he looked at her. He had been very young when she left. He had not realized what a beautiful woman she was. She had been but a memory in his mind.

"My sister, it is good that you are back. Our family has not been the same since the day you left. I have missed you." As a token, he handed her some shells he had found .

In a short time, Schalute ushered them all out. Morning Glory was very weak.

"Where is Two Moons, Father?"

"Two Moons. . . . You know Two Moons. Two Moons comes when he feels like it. I have not been able to find him since your return. He'll be along shortly," Schalute said with exasperation. "I'm sure he feels your presence."

Morning Glory put her head down and nervously asked, "Father, what of Dancing Eagle?"

Schalute knew she would ask sooner or later. He tried to find an appropriate answer. "Dancing Eagle is not the same man you once knew. Your leaving was hard on him. I will try to find him for you, but be prepared. Don't expect too much. You have been gone a long time."

"Did he take another woman, Father?" Morning Glory asked with hesitation.

Schalute simply said, "No, he did not," then left to look for him.

"Runta, how do I look?" Morning Glory asked, realizing for the first time the toll her illness must have taken. "I want to look beautiful for Dancing Eagle. It has been too long."

Runta turned away from Morning Glory as she spoke. "Morning Glory, it has always been your spirit that was beautiful. Even though you have gone through many trials, you are still beautiful. That is why your loss has changed Dancing Eagle so. Do not expect much from him when you see him."

Morning Glory did not know what they were talking about. The man she'd left was so vibrant. It was his fiery soul that excited her like no other. They could share with each other as they could share with no one else. That was what was so special.

Morning Glory heard footsteps approach her lodge. She could see a man's leggings and moccasins by the entrance. The man was hesitant to come in. Her heart pounded. She could barely think. Was it Dancing Eagle?

She heard him take a long, deep breath, then sigh. He ducked in the door and stepped through. Runta immediately excused herself and left.

Morning Glory looked up at him. Her heart pounded wildly. Oh, he was still handsome and strong, but so sad-looking. Wisps of silver streaked his hair.

He folded his legs and sat down across from her. His head was down, looking at the ground. He could not bear to look into her eyes. She silently looked at the top of his head. He was wearing his hair loose, with a headband and three eagle feathers. His chest was bare except for the wind bone he wore. He had an arm band on his left arm.

She tried to read his thoughts, but he blocked her. He could do that very well.

Finally he looked up, straight into her eyes. Her heart pounded and tears welled. She tried to swallow the lump in her throat.

"Oh, Dancing Eagle, I have missed you every day of my life," she started to say.

Dancing Eagle looked at her in bewilderment. "You left me for a white man! My heart died a long time ago. It turned cold. Now I see you before my eyes, more beautiful than ever before. Why have you come back? Is it to torment my soul?"

Morning Glory was in shock. She stiffened and froze. What she feared most was happening. She had brought him disgrace. Words were locked in her throat. She could see that no matter what she said to him now, it wouldn't matter.

She wanted to hold his hand, caress his hair; but he just stared at her in confused pain. She wanted to explain to him how she had to protect the People. How could she ever explain to him that she had to do it at his expense?

He looked down into the dirt and toyed with the lacings on his moccasins. She could see into his soul. He couldn't bear it. She couldn't talk. He couldn't talk. Minutes seemed like eternity.

Dancing Eagle rose to his feet. "Schalute insisted that I not stay long. I can see that you have traveled many days to get here. We will talk later." He abruptly left.

After all those years of calling to his spirit, talking to him in her dreams, yearning for him day and night, he simply got up and walked out without even touching her. Dancing Eagle was in too much pain to have done anything else. She could see that. He had no idea how much pain she too had been in. He only remembered the rejection.

During the day, gifts were laid outside the lodge. She was gifted with beaded dresses, robes, blankets and food. Her People knew that it was their honor to give. They knew that she had arrived with nothing in her hands.

Throughout the day Runta tended to her wounds, made her drink special herbal brews and fed her small portions of food. The braves went on a hunt. The women gathered flowers and berries. The village carried an air of joy. They thought they had reason to celebrate.

Schalute asked Dancing Eagle to build Morning Glory her own lodge. Dancing Eagle built it next to Schalute's lodge, with the help of Lone Star. He painted it with the picture of a rising sun, which symbolized the daughter of a chief, and the feathers that she was to be gifted with at tomorrow's ceremony.

Morning Glory, on the other hand, was trying to summon the courage to tell Schalute and the council of their impending danger.

During the day she succumbed to sleep. She rested but in a fitful state. In her visions she saw a row of corn. The corn produced a beautiful kernel, very rich in nature, very fertile. At first, she touched the corn. It had the feel of power, energy and life. When she peeled back the husk, she found that the corn was eaten away. The cob was all that was left.

She knew this was an omen that, as the corn produced life and projected life, death was also there. The corn fed the life. And the corn fed the death.

When she'd first arrived in the village, she was the Glory of the Morning, the dawning of a new day, a new life. Now she felt that she would be the Glory of the Mourning.

When she awoke from the vision, she was called to the council meeting. She put on a clean new dress and moccasins. Runta helped her cleanse her hair and put in new braids. Even though she had a deep wound near her temple and her fever had just broken, she still carried beauty. It was obvious, though, that she was still weak.

It was a closed council meeting. Only the medicine men, the elders and the chief were present.

After the initial cleansing with sage, the pipe was passed, according to custom.

Morning Glory sat quietly until the pipe had been passed and all looked her way for her to start.

"My People, it is my honor to be back among you. My heart has never left this place. I stayed among the whites so the whites would not come. The man I married promised me this."

"The whites' big chief from Washington sent a new man to the fort. This man will not honor my husband's arrangement. He says you must move off this sacred land."

The council members looked at each other in alarm. They shook their heads and let her go on.

"I have seen the hearts of the whites. They do not honor our People or our land. I fear that our village will perish if you do not leave immediately. Many whites carry greed in their hearts. They may not give you time to negotiate. They now have an excuse to just take."

The council members began to talk softly among themselves while Morning Glory paused to choose her next words.

"I had a vision. It was a vision of death! Our People must leave now. The whites have many weapons and many men. Our small village cannot win such a fight. Our brothers have already been forced to move west. They are no longer here to band with us in a fight." Morning Glory stopped so the elders could share their feelings.

White Feather, an elder with gnarled fingers and few teeth, chose to speak. "Long ago, our People were chosen to leave the safety of their tribe and the home of their ancestors in the north to come to this sacred land. This is the home of the ancients. We are here to guard an entrance into the inner world. Our temple in the cave holds the spirits from the inner world. We cannot so easily be told to leave."

The council members nodded their heads in agreement.

Deer Runner then asked to hold the feather in the circle so he could speak. He was the youngest member of the council but still very wise.

"What you have just said has been passed down to me through my father. I did not travel here from the north, as some of you have. But I have been here long enough to remember the day the Spirit of the Sky sent us his daughter. She is a gift. She has wisdom. We must continue to listen to her. She has risked her life to come back to us and give us this message."

Morning Glory continued. "My People, you have been faithful guardians of this land. If you stay, I fear you will die. I have come to warn you that your job is now to move west. There is not much time for you. You must move quickly. It is time for you to rejoin your relatives of the north. They will greet you with open arms once again."

The members of the council were old and set in their ways. Nothing of such importance could be decided in a moment's time. They would seek vision and rejoin once again to decide. Morning Glory understood but was fearful. She knew time was not in their favor, but she could not get them to decide immediately.

Schalute could see that Morning Glory's strength was drained. He quickly led her from the council lodge back to his lodge for one more night. He did not want her to go to her own lodge until she was better recovered.

Two Moons had stayed in vision the entire day. He had not yet come to see his sister. She understood. She no longer questioned his ways or his timing. They were his own.

Even though she was exhausted, Morning Glory could hardly sleep. Her shoulder still throbbed. Her head pounded like thunder from the wound. Her body ached from loss of blood. Most of all, her heart ached. She missed her sons. She was worried about her

People. She wanted Dancing Eagle to hold her in his arms.

The night was long. She listened to its familiar sounds, of owls hooting in the woods, the horses stomping bugs in the field, crickets within the bushes and the curious sound of wolves surrounding the village. Never had the sound of wolves stirred her senses so. She would have to talk to Two Moons about that when she finally saw him.

Morning Glory rose before the sun's rays struck the east side of the tepee entrance. She freshened herself by the river and returned to her lodge to find a little girl named Little Red Flower, Blue Dove's daughter. She looked as though she had seen about six winters. Little Red Flower was quiet but alert. She brought a basket of fruit as a gift.

Morning Glory gave her a gift. It was her heart-shaped turquoise stone.

"Any time you want to see me, look into this stone," she told Little Red Flower. She gave her a peck on the cheek and let her scamper off.

Dancing Eagle saw the sun's rays peek through the flap of his tepee. The sounds of the village started to come alive. The dogs barked for scraps of food. The children ran about, chasing one another to the river. As the women began to prepare meals, the smell of smoke began to permeate the air. Horses nickered in the far field.

Part of him felt alive for the first time in many winters. He faced the east and thanked the rays of the sun for sparking new life in him. For the first time in years, he had a reason to greet the day. He would continue to work on Morning Glory's new lodge.

Morning Glory spent the morning being assisted by Gentle Breeze and Runta. Her wounds were attended to, she was cleansed in the river. Her hair was washed and braided with flowers. A beautiful beaded, fringed buckskin dress was brought to her to wear, along with beaded moccasins.

Her wounds were healing and the throbbing had lessened. Her strength was starting to come back. Gentle Breeze doted on her, hoping to make up for what she had been involved in many years ago.

By midday the celebration was about to begin. On this hot summer day, the sky was blue and cloudless. For the first time, Morning Glory was brought out before the People. They gathered in a center circle.

The council gifted Morning Glory with one of the finest horses from the herd. It was a stout buckskin mare of profound endurance and speed. It was brought to her with a beautifully braided bridle decorated with beads, stones and feathers and blanketed with a handwoven blanket cushioned with fleece.

Morning Glory slowly walked toward the mare and stroked its wise face. The mare immediately nuzzled her, becoming an instant friend.

"I truly thank the People for such a fine gift," Morning Glory announced. The mare was so special to her, she didn't want to let it be led away, but the ceremony was about to begin.

A great feast had been prepared. There was plenty of venison, corn, potatoes, apples and fish. All in the village gathered to share the food.

A fire was built within the circle, which still contained soft sand for dancing and was bordered by rocks for the People to sit on. The medicine men sprinkled special herbs into the fire and the drums began to beat.

Schalute started the first dance. He danced to wash the stain of the white man away from her. While he was dancing, Two Moons finally arrived in the village. He sat so he could observe, yet not be observed.

Dancing Eagle performed in the next dance. Morning Glory watched him enter the circle. He glanced toward her and his heart throbbed. During this dance they chanted for the Eagle to fly over the ceremony and drop a petal to signify that everything would be all right. It would be a petal of purity.

Dancing Eagle was truly a gifted dancer. All in the tribe loved to watch him move with spirit. Morning Glory couldn't take her eyes off him the whole while he danced. She had missed both him and his dancing more than she realized. Every beat of the drum became the beat of her heart. Every movement he made, she made quietly within her limbs. She was dancing with his spirit. He could feel it too. He danced with more life this day than he did in all those years she was gone.

Two more dances were performed by tribal members. Then the People waited for the Eagle.

While they waited, Morning Glory worried about the vision she had seen. She knew that she was to be part of that vision.

The Eagle never appeared. Two Moons felt this was a very bad omen. He had watched her during the ceremony. She carried much heaviness in her heart.

As the ceremony ended and the People started drifting back to their lodges, Two Moons pulled Morning Glory off to the side. The two embraced tearfully.

Two Moons did not waste words on what they already knew between them. He knew that she had come because she had to warn the People. He had been expecting this for some time now. His visions had already shown him it was coming.

"Morning Glory," Two Moons softly said as he led her toward a quite place, "tell me what troubles your heart."

"Three bright sons!" she started to sob.

"You mean three moons?" he asked, confused.

"No. Three sons," she said as her head hung low.

"Sons that you conceived?"

"Yes," she confided.

"Have you told anyone yet?" Two Moons inquired.

"Not yet. That would be one more complication. I'm trying to convince the council to move immediately. They aren't moving fast enough on this. My husband's men are probably coming toward the village this very moment!"

Two Moons confided, "Now I know why the Eagle did the Dance of Death yesterday. That is why the Eagle didn't drop the petal of purity. In my visions, I saw white men coming by canoe and by horse. They are on their way now!"

Then with certainty Two Moons said, "The council must meet again tonight. I don't think we can make the move fast enough. We must prepare the best we can, making provisions for the women and children."

CHAPTER 27

Schalute too was disturbed that the Eagle had not appeared during the ceremony. It was not a good sign. Upon returning to his lodge, he saw Two Moons and Morning Glory standing together. Their faces showed great concern. He knew that Morning Glory had not told him everything.

"It is about time you showed yourself, Two Moons," Schalute said. "Your sister returned some time ago. Where were you?"

"In vision," he simply stated without further explanation.

"Of course. In vision. That's where you always are! But what is going on here now? Morning Glory, it is time you tell me everything. Why did the Eagle not come?" he demanded.

"Father, let us go to the lodge. I must talk to you privately. Besides, Two Moons needs to gather up a council meeting. I will inform you further while he gets things set up."

The sun was about to set past the heavily wooded hills. As the sky turned red, they stepped into the lodge entrance, closed the flap behind them and sat down on the ground.

Morning Glory did not know how to begin, except to just dive in. She straightened her back and looked at Schalute. "Father, I have left behind three sons."

Schalute's head shot up with alarm. "By the white man?" he quickly asked.

She nodded her head. "Yes, Father. He promised me that he would make sure the village was unharmed if I became his lawful wife. You know that was the last thing I wanted to do. What choice did I have? Now I have three special sons. They have straw-colored hair, as does their father, but they have my blue eyes. They are the bridge between the two peoples. Can't you see that?" she asked, hoping for some understanding.

Not waiting for an answer, Morning Glory continued. "I know that their father will come to try to take me back. I do not want to go. I only stayed with him to protect the village. He has no power to protect it anymore. I have to find a way to get my sons back soon. The time is not now. Our village is endangered. Two Moons saw that some of the whites are already on their way. I'm sure my husband is among them!"

Schalute was silent for a while, then spoke. "Was he the one who wounded you? Is he the one who branded you?"

Morning Glory lowered her head in shame and simply nodded. "He thought that if he branded me, no other man could have me. He wanted to keep me. But my heart was never with him, it was always with Dancing Eagle."

Schalute arched his head back and shouted, "Upon my bones and the bones of my father, I shall slay this man and scatter his bones to the wind. This man will have no peace and no spirit. This man will not take part in any pleasure, just the pain."

"Father, this is not what I want to hear!"

"It is my right! Something that has been stolen from me has to be taken care of."

Schalute jumped to his feet and abruptly left the lodge to join the council meeting. Morning Glory was shaken. She did not want to be with Tom Shaye ever again. But he was the boy's father. She did not want Schalute to avenge her. She wanted no blood on her hands.

The moon was full that night. She was restless and distraught so she walked to her favorite place along the river. Her heart began to beat like thunder. Dancing Eagle was there, waiting for her. He sat upon a large rock, throwing stones out over the water. The moon shone in a path across the water. He heard a twig snap and got up to face her.

Morning Glory stood there with a lump in her throat. The moon shined off her blue-black hair. The gentle evening breeze, brushing against the long fringe that decorated her soft, white buckskin dress, created a soft chiming among the beads that decorated it. Her chest heaved as her breathing quickened, and her heart pounded in anticipation and fear.

Dancing Eagle stood there staring at her. She had only seen twelve summers the last time he saw her. She was a bit taller now, more refined. Even though she had a large gash on her forehead, she was still the most beautiful woman he had ever known. Motionless, she stood before him elegantly, regally, but with an incredible sadness in her eyes.

He stood before her, bare-chested and sinewy, wearing his buckskin leggings, breechcloth and an arm band. His long hair was loose, bound by a headband and eagle feathers. The red arm band set off his hard muscles. He still captivated her. No one could fully hold her heart but him.

He stepped toward her. Somehow she found herself in his strong arms, feeling his heart beat against hers.

"Just hold me," she whispered.

He caressed her hair and held her strong. She started to sob. He greeted her with salty kisses. Dancing Eagle had been so blinded by sorrow and rage through the years that he had forgotten, until this moment, what it felt like to love, to have her breath move with his own. They had together a rare harmony of spirit and mind that they could find with no other.

Dancing Eagle suddenly heard some birds flutter from a nearby tree. He became alarmed and pulled away, turning sideways.

Morning Glory heard a whoosh and a thump as Dancing Eagle flew backwards onto the ground, pulling at an arrow in his left shoulder.

Morning Glory fell to her knees at Dancing Eagle's side. She gasped as she saw feet next to her. When she dared to look up, she saw those cold eyes. It was Thomas Shaye!

"Spare his life," she pleaded. "Please spare his life!"

He gripped his gun in both hands. The barrel was pointed at Dancing Eagle's head, the hammer was cocked. The face of this man showed total absence of all thought except to kill the man who stole his wife's heart.

Tom flashed a wicked grin. "I will spare this brave his worthless life if you will come back with me."

Morning Glory nodded affirmation. What else could she do? If she did not, Dancing Eagle would die.

Tom grabbed her by the hair, swung her wide and held the gun to her side, to make sure Dancing Eagle did not make a move toward them.

Into her face Tom snarled, "Never leave me again, do you hear?" He shook her fervently. "Never leave!"

Tom looked down at Dancing Eagle, who was bleeding. To add insult to his pain he said, "She will go the way of the white." He kicked Dancing Eagle hard to the head, rendering him unconscious.

Within a second Tom had dragged Morning Glory off into the trees and disappeared.

When Dancing Eagle awoke he did not know how much time had lapsed. He couldn't think clearly. When he tried to get up, the pain in his shoulder reminded him what had happened. Rolling to his side, he groaned and clenched his fist in rage.

With an awful growl through his teeth, holding on to the ground, Dancing Eagle pledged, "By the ancient spirits that have flown on this land, I will find this man Shaye and take his life. This will be my time to cut out his heart and let a horde of locusts on the prairie eat away at the darkness that is there and the despair that he has in his mind. I will feed it to the wolves so that in time we will know who he is. His body will never rest as long as I have a breath of life in me. I pledge to thee. The Great Spirit Eagle that protects me will witness as I watch the sun rot his flesh and soul. I will hang his hair from my lodge. I shall spit upon his bleached bones."

Two Moons had sensed something was wrong. Dancing Eagle looked up to see Two Moons at his side.

"He took her again, Two Moons. He took her again," Dancing Eagle said. He pulled at the arrow, snapping it off at the shaft, and passed out cold."

Dancing Eagle awoke in his lodge to the beat of the drums sounding an alarm. Runta was attending to his shoulder.

Dancing Eagle shot up and tried to rise. "I have to find her. This can wait." He tried to push Runta aside but didn't have the strength. He faded out again.

CHAPTER 28

Tom had dragged Morning Glory to a clearing where four other men waited with horses. They had an extra one for Morning Glory. It was clear that Tom wasn't going to leave without her.

He pushed Morning Glory toward her horse. She refused to mount. Tom pulled her sideways and with one sweep of his arm, smashed her across the face.

"Get on . . . now! I'm not fooling around here, woman!"

Morning Glory nodded submission as he swung her up onto her barebacked horse. She never rode with a saddle as he did. As Tom released her reins and turned to mount his own horse, she whirled her horse around and wildly kicked it into a full gallop, catching the men by surprise.

With her bolt, Morning Glory had a slight lead, plus she was bareback and lighter. Her sorrel gelding had not had a rider on it all day, as had the other horses, so it was fresher. Momentarily, she galloped ahead of them.

All five men charged after her. Tom could see that they would be hard-pressed to catch up. She always did ride like the wind. Soon she would be within sight of the village. He had to stop her.

Tom pulled out his long-range rifle and reined in his horse. He took a quick but accurate aim and fired a single load. Morning Glory's horse had just begun to run up a hill. The shot caught it on the right flank. Her horse reared up and lost its balance on the slope, falling on top of Morning Glory. The horse screamed out in agony as it struggled vainly to get up. Morning Glory lay deathly still.

"Damn!" Tom yelled. "I didn't mean to kill her. I just wanted to shoot the horse out from under her," he said in disbelief.

The shot alerted the braves from the village. They leaped onto their ponies and galloped toward the hill.

"Let's get out of here now, Tom!" McVain yelled. "If she is alive, they will take care of her. The five of us can't fight off an entire village. If they catch us now, we won't want to be alive."

The five whirled their horses around and galloped as fast as they could into the woods. Tom looked back, thinking, If I can't have her, nobody can.

Two Moons and Schalute were among the first to arrive, and leaped off their ponies in panic. They walked slowly toward the struggling gelding. Each time it struggled, it crushed Morning Glory even more.

Schalute placed his hand upon the horse to calm it momentarily. Its right leg was clearly shattered. With one quick sweep of his knife across its throat, he put the poor creature out of its misery.

Lone Star and the other braves lifted the horse up off the ground, while Two Moons pulled Morning Glory out. They laid her upon the ground, trying to awaken her. Once again her spirit had left her. Judging by the position of her right leg, it was clear that her leg had also been shattered.

Schalute jumped to his feet. "Lone Star, you gather twenty of our braves. I will join you at the village circle and ride with you. We cannot let that man get away again. Morning Glory will never be safe as long as that man lives."

Two Moons scooped up his sister and carried her in his arms. "I will take care of my sister. I will bring her to the healing cave. Let no one disturb us for three days and three nights. When she is better, I will bring her back to the village."

With Morning Glory limp in his arms, Two Moons silently walked off toward the point, which housed the cave. With great pain in his heart he carried her against his heaving chest. He could not bear to see her in so much trouble and pain.

Two Moons carried her to the cave's entrance down by the river's edge. It was hidden under a cliff, surrounded by bushes and vines. The opening was invisible to anyone unaware of it, even if they were standing right next to it.

Two Moons had spent much time in this cave. Inside, it had three tiers. The first level was his altar. The altar contained herbs, rattles, sacred objects and turtle shells painted with pictures of the elements. On this level was a curious, large crystal cluster, standing almost two feet in height. The cluster faced the opening in the cave and caught its light.

He laid her down upon the second level. The third level or tier was sandy. In the crystalline sand, he drew the outline of her being. It was his intent to heal her spirit in the crystalline sand.

Morning Glory's right leg was shattered in three different places. She had another concussion. Her spirit had to decide if it could go on. She had endured much, and there was much ahead of her.

On the walls of the cave were sacred totems — a buffalo head, the head of Marona the cat, and a spider. During the next three days, Morning Glory's spirit would run with the cougar, charge with the buffalo and talk with the spider. They would become alive in spirit, as her spirit soared in their world. The buffalo gave her strength. The cougar gave her heart. The spider gave her wisdom.

Few People understood, but Two Moons' and Morning Glory's souls were but opposites of the same. The People knew that the Creator does not allow twin stars to be truly together until the Creator takes them home, to the Sun.

In this rare instance, the Creator allowed these twin souls to work together, because the day they could return to the Sun was not far off.

Two Moons chanted to the oneness of his soul, to bring her spirit to the outline in the crystalline sand to heal, while he worked to heal her broken body with herbs, poultices, and brews to drink. He set her leg and put comfrey root poultices on her leg. He put drops of comfrey root tea into her mouth. He gave of his strength to heal her as no one else could.

The spirits of Morning Glory's sons appeared to her. They called out to her. She knew she had to come back for them. There was a purpose and a plan for these boys. They were to be a bridge between the red and white.

When her spirit knew she was to stay, the Creator sent a gift. Two Moons looked toward the opening and saw a bright light. The sun had already started to set in the west. This opening faced the east. At first he thought it was the moon, but it was not yet night.

Suddenly a ray of orange light shot into the cave and struck the crystal cluster. Rays of orange light reflected off the cluster and bounced from every angle in the hallowed cave. They dazzled the eye and shot all about, making a wondrous sight. The room filled with a gentle heat and began to spin. The reflection off each cluster amplified as it bounced off each plane of the crystal; it reverberated off the crystalline walls and the crystalline, sandy floor.

Morning Glory opened her eyes to find Two Moons quietly sitting beside her. As usual, few words were exchanged. Words were unnecessary for them.

He brought her comfrey root tea to help heal her broken bones and some food to give her strength. By the end of the day, she was ready to return to the village. Two Moons made her a walking stick and bound her leg with a splint.

She was able to hobble on her leg pretty well, considering that only three days had passed. People in the village were amazed that she returned on her feet. Gentle Breeze, Blue Dove and Shadow Dancer ran out to greet her.

"Where is Father?" she asked.

Shadow Dancer said, "He has gone after the whites. Father vowed not to return until that man is dead. He said, 'As long as Shaye lives, Morning Glory will never be safe. He will never live to take her away from us again.'"

Morning Glory's heart skipped a beat. She knew that either one or both of those men would die. Schalute never went back on his word. It was not what she wanted to hear. Two Moons also felt despair. He knew nothing good would come of this.

"What of Dancing Eagle?" she asked with fearful anticipation.

Blue Dove replied, "He is in his lodge being cared for by Runta. The wound in his shoulder has festered. He is with fever."

"I shall go to him immediately," Morning Glory said as she started to hobble briskly toward his lodge.

Gentle Breeze tried to stop her. "You are weak yourself. You need time to heal."

Morning Glory didn't take time to stop as she replied, "He is wounded because of me. I will not leave his side until he is healed."

Runta smiled as Morning Glory peeked her head into the lodge entrance. The flap had been left open because it was a warm day. "Morning Glory, you are back so soon. Two Moons certainly knew what to do!" Runta exclaimed.

Morning Glory didn't even reply. Her eyes fell to Dancing Eagle, who was lying on the robe at her feet. He was sweating profusely and sleeping fitfully. She pulled back the poultice on his shoulder. The wound was full of pus and hot with fire.

She sat on the ground beside him and put her hand over his wound, closing her eyes while she concentrated.

"Pieces of the arrowhead are embedded within his bone,"

Morning Glory said to Runta.

Runta said, "Yes. I know. We got out what we could see and feel. We did the best we could."

Morning Glory sat beside Dancing Eagle for a while, stroking his hair. "Dancing Eagle, come back to me. It is I, Morning Glory."

Dancing Eagle opened his eyes for a moment and smiled as he reached out to her hand. She gripped his hand, but it was weak.

"Runta, please get my uncle Lone Wolf. He must hold him for me. I have watched the doctor at the fort many times do this thing. I must try or the wound will not heal," Morning Glory said with strong determination.

Morning Glory picked up a stick by the fire and scraped the bark off it. She put a knife into the fire to heat it while she waited for Lone Wolf.

Lone Wolf arrived and took his position, placing Dancing Eagle's head between his knees so he could firmly hold it and keep it from going side to side. He leaned over and held on to Dancing Eagle's shoulder and arm, while Morning Glory knelt at Dancing Eagle's left side.

The doctor at the fort had drugs to kill the pain whenever he dug arrows out. She did not. Morning Glory caressed his hair for a while to stall for time to build up her courage.

"Dancing Eagle," she called out, "put this stick between your teeth. When the pain starts, direct it into that twig."

Dancing Eagle could barely hear her, but weakly opened his mouth to receive the stick.

Morning Glory prayed to the Creator for guidance and to help ease his pain.

"Dancing Eagle, I'm so sorry for the pain I have caused you. Please forgive me." She took a deep breath, removed the knife from the fire and put its point to his wound.

Dancing Eagle jolted with the piercing of the knife and arched back as she dug in. Harder and harder he bit into the stick as he tried to muffle his screams. His back arched and his toes curled in, while his face turned a purple hue. He was very weak but he suddenly became strong in trying to dodge this pain.

Morning Glory pulled out a piece of the shaft, but she knew there was still more.

"Take a deep breath, Dancing Eagle. I'm afraid I have to go in again. Hang on!"

Dancing Eagle stiffened as he braced for the next wave of pain.

It was almost more than he could bear. Morning Glory could feel his pain as if it were her own. She pulled out two more pieces. Now she was scraping on bone and could go in no farther lest she should shatter his bone.

Dancing Eagle was heaving from pain, breathing at a rapid rate and moaning as he writhed on the ground. Tears flooded Morning Glory's eyes.

She caressed his head. "It is over, Dancing Eagle. You can rest now." She took the stick from his mouth and offered him some water.

She sat beside him all through the day and night, applying fresh poultices, bathing down his fever and encouraging him to drink herbal teas.

By the second day his fever had started to go down. She sat with him while they both healed. On the third day his fever subsided. He was able to eat a little and sit up. His spirit came back to be with her. He now felt that he wanted to start with her anew.

The two of them were side by side for three days. They felt so comfortable, so at peace with each other. Just being together, even without words, gave them joy.

Morning Glory still had not told Dancing Eagle about her three sons. The timing was just not right. He had been so very ill. She had missed his companionship so very much.

Dancing Eagle sat up on the third evening and looked out through the flap. It was a beautiful starlit night. He looked toward Morning Glory and with a spark in his eyes said, "Let's walk past the village. The stars are out and will light the way." She agreed.

They walked slowly, Morning Glory hobbling, Dancing Eagle still recovering. They found a big rock within a grove of trees, just outside the noises of the village. The stream gently trickled by. Dancing Eagle appeared anxious. He obviously had something on his mind that he wanted to say.

Dancing Eagle started to pace. He dared not look into her eyes for fear he might lose his courage to speak.

He was wearing just his buckskin shirt, leggings and loincloth. He had left off any other attire in the warm night. She wore a simple buckskin dress, but her silhouette in the night drove him to pace wildly.

"My heart speaks to you, Morning Star. The Creator once spoke to me and told me that your heart was the essence of all life. The spirit that forms itself in you is of the love of the world!"

"I knew you when peace reigned among our People. Together we could bring back the love that escaped our village and the sense of unity within our tribe. Both of us, together, can be of the highest nature. I pray the Creator will not separate us again.

Dancing Eagle continued to pace, still not daring to look at Morning Glory, who sat quietly upon the rock.

"For many moons I had pondered my being and asked Spirit to help me find a reason to live, since your life had been taken from me. Our People have since taken a path of their own, leaving the Creator outside of our world.

"The white ones have brought into our world their own spirit, one of destruction and lies, a deceptive spirit who only takes and never gives. He came in the form of a white called Shaye, who stole my heart from my very soul when he swept you away from my eyes.

"The spirit of our village left. I did not have the strength to combat the evil that the white spirit produced when the golden glow of our village disappeared.

"You were the embodiment of all things to me, only to be scarred by the face of destiny. But now we can produce a new world of life in which our Creator will be satisfied. Our youth shall rule forever. The ancestors of our beings will again smile across the land as our spirits fly in the sky.

"Our union will provide the freedom for our People to sing and dance and celebrate life once again. The fires will burn bright. The council will decree that our love shall light the way for our People to cherish the life of their own destinies."

Dancing Eagle finally turned to look at Morning Glory. To his amazement, she was crying. He had just told of his passion and plans for their future life. He had bared his soul to her, and she was crying!

Puzzled, he said, "Oh star of my day, why do you cry? Have I not shown you the way of my love? Have I not spoken the words your heart needs to hear? Is it I whom you do seek and find shelter in, or is it another that you do cry for? Woman of the sky, your eyes sadden my heart. Why have I brought you tears?"

Morning Glory could barely look at him. He was the embodiment of a brave, a chief, a most masculine man, who had bared his soul to her, leaving him vulnerable. She had never wanted to hurt him but she would have to, once again.

Reluctantly, trying to find the words, with a lump in her throat, she softly spoke. "You don't know the torment I have endured for so long, away from our village. I have spent a lifetime in the grip of a spirit who knows no love of any kind. I asked the Great Spirit to take my soul to the place of our fathers, to leave my bones in the dust of eternity. The Great Spirit had other plans. It was not time for me to seek shelter. It was not time for me to go to the Sun of our home.

"The white spirit swept me away to torment and pain that will cost dearly the lives of my father and my family. A curse was placed upon our village. Death will follow. I have been shown this in my dreams.

"I have brought to you a sentence in time in which I must leave shortly to find my destiny elsewhere. Our love will be shattered against the hope of the survival of our People."

Dancing Eagle's eyes were wild with puzzlement. He did not understand what she was saying. He was about to interrupt, but she put up her hand to forestall him and continued.

"I have borne for this white devil three sons. I can bear no more."

Dancing Eagle sat down in shock. His muscles suddenly failed him. He became weak.

Morning Glory continued, "So you can see, my love, the love you held for me is of a false hope. The courage that you share with me now is forever in my heart. The only way we can go on is for you to accept my three sons. If you cannot find it in your heart to do this, I must go and find the true course of my destiny. I will have to do this soon.

"I have cried a river of tears, for I have lost so much. I also cry for you, my only love, for I will always carry your love in my heart."

Morning Glory tried to look directly into his eyes so that she could continue. Dancing Eagle could only look at the ground. He could no longer bare his soul to her. She went on.

"Dancing Eagle, when I was taken from you, I was carrying your child!"

Dancing Eagle shot up. "You mean one of the three is mine?"

Morning Glory shook her head. "The embodiment of that child chose not to stay. Your child could not be raised by Shaye. The same spirit of that child chose to come as my third son, Chata. We could raise him together. If only you could see his eyes . . . ."

"No . . . I shall not have a white-eye as a son, not by Tom Shaye, never. You told me that you were taken, that you did not go willingly, and yet you have three sons! I am not a fool. How can you expect me to believe that you did not want to be with that man when you come back with his three sons? "

Dancing Eagle again started to pace. He picked up a stone and flung it into the stream. He started to think . . . three likenesses to a man like Shaye – the man he hated! My love, the star that filled my night, the sun that split the morning dew, bore three sons from a demon who had no destiny but only hate in his life. At heart, he only hated . . . .

His mind raced with rage. Never, never shall I let this man come between me and my love again. I shall seek this devil and destroy him and the sons that she bore to him. He stole my being, for the seeds were to be planted by my spirit and no other. My spirit!

Both of them were emotionally and physically exhausted. There were so many forces trying to keep them from sharing their love. Dancing Eagle sat down beside Morning Glory, holding his head in his hands. She leaned back against the tree for support.

Morning Glory watched a bright light in the sky that was coming closer. As it neared them it formed into a cloud that seemed to speak from the sky.

The cloud came down, spoke to them of the time of their eternal youth and said, "Now the time has been chosen for the two to go and be part of what they have to show the world. Of the tribal man, take now the skins and shed them. Of the woman, take thy heart now, spread it to make a new start of thy life."

"Do not harbor what has come between thee two. It has not been of the full view of your being. That you were taken and swept away by the eyes of the white, was not for any purpose other than the plan, the plan of the cosmic man. As the two beings now form again, return, re-form what we call friend. Do not hold thoughts of despair. Come back now into the air of enlightenment.

"Note, woman, thy heart is pure. The vision will be near. You will teach others what you have learned."

The cloud formed back into a bright light, split off and spread into the night. They thought it was the Eagle speaking to them. The message, coming in that formal language, they knew to be straight from spirit.

Dancing Eagle felt it, saw it, but couldn't understand. He couldn't shed his skin. His spirit had not been formed yet for service.

His anger was high and love was taken from his heart. He

could not hear what he was to hear. He could not see beyond himself. He did not know of her vision of how to take care of her People. Her sons were part of the plan, but he could not see that. His thoughts were only of hate when he thought of the white man.

It had always been this way between the two of them. When they were together, clouds would talk to them. Eagles would fly over them. Their times were special. Dancing Eagle could experience this only with her. He missed those special moments they shared. But this time, too much was being asked of him. How much could a man take?

"Morning Star," he called out to her with pleading eyes, "I will again take you as my wife, but leave those boys with the white man. There is a curse upon us because of that man. Those boys are white. Leave them at the fort with the whites. We will have our own son who will grow to be a mighty chief. He cannot be white!"

Morning Glory took a deep breath and whispered, "Dancing Eagle, you did not hear what I said. I cannot have another child. That wicked man has put a curse upon me. But the spirit of the child that we were to have together is in Nathanael, Chata. If only you were to see his eyes, you would have no doubt."

"No, woman! You bring me shame! I cannot have it that way. How am I to believe that you did not willingly go with that man? He promised you riches. You stayed away for ten winters. You gave him three sons." Dancing Eagle was shouting and pacing, enraged. "Do you think me a fool? So now he treats you poorly and you come running back to me?"

Morning Glory looked down and shook. She could not think. She could not speak. She could only feel his pain and rage. She was beginning to realize that the situation was hopeless. She didn't want to leave him this way.

With one last attempt, Morning Glory pleaded. "Dancing Eagle, I can understand that you are angry, but I cannot understand your anger toward me. How can I make you understand that I had no choice? The People had to be protected. My every waking thought had been of you, since I was just a little girl and throughout all of these years. I have always loved only you, right up to this very moment. Now I have come back to you. Please, Dancing Eagle, I cannot give up my sons. They are . . ."

"Woman, speak to me no more of your white-eyes. They will bring destruction upon our village. I will be happy to put them to rest!" he shouted.

Dancing Eagle spun on his heels and went back to join the council meeting, leaving Morning Glory to sit there with the evening dew and the hooting of the owl.

CHAPTER 29

It was a warm night and the entire village had been summoned to hear the council. Two Moons had called for the meeting. Schalute and his band of braves still had not returned. The council feared for his safety.

Dancing Eagle was next in charge, but all knew that he had other things on his mind. At this point, Two Moons seemed to take over.

A fire was burning in the village circle. Sage was spread. The pipe was smoked and passed to anyone who wished to share it. When formalities were out of the way, Two Moons began to speak before the People.

Dressed simply, without decoration, his silver hair glowing in the moonlight, he spoke with determination. "My People. It is time for us to leave now. My visions are clear. The whites are coming to take us from this land. Their numbers are too great for us. It is time for us to return to the land of our ancestors while we still have time. We must move immediately!"

Shadow Dancer spoke out. "My father has not returned yet. He is chief. How can we leave without our chief?"

Many mumbled to acknowledge this fact. "Yes. If our chief returns, his People will be gone. We cannot do that," one of the elders replied.

Two Moons was frustrated. "You do not understand. If we do not leave immediately, my father will return – if he returns at all – only to bury the dead!"

The old squaw in the village, Keechamanata, rose to speak. "I have seen shadows in the night. They dance all over the firelight. I have seen shadows from dancing dead! I see smoke rising above our heads! I see this village being wiped away!"

One young brave, Willow Wood, rose to speak. "You are an old woman. You don't know. We cannot be pushed around by the whites."

Other young braves affirmed their courage. The council steadfastly refused to decide until Schalute returned.

Dancing Eagle then rose. "We will wait until the sun rises and sets one more day. If our chief has not returned by then, I will take my band of braves to find Schalute. We will not come back until we have found him."

The council agreed that this was the best solution. Two Moons, on the other hand, was sure this was the wrong thing to do. One more time, he arose.

"My People, I have told you my visions are clear. My father is on a mission of revenge. If we wait for him, it will be our end!"

But the council had decided. They would wait for Schalute.

CHAPTER 30

The next morning arrived, a familiar, typical summer day. The sun warmed the air. Birds chirped in the new dawn. Fish offered themselves as food from the river. But the hearts of the People were heavy.

Two Moons and Morning Glory knew trouble was at hand. They were trying to devise a plan, but few would listen.

Dancing Eagle could not face Morning Glory's disgrace. He welcomed the opportunity to leave the village tomorrow so that he wouldn't have to face her. Every time he saw her, his heart ached even more.

Two Moons thought it best to gather the children to teach them one more lesson. He took them beyond the bustle of the village into the woods and softly spoke.

> All life forms must have spirits. We must respect the spirits, for in this way we can learn the truth of the Creator. The forest is alive with wondrous things. We can sense this wonder with our hearts. We can hear this wonder with our minds. All things speak to us as brothers.
>
> All things are real in the natural world of spirits. The plants, animals, rocks and even the water have a spirit of life. You must practice the ceremony of inner sense. We must always prepare ourselves for the sacred lessons to be learned by the voice of the Creator.
>
> We must always give praise to the Creator for making all things possible. If you are to take a life, you must praise that life, for the Creator only deals in forgiveness. We must learn all aspects of the natural cycle of our being

and the spirit that is housed within.

Our tradition teaches us to respect all things. We must live by that golden wisdom. You must never take a life without establishing an extreme need for such an act. Be it small or large, never do it without guidance by the Creator. Don't do it on impulse. Listen first. Give it that moment of time to listen to the truth of it.

The heart is where all things begin. All life flows from the heart. Listen to your heart, and the gifts of life will present themselves to you. A need and a way must be found before life can surrender. Never feel ill will against the world, for the feeling will disease you. The spirit's flame will be low. Your being will cease to exist.

Listen to the voices of the land. They will tell you truth. And with all your heart, listen to the Creator. He will guide you on your long journey through life. Always present a gift of life when taking a life. Make a sacrifice of yourself and show the Creator that you care about all things.

Never take a life carelessly. The Creator will show you no comfort for this act.

What makes the river flow? Spirit.

What makes the bird sing? Spirit.

What makes the grass tall? Spirit.

Spirit is in all things and in all of us. Life is death and from death springs life. Spirit must move on.

Life and Creator should be a part of you that lives on forever. Once you communicate with all things, the Creator opens up His door to you. The sun speaks. The moon talks. The sky opens and listens.

All of Earth's knowledge is passed on to your spirit. You will receive all physical and spiritual rewards. All beings are close to the Creator.

The best way to express your thoughts and desires is to talk to the land, the plants, the animals and the river. Talk to everything. Talk to all nature. Listen to your heart's reply. Give it a moment and listen.

All things are teachers. Observe the ground for planting. It will tell you what it needs. We are all brothers and sisters of the Creator. Be in oneness with it.

How do you think the fox knows where to burrow its

> lair? It uses its heart. The eagle its nest? It uses its heart. The man that plants his corn? He uses his heart. We can only work and live by the heart. Sense of all things is in the heart.
>
> In peace we find good. The good is right. In war we find hate. Hate produces only more hate and death. Only good is right.

Two Moons looked up from the faces of the children to see Dancing Eagle leaning against a tree, waiting for him to finish. He looked again at the children, into their eyes, hoping they would always remember what he had just told them.

"Children," Two Moons said, "it is time for you to touch flowers along the riverbank. When you do, ask the Creator for feelings so you will know the spirit of the flowers. Go now and remember these things in your heart."

Two Moons walked toward Dancing Eagle, seeing from his posture and his expression that he was disillusioned.

Dancing Eagle blurted out to his brother-in-law, "Two Moons, my heart will grow old without your sister. Why did the white-eye take her away from me?"

Two Moons never answered immediately. He stood by an old oak that stood very tall, and became one with it and part of the gentle breeze upon the trees. Now he was ready to speak.

"Upon the brook that runs within this field, do you know what you feel and what emotions well from you?"

Dancing Eagle became incensed. "Don't start with me about the abundance of light and the nature that I cannot see. Don't tell me these things, Two Moons. I am not in the mood for your lessons. You can tell these things to the children, but I am not a child. I am a man. My heart is like a hand in a fist that rages and will plant itself in the faces of the ancients if you don't tell me the truth.

"Why didn't you tell me about her sons? Why didn't you tell me these things, my friend? Why didn't you tell me these things?" Dancing Eagle pleaded for understanding.

Two Moons looked into Dancing Eagle's eyes, which burned from the darkness within, showing that his heart had split. He tried to be a friend.

"Why do you not follow the true meanings of your patterns of being? Why do you not come to seek me on a better level than this?" Two Moons said indignantly. "Your vibration is amiss. Now this tree vibrates with your anger. You know you have put it into the ground and it will forever grow. There are going to be plants and trees here seeded by your thought!"

"What has this to do with my nature?" Dancing Eagle impatiently flashed back.

"All nature comes with all things. You have now planted seeds unto the end. You have brought hatred here. Now I have to cleanse this land. Do you understand the concept of your manhood?"

Dancing Eagle shifted his weight from one foot to the other in exasperation. Becoming even angrier he shouted, "You talk about my manhood; I have many hoods, my friend. I wear many. I have taken many scalps in war, you know."

Two Moons shook his head in despair. "Of this embodiment, my friend, you will also reap what you sow. With the sorrow you have placed upon yourself, my friend, you have committed yourself to death!"

Dancing Eagle sighed. "That is typical of you, Two Moons. You are always walking around in a dream, never telling me the truth straight."

Two Moons knew that Dancing Eagle didn't fully understand what he was talking about. "What the truth is, is the truth in your eyes, my friend. Your heart breaks. I know the end. It is my sister we are talking about. I am trying to give you some comfort. You have come here now as a hard little boy. Sit on the ground. We will smoke the peace. We will smoke the pipe. We will smoke a newfound friendship."

Dancing Eagle threw his hands into the air and paced. "How can I be friends with you when you lie to me? You wouldn't tell me what had happened to her. You knew in your heart." With intensity he continued. "You heard it from the bird. You did not tell me that the Great Eagle had spoken to you. He would not talk to me.

"I cannot talk to you, Two Moons." Waving his fist in the air, Dancing Eagle yelled, "Why is that?"

Two Moons kept his voice at a soft, steady flow. "Because you would not listen. You are not listening now. The Eagle only speaks to the ones who show pride. The Eagle heart speaks from them, not from me, not from you. The heart speaks from the spirit. The spirit is surrounding us like a hue. Don't you know this, my friend? You have not learned the lesson in the end. You will pay the penance of your pipe. The price at the end will be your life."

Dancing Eagle rolled his eyes. His voice trembled. "Now you speak of my life. I am talking about hers. They stole her from me. You know this to be true. You saw it in the stars. You didn't tell me what to do."

Two Moons grabbed Dancing Eagle by the shoulders. "Calm yourself. Sit upon the ground. I will place a circle about you. I'll have to heal what you cannot."

Dancing Eagle tried to soften his rage. Quietly he admitted, "Oh two Moons, I fear my true being. Tell me what it means. Talk to me about the sky, the moon and the sun. It is a life that I have not seen. I cannot feel anymore. I am dead inside. Dead! Why does this happen to me all the time? Why do I lose so many that I love?"

Two Moons tried to explain. "Do you hear how you always say in the end that it is you? You don't understand the concept of the view. It is larger than you can see. We are just a part of everything. In the spirit hand we come to roam together. Calm yourself. I cannot shake the tree. The tree is saying, Take me away from here. The tree does not want to be. Calm thyself, friend. I cannot speak of these things in the end when you are of this nature."

"Well. Well. I'll calm myself. But you make me so restless. You do this to me all of the time."

"I do nothing, my friend. You do it to yourself. You do it to yourself."

"All right, Two Moons, don't lie to me. Tell me what you see my future to be."

Two Moons stated with certainty, "Until you break the hatred form, my friend, you will never be reborn. You will carry a black heart to the desert prairie land. You will say you knew of the white man land. You have killed men. You have killed many before. You will kill more. You will then hide within yourself. You will wear disguises, many frames. You will come in many ways, many names. When you become old you will know the same. That is the truth of your heart!"

Dancing Eagle said in alarm, "What are you telling me? Are you telling me that I am not to see her again?"

Two Moons nodded. "That is a fact, my friend."

"No! I will not listen to this! Now you will set the ground against me. You set this tree against me," Dancing Eagle shouted. "You set these bushes and the sky against me. You set the spirit against me. Why do you do these things, Two Moons? You are my friend. Don't leave me!"

"I don't leave you. You leave yourself. You forgot that the Great Spirit has brought life into us. We are of peace. Your heart wars out for more blood. I cannot control that, Dancing Eagle. I can only tell you in the end what you are going to be: a lifeless soul on a desert sea, flowing here and there and never knowing the peace in the air. But you can find it now if you listen to a friend."

Dancing Eagle shouted in disbelief, "It is so typical of you – round and round you go. You tell me of things that aren't so. I don't know these things! I am not of your embodiment, but you know her. Speak to me of her now. I don't want to know about myself. I can care for myself. I am a warrior chief. I am one to be seen. I ride the horse. I go to war. I will fight to keep this land free for you to stay here and tell me what to do!"

Two Moons continued to keep his voice steady and low. "You missed the whole point, my friend. The point is that this land is not ours to defend. This land will be gone when our bones are washed ashore. This land will be of the white man, not ours to set free."

"Oh, well, the white man, the white man. Everything of the white man!" Dancing Eagle shouted. "I will take his scalp. I will roast him to death. Then I will take his bones. I will not let his black heart go."

"You think these things," Two Moons said. "You think they will become true, but in the end, look at the vision of you. The more you hate, the more you disgrace me and my world."

"Oh, now I disgrace you. Now I disgrace you? Go . . . . I don't disgrace anyone except myself."

"Ah, but you said it yourself! Do you want to go through torment and fear? Do you want to go through the years not knowing who you are? Fine, then go, because I separate myself from your soul. I once called you friend because I found a love there within. Now I can find only anger."

"It is not you, Two Moons," Dancing Eagle said. "Don't leave me now. It is your sister. What has she found in this man?"

With quiet resolve Two Moons said, "Nothing but emptiness, a broken heart. But three new beats came in to make a new start. She has to take care of them, of those three endless waves. They have to sweep in a brand new day. You can't see it now, but one day you will say, 'I know that what he said was right.' I can speak to you all day and all night, but I know now is not the time. Friend of mine, peace and love. Go now. I have to heal the Earth with love."

Two Moons turned from Dancing Eagle as though he no longer existed, and said a blessing upon the land.

Dancing Eagle hung his head and pledged, "Death this day. I will hang on my tribal council wall this man's scalp. I shall never fall again."

Two men had come together to pray for love and peace. One man went with the rhyme of his heart, and that was love. The other man went with hatred. There was a separation that day of two; one would go to the mountain and one to the desert. One to find peace, the other to let it go.

Two Moons had told Dancing Eagle that he could never see his sister again. She had larger plans than he: the plans that were laid far before the time when he even knew he was of his rhyme.

Dancing Eagle now felt that his birth meant nothing, his position meant nothing. The land was being washed away by the white man who would say, "We are just getting rid of the scars, the red man."

Two Moons had to separate Dancing Eagle and Morning Glory. Dancing Eagle was now an embodiment of hate. Everything that Two Moons had hoped wouldn't rear its ugly head, came up now and said, "I am dead."

Two Moons could see in Dancing Eagle's eyes that the man was to die. He would not die a death as we know, but a dying of heart. Two Moons saw what was going to happen to him. He was to be on the run forever. He would not leave that hate alone. It would eat him like a cancer until he was gone.

CHAPTER 31

Tom Shaye and his small band of men rapidly left the village after shooting Morning Glory's horse out from under her. They were to rendezvous near Beaver Creek to join up with a much larger band of soldiers from the fort.

Colonel Clemens had sent Tom ahead to scout the area. He wanted a new headcount of the Indian nation in that territory so he would know how many men to send when it came time to relocate the village. The colonel did not, however, know that Tom would go ahead to the village looking for Morning Glory.

Schalute and his braves rode south along the river for half a day before their lead scout found the camp where the cavalry stayed at Beaver Creek. He devised a plan while they awaited Shaye's return. Astride his black stallion, wearing a war bonnet and holding his spear, Schalute sat proud. He and his twenty braves quietly hid among the trees behind the hill. Their war ponies were trained to be still. The braves soothed the ponies by talking to their spirits.

The soldiers came into view. In the lead, astride a white horse, was a tall, blond, scar-faced man wearing a long coat and a wide-brimmed hat. He carried two buffalo rifles, one on each side. Schalute knew it was Thomas Shaye!

Schalute sang his death song. "Brave painted warriors of red, white and gray will mark the date with all the special words they have to say."

Schalute sat quietly on his horse until he saw the eye of the man he hated the most. He broke rank, let out a war cry and kicked his horse wildly, splashing through the slippery riverbed. The rest of the braves galloped behind him with their arrows flying.

Tom raised his rifle and fired straightaway, as did his men.

Schalute kept riding straight toward him as though he didn't even feel the bullets that riveted his chest. The braves behind him were falling to their deaths.

Schalute waited until he could see the whites of Shaye's eyes. He raised his spear and yelled, "This is for our Glory. It is time to die!" Schalute's spear whistled past Tom's ear as Shaye's bullets brought down the great Schalute.

With the beat of the drum, the warriors grabbed their courage. All through the day, the sons of many men died. Many an arrow lay wasted.

As the sun's first rays glimmered through the morning sky, Dancing Eagle and fifteen braves mounted their ponies to look for their chief. Although the heat of the day had not yet begun, the ponies' tails swiftly fought the flies that brought blood to their hides.

Morning Glory in her tepee could hear Dancing Eagle organizing the braves. Her heart knew that this was not a good day. She didn't want him to leave. There was still so much in her heart that remained unsaid.

She stepped out of her lodge just as they were about to leave the village. Dancing Eagle felt her presence and turned. Morning Glory's chest tightened. A lump formed in her throat. He glared at her with pained eyes and rode away on his paint pony.

The band of braves picked up the tracks leading out of the village. The sun no longer stood straight up in the sky when Dancing Eagle noticed that the creek had turned crimson. They rode up the creek and went around the bend to find their dead. Many horses lay on their sides in the stream.

His heart beat wildly. He looked around to find the bodies of his cousin Lone Star and his friends. In the corner of Dancing Eagle's eye was a body wearing a war bonnet bobbing on the edge of the water near the bank.

He jumped from his pony and splashed through the water to reach this man who was lying face-down in the water. He turned Schalute over and held his head in his arms as he whispered in fear, "Where has the Eagle gone? Are we all dead?"

Dancing Eagle stood to face the red of the setting sun. With clenched fists he stood with his feet spread apart. "No . . . not this way!" he screamed to the skies.

Dancing Eagle decided not to bring him back to be buried on their own land. In his heart he knew the soldiers were coming to desecrate their village. He had to bury him there under the skies.

Dancing Eagle and his band of braves buried their People alongside their chief. Dancing Eagle was now chief, but he considered himself chief of a dying tribe. It brought him despair.

Tomorrow they would head back to their village with the news of death. They were all too exhausted to travel through the night. There was no moon to light their way. It was a dark day.

Dancing Eagle slept fitfully, full of nightmares, talking aloud. "Land lost! Great army come!" Thrashing about, he continued, "Must stay ground. Eagle fly! Land of forefather! Ancestor right! This is not the way to stay! Peace!"

It was not yet daylight. Dancing Eagle sat bolt upright. Still half-dreaming, he started to shout, "This is the land where we shall live! This is the land on which we will die! This is where I should be buried, in the eye of the Eagle. This is my land! No other can take it away. This is our right!"

"Of the birth, of the one form, the woman form, the life factor. Don't take her away from me. . . ."

Wildly he looked around. The hobbled horses stood where they had wandered, herded to one side. Short Leg, the one who was to stand watch, had fallen asleep.

Leaping to his feet, wide awake, he shouted to his braves, "They come! They come in force! Many come on horse!"

A rumble of hooves became a roar and the white men, led by a large, blond man on a big white horse, galloped into the middle of the camp. The blond man thrashed a sword in the air.

Dancing Eagle stood his ground as the man rode closer to him. He saw the long coat that he wore, the buffalo guns and the scar on his face. He recognized the cold eyes of Tom Shaye!

Dancing Eagle was caught off-guard. His pony was gone. His arrows were not with him. All he had was a spear at his side.

Tom spurred his large white horse straight for Dancing Eagle. With feet spread wide, Dancing Eagle waited until he got closer.

The two men looked into each other's faces. With their chiseled expressions, there was no love in either's eyes. Tom's lips formed a surly grin as his horse charged straight at Dancing Eagle. Dancing Eagle waited until he was close, lifted his right arm behind him and flung his spear with all his might.

Tom reeled back on his horse as the spear caught him in the gut. He grabbed the spear, pulled it out and laughed a hideous laugh.

Dancing Eagle stood there without a weapon left. He could barely hear the sounds of battle. This particular match was between just the two of them. Nothing else existed.

Leaning low and brandishing his sword, Tom spurred his horse. Dancing Eagle could hear the horse's labored breathing above the sounds of his pounding heart. He heard the creak of the saddle leather near his ear as the awful, searing pain of the sword tore into his left side.

Tom pulled out the sword. Dancing Eagle fell to his knee, clutching his side.

With his last breath, Tom laid a curse upon Dancing Eagle. Through clenched teeth, with blood trickling from the corner of his mouth, Tom hoarsely said, "If I can't have her, nobody can. Today we will both die!"

Tom gave out one last strangled laugh, fell from his horse and sighed as his spirit left.

Dancing Eagle finally got to watch that man die, but he knew Tom's spirit would never fly to the skies. It would always be there, in the woods, in the trees, looking for Morning Glory in every breeze. It would never let her go, not now, not even in the next life.

Dancing Eagle collapsed in a crumpled heap upon the ground, next to the man who had taken away everything he loved. Death was all around him. The wolves started to gather, snarling through the cover of the trees.

The gunshots had ceased. All of his braves were dead. They didn't have a chance against the white man's guns. In the corner of his eye he saw the surviving cavalry men drag off their dead.

Dancing Eagle's blood was pouring upon the ground from his side. The sun's rays blinded his eyes and he blinked to clear them as he rolled to his right side. He thought he saw Morning Glory. No, he couldn't have.

The wolves scattered. What drove them away? Then, in his misery and his pain, she stood before him. She had come with the morning; the spirit of her glory had come to his side.

With tears coursing down his cheeks, he breathlessly whispered, "In a time when life means nothing, there is no peace upon the land. When a time in life means nothing to the hand, I took up the spear and I slew the man. I was given one life. One life I do leave. The Eagle has left us.

"Where is the sky? It is turning dark. Glory, do you see the form? It is the great red bird. It comes to speak to me. It must be heard.

"I lie now, off my horse, on a finished battlefield. I lie, a wounded brave.

"Have I not given my life a thousand times for what I have believed in? Have I not left this life true? Have I not left a love . . . ?

"Speak to me, woman. It will not pass. I know my days will not last. My bones shiver. My eyes do not see. The great bird wants to take us away.

"Man's home is of the Sun. That is home, you know. The white man will never know. He has stolen us, but we are his brothers. Spread the word. We are his brothers . . . .

"A great coldness is coming over me, but it is of peace I see. I find harmony as I sweep myself now into the breeze. I go and fly. I follow the sky. Toward home I fly. Toward home . . . .

"Bury me deep. My body will seep into the soil that was planted this day. From thee I go. I go. I hear the great horn. The great horn blasts. At last I find life."

Dancing Eagle's outreached hand dropped helplessly to the ground. Morning Glory's tearstained face faded from his view.

CHAPTER 32

Thomas Shaye's body and the bodies of several other scouts were brought back to the main encampment. Colonel Clemens had wanted to negotiate and have the Eagle tribe moved. But Colonel Clemens was back at the fort, and it was McVain who was here.

McVain spit into the grass and waved his fists in the air. "Look what those vermin did to our men! Tom was married to one of them. He protected them, and look what they did. Let's get them now, every last one of them stinkin' redskins."

Tom had been a popular leader among the men for a long time. They wanted revenge.

The main camp was immediately struck. The horses were watered and grained. The men were ready to fight in Tom's name.

Two Moons and Morning Glory had sensed that something was very wrong. Two Moons turned around to face his brother. "Shadow Dancer, I will meet you at the cave with the women and children. We must hide them. With Schalute gone with twenty of our braves and Dancing Eagle gone with another band, there are precious few braves left to protect the women and children. We must hide them."

As they left the tepee, Two Moons and Shadow Dancer gathered the old women and children and ushered them through the village, toward the thumb of land that jutted out over the river. Below that point of land, in the cliff wall, stood the sacred cave. Normally, only the medicine men were allowed to enter it. Now it was to become a sanctuary.

With urgency Shadow Dancer lowered himself first into the

cave so that Two Moons could lower the women and children. He had not found Blue Dove but sent her daughter and Gentle Breeze's baby into the cave to be with Runta. The cave was very small. It could only hold the children and a few old ones.

Two Moons left Shadow Dancer in the cave to guard the children. He then left to post some braves around the perimeter of the village.

Morning Glory was in her lodge, frantically trying to put things together. She felt the Earth rumble. Women began to scream. Dogs were barking wildly. The drums began to beat.

Through a cloud of dust, horses thundered into the village. Morning Glory ran out of her tepee, straight toward the charging men. She knew these men. Maybe she could stop them, she thought.

McVain was in the lead, shouting, "Rally, boys. Rally, boys, around me. We shall kill all these vermin. Scourge the vermin from the land!"

McVain saw "that blue-haired wench," as he called her, running toward him. His horse was shot out from under him but he landed on his feet. He aimed his pistol straight at Morning Glory. As his gun kicked back, she fell backwards to the ground, bleeding from her left shoulder. From behind, Elk Skin clubbed McVain across the neck. McVain fell dead to the ground.

Gentle Breeze saw Morning Glory fall. She screamed and started running toward her, past the troops. She felt a searing pain as a knife was thrust into her heart. She fell lifeless to the ground, ten feet from her sister.

Blue Dove ran helplessly through the village. Tepees were burning. People were screaming. Fire—gunshots!—a bullet burned across the side of her head and one lodged in her leg.

Shadow Dancer ran from the cliff toward the village to find his sisters. A searing pain tore through his leg and he stumbled to the ground. He lay low, head down, watching horrified as the troops quickly rode through the village, burning every tepee and killing every man, woman and child they could find. They even shot the dogs.

As fast as they rode in, the troops rode out, leaving behind only fire and death. The village had been ill-prepared to meet such an attack. There were few braves left to fight in the village. The village consisted mostly of women and children.

Shadow Dancer stumbled through the smoke toward his family

lodge. Gentle Breeze lay twisted on the ground, her life source pouring from her chest, her face blue and her hand reaching out as if it were still trying to hold on to something. He gasped, shocked. Through the dust and smoke he could see that it was Morning Glory she had reached for with her last breath. Gentle Breeze was gone.

He crawled toward Morning Glory, who lay very still. Blood covered her, her face was ashen, but still her heart beat.

Shadow Dancer looked up to see Two Moons running toward him. Two Moons quickly checked on Gentle Breeze and knew it was too late. Together they picked up Morning Glory and carried her to the point. Two Moons lowered himself down the rope as Shadow Dancer helped lower her down over the side and into the cave for Runta to attend to.

Two Moons ran back through the smoke in the village, looking for Blue Dove. She was lying just outside her smoldering tepee. He picked her up and carried her to a canoe in which a brave waited. Instructing them to meet others in a clearing about two days down the river, he pushed their canoe off from the shore.

Shadow Dancer grabbed Two Moons by the shoulders and told him in alarm, "I have to get to the village over the hill. My People are being massacred, slaughtered, because I am not there!"

Two Moons, knowing that even with arms there was no chance to save them, said, "Go in the canoe. Quick, into the water."

He handed Shadow Dancer snake eyes. "If you ever have to contact me, shake them. You will see my image."

"Take up your arrow and bow. Get your knife," Shadow Dancer yelled to Two Moons.

"No. I will just try to help," Two Moons solemnly stated.

Shadow Dancer stood up in the canoe, about to step out. "I will take my knife. I will kill for you."

"No! Stay in the water." Two Moons pushed Shadow Dancer's canoe away from the shore.

"You are all that is left," Two Moons told him. "I might end my days here, but you are all that is left. Take the People away. Take them to the south, down the big muddy river. Take them to the tribes of the south. They are our friends. Someday I will join you again with the others. Look for the land of the firebird where there are two peaks. I will take the others north. If we split, they cannot follow us as easily. We will join again. Now go, quickly."

Two Moons ran back to the village, ushering all survivors to the few remaining canoes. An unconscious Morning Glory was being carried to the canoe by Willow Wood. As two braves lifted her into it, shots cracked out from across the river where snipers waited in the brush.

Two Moons jumped into the canoe and, together with Willow Wood, paddled swiftly upstream, until they were out of firing range. They would follow this tributary until it connected into the big river to the west of them.

He had told the rest of the villagers to go two days up the big river. Morning Glory still bled too badly for the journey. He didn't know whether she could survive. The other canoes went on while he pulled ashore to find the herbs that he needed to treat her wound. She was still bleeding and burning with fever, and he felt she could travel no more.

Through the night he tended again to his wounded sister. Before the sun glimmered in the east, they were rapidly paddling upstream, slipping swiftly through the water. Morning Glory was still mostly unconscious but her fever had broken in the night.

Two Moons knew that Morning Glory's spirit could not yet bear to come back to face the heartbreak. He would simply give her time. It was the People she lived for; it would be the People she would die for. The Creator spared her from having to watch her People die, Two Moons told himself, by having her shot first.

By nightfall Two Moons had paddled north, connecting with the big river, to the point where he had sent some of his People ahead. It was also where he had sent Blue Dove.

The moonless night was black, and dark clouds covered the stars. He didn't want to be shot at by his own braves as he entered the encampment. He gave his personal birdcall. Some of his braves whistled back. He beached the canoe and walked toward them, carrying Morning Glory in his arms.

Two Moons had always worked well in the night. His vision was as acute in darkness as it was in light. He could see and feel that misery and pain were carved into the faces of his People.

He brought Morning Glory over to Runta. As he placed her on the ground, a brave approached him. In a low voice the brave said, "Two Moons, the riverbanks are peppered with soldiers. We lost many trying to come to this spot. Many were shot from the banks as we fled. Other canoes turned over. One of the canoes had Gentle Breeze's baby. I am sorry."

Two Moons listened in silence. He had known this was going to happen. He saw it clearly in his visions. His People should have been moved before this happened, but the council would not listen. Morning Glory had risked her life to come and warn them. They simply didn't listen.

Short Leg approached Two Moons. "The river to the north is barricaded by soldiers. We can travel no farther north."

Two Moons said, "Then we will head south and join Shadow Dancer's group."

"No, Two Moons. Apparently Shadow Dancer got through because he left earlier. That too is blocked to us."

Two Moons shook his head. "We have no choice. We must travel south as soon as we go back to bury our dead."

Runta approached Two Moons. "You must join me now, Two Moons, or it will be too late." She pointed to a woman lying under a tree. It was Blue Dove. Her daughter, Little Red Flower, slept fitfully beside her.

Two Moons carefully pulled back her blanket. Blue Dove's leg was festering from a bullet wound. She also had a head wound.

Blue Dove grabbed his hand and fought back the tears. She was frightened and in pain.

Two Moons stroked her hair and said, "Don't worry. I will take care of you. Now sleep. I shall look for herbs to heal you."

Runta sadly looked at Two Moons. They both knew that soon the Eagle would come and take her away.

In the middle of the night, Two Moons was drawn to Blue Dove's side. He held his sister in his arms as she said with her last breath, "Be with me, Two Moons. Be with me . . . ." She breathed her last sigh and her head dropped to the side. Little Red Flower whimpered softly as she stroked her dead mother's cheek with her small hand.

Two Moons' father, his sisters, and the baby too, were all dead. Two Moons raised his hands and tore at his hair. "How do they dare touch this land of the Great Eagle?"

Two Moons buried her on a ridge. The mourning brought the rain. He couldn't tell his tears from the rain, his heart was in so much pain.

Tall Trees and his wife had no son. They took Black Wolf, who had seen ten winters now, as their own.

CHAPTER 33

The wetness of the morning dew had already burned off of the prairie grasses. Flies swarmed over the bodies of dead braves and two dead ponies. The surviving ponies grazed nervously, away from their bloated friends. Coyotes yapped in the forest, telling others of their find. Crows cawed loudly in the trees, carrying their sounds through the breeze. The woods were animated with sounds of alarm. A small hunting party of Sacs became aware of this. It was in the air.

Cautiously they came to the edge of the woods and peered into the clearing to see the bodies of their neighboring brothers. All were dead with the exception of one.

Dancing Eagle had been seriously wounded. The sword wound had pierced deeply into his chest. He bled from within. In his mind and heart, there was only pain and doubt. He could hardly breathe. It took him many, many days before he could even sit up.

He was in a Sac village. Upon Dancing Eagle's request, a scout was sent to the village of the Eagle Tribe. The scout solemnly returned with a report that he didn't want to give to this new, young chief.

The scout asked permission of Dancing Eagle to enter the lodge. When Dancing Eagle saw the look on his face as he stood at his tepee door, he feared the worst.

The scout sat before Dancing Eagle and paused, trying to find the right words to deliver a most horrible message.

"My friend, your tribe was a quiet one. They were our brothers. The village exists no longer."

Dancing Eagle sat as if frozen, his hands clutching at the dirt on the ground. "Everything that I know to be, everything that was true to me, gone? How could that be? Where have they gone? Did none survive? I cannot see with the Eagle's eye. If they survived, where are they? I am chief. I should have been with my People."

The scout shook his head and took a breath. "I found many new graves. Every lodge was burned to the ground. All tracks of horses belonged only to the white man. All tracks of Indians led to the river. I'm sorry. It doesn't appear that too many survived." The scout rose, to let this man grieve privately.

For days Dancing Eagle did not eat. He did not cry. He did not even know the People before his eyes. He was all alone. He did not even want to survive.

After fourteen suns had risen, Dancing Eagle could rest no more. They gave him a horse to ride, helping him to get astride. He grimaced as he held his side, for his ribs ached with every breath.

Slowly he rode back toward the place of his village. He had to cross back over the Mississippi River and head east to reach it. His heartbeat quickened as he neared the place he once called home.

His pony snorted, putting its head down and sidestepping as they rode past an entire field of new graves. Dancing Eagle's skin prickled from the spirits abounding. Who was in those graves? Was Morning Glory among them? What of his mother, Runta? Where were his People?

He silently rode down the trail that had so often bustled with children and dogs barking. Now there was nothing but deathly silence. Unbelievable silence. The birds were not chirping. There was no campfire smoke. No ponies grazed in the fields of the lush valley.

With great apprehension he rode farther, to the center of the village where so much had once gone on. Around him were burned trees and circles of blackened stakes that had once supported coverings of hide.

Dancing Eagle slid down from his pony, his right hand holding his left side. His knees buckled when his feet hit the ground. Dancing Eagle fell face-down and put his ear to the dirt. He could pick up the screams of his People as they were being murdered. In his mind's eye, he could see their terror and their pain. He could see them running for their lives through the flames. He could see the smoke and the dust hiding their shame. Oh, he was in so much pain.

A motion caught his eye. Through the burned trees he saw the glint of the eye of a wolf.

"What is it in your eyes, in your heart, that I see?" he asked the wolf. "Why do you look so familiar to me? Why do you always come to me when I am near death and pain? Is it you that I flee? Be gone, before I put an arrow in your hide. Be gone!"

The wolf walked two steps away, then turned its head and stared back. It gave out a howl then confidently stalked away.

Dancing Eagle slowly pulled himself to his feet and found a rock to lead his pony to. He was too weak and sore to simply jump up onto its back as he used to do so easily. He crossed the river and rode for a day, coming to a village that his People once knew.

Dancing Eagle rode into the village holding his side, barely able to sit any longer on his pony. Chief White Feather appeared and recognized him to be of the Eagle Tribe.

"My brother, you must join us and eat. We have much to talk about at the council fire tonight."

Dancing Eagle simply nodded, too traumatized to say anything.

It was a cool night. The fire in the council lodge soothed his aching bones. He watched the shadows of the flames dance on the tepee wall.

"My friend, a moon ago our scouts saw a small band of your People heading west. The one known as Shadow Dancer was leading them. Many were wounded. There were mostly women and children, just a few braves," the chief sadly informed him.

Dancing Eagle's head shot up. "Was the blue-eyed one with them? Was our princess with them?" Dancing Eagle asked earnestly.

The council members just looked at each other for an answer. No one seemed to know.

With bowed head, Dancing Eagle sat and talked from spirit before the council.

"Why has time now been lost upon this land? Why now does man not know of the war and the violence that was projected upon the land by a race of whites? They had so many other things to go and see. Why did they want this land? Why couldn't we be free?"

The council members understood. There were no answers for this man's plea.

Dancing Eagle said he would always remember that hot day. "Whites came this way. They tried to strip us of our land. They broke treaties that we had made with them. They ran us off, killed our braves. They dispersed our tribe."

The only thing Dancing Eagle had left was the memory of a tragic day. Love, war and hate wrapped around his life.

CHAPTER 34

Two Moons and his band of People continued to travel down the river. Morning Glory was not doing well. She was awake but her spirit was not. She could not handle the death of her village. She worried about her sons.

Many of the People in their anger blamed Morning Glory. "It was her white husband who brought death upon this village," they would murmur.

Two Moons would sharply stop them. "You do not know what you say. We have to make a new day."

Two Moons was skilled at covering up their tracks and finding hidden caves. The Eagle would always show him the way.

The People became hungry and tired; they were parched by the sun. They slept under the moon, the waters would flow, but it was too soon for them to stop. They had to go on, looking for a peaceful valley.

Along the shores of the river they would hunt and feed on the fish that offered themselves. They looked for a land to call home, but they feared trouble was brewing. The white man's law was a kiss of death on their souls.

The People traveled for weeks on end through lands that were hostile. No tribe would welcome them. Food was scarce. The sun beat down. The women cried in their weariness. They had to find a home.

Morning Glory became almost totally silent. She was very weak for a long, long time. She constantly prayed to the Creator to have the Eagle come and take her away. Instead, each day the Creator gave her a little more strength.

Morning Glory functioned methodically day by day. She

tended to the sick and wounded, fed the orphaned children and hunted for herbs, but she rarely talked. She couldn't. Her heart was in her throat. Almost everyone who was dear to her was gone. Her People said that she now walked the "trail of the lonely moccasin."

Little Red Flower followed Morning Glory about. Morning Glory adopted her as her own, often simply holding her and rocking her without words, just offering her love.

Two Moons, as he always did, would go off into the night. His silver hair seemed to glow as his body eventually faded from their sight in the darkness. It was as if he were walking toward a blinking star that would appear from afar.

Two Moons prayed to the Creator for help in their plight, to give him might to find a home for his People. Late in the night, the People would hear a rumbling and the ground would shake. Hours later, as the sun started to rise, they would see him sitting alone.

What the People didn't know was that he called upon the forces to change the landscape, to cover their tracks. He didn't want the soldiers to track down the People or to find Morning Glory. What had been passes to cross were not passes anymore.

Two Moons was always in vision. He would be shown hidden caves in which to hide the People for a few days while they rested and sought food.

He was heading them south toward a land of hot healing waters, into the land white man called Arkansas. The People were sick and wounded. They needed to rest and heal.

The Eagle Clan sought shelter with a small band of Indians who came across them and saw their plight. They camped about a mile from Crater Lake, in a grove of trees. The People were weary. There were not many braves to guard the outskirts of the camp.

Seven suns had risen and set during their encampment. Morning Glory suddenly awoke to the sound of rolling thunder. It was the thunder of horses coming again! Her heart pounded as she leaped out of her blanket to see fire! The village was surrounded by fire!

No — not again! Not again . . . . Shooting, shouting, screaming, People falling about. Smoke. The smoke was burning her lungs! She could hardly breathe!

Little Red Flower, gasping and coughing, ran out of the tepee to be at her side. As Morning Glory was about to pick her up and run, a shot rang out. The child fell at her feet.

Blood ran from her head. The child could not breathe. Panicked, she looked at Morning Glory for help. Morning Glory held her in her lap, bending over, shielding her. She did not know where to go. The fire surrounded them! The soldiers kept throwing torches and shooting. Tepees were burning. Trees were burning.

Morning Glory could only rock the child, trying to get her to breathe. She rocked and sang a song to the Creator for help. She kept singing and rocking, singing and rocking, as if nobody were around. People were running past her, screaming, falling, but she just sat there rocking the child and singing.

She saw a dove, a gray-blue dove coming toward her, wings outspread in the breeze, through the smoke, through the trees. The blue dove hovered over the child. The little one's spirit began to rise, like a flower carried by the dove to the skies. She was gone.

Tears flowed down Morning Glory's cheeks. She became numb. Whites, some with uniforms, some without, rode into the center of the circle. The People had been herded to the middle by the soldiers.

Morning Glory looked up to see Two Moons struggling between two soldiers. She put Little Red Flower's body down, but not before she closed the child's eyes. She brushed the child's hair back and laid her straight out on the ground. Morning Glory then sang out a wailful death song. It sent chills up and down some of the soldiers' spines.

For a few moments everyone stopped what they were doing. Even the soldiers stood and watched as Morning Glory finished her song. It was a curious thing that time seemed to stop as she sang the Song of the Swan.

Morning Glory stoically stood up and looked without expression into the soldier's eyes. Thunder struck. It began to rain.

With a Scotch-Irish accent, Morning Glory said, "You have brought tears to the Creator's eyes," as she pointed to the sky.

"I am ready. I will go with my People now. Do not harm them anymore. We are mostly women and children. You can see that. They are hungry, sick and weak. In my eyes, you are not men. You need not kill anymore, for we are already dead. We have nothing left to fight for."

Morning Glory picked up a sobbing child and carried it as her People followed behind her. Two Moons and the other braves were under heavy guard.

The night was cold. The surviving women and children huddled around the fire. There was quiet in the ranks. Only a few of the soldiers felt good about what had happened. In fact, some wondered why they had done it at all. They felt no glory in killing children.

The dusky light that precedes the dawn had not yet appeared when Morning Glory heard birdcalls within the trees. She heard Two Moons give his signal back. There were a few braves, a hunting party, that had not been in the camp that day.

Suddenly, shots rang out. The horses were spooked. Soldiers were running around trying to stop the herd and fighting off the braves. Morning Glory directed the women and children into the trees, toward the sounds of the signals. Braves were at the riverbank with canoes. The women and children were swiftly paddled away.

Morning Glory was about to run back for Two Moons. She couldn't leave without Two Moons! Willow Wood, seeing her begin to turn back, scooped her up and put her into the canoe while another brave held her from getting out. She could not get away. They would hide for the day in a small cove down the river.

When the sun began to slide behind the western slope, Two Moons arrived with the rest of the surviving braves. The soldiers had been so scattered, running about, that it had not been hard to get away from the few whites tried to stop them.

Two Moons had in his arms the body of Blue Dove's little girl. "I could not leave her there. We shall bury her with love and send her properly on her way." It was another sad day.

Morning Glory wearily whispered, "When will we find a home again? We are from the Sun, but we are not free to roam?"

Morning Glory hung her head and gave out a song that went through the skies to find the Eagle's eyes. "One day, one time, I will bring my People back to where they belong. With the Creator as my witness I promise this," Morning Glory vowed.

Two Moons tipped Morning Glory's head back to meet his eyes. "It is time to head back west. We must find our brother and the rest of our People."

CHAPTER 35

Young Shadow Dancer and his band of People were having a hard time. The land they journeyed upon was dry. The women didn't know which herbs to use in this part of the world. Food was not plentiful in the desert plains. His People did not speak the languages of either the white or the red men they met in their travels.

They needed horses and food. Shadow Dancer was now their chief, although he had seen only sixteen winters. Shadow Dancer began to steal to provide for them. This angered the settlers. The Texas Rangers were hot on his trail, so he took his People south to Mexico.

Just over the border he met bandits and hostile Indians. His group was always on the run. He learned to hide his People well, but they never had a place to call home.

This was not the land of the eagle. This was not the land of the phoenix bird, where he was to meet Two Moons between twin peaks.

About this time, there were problems around the Rio Grande. Texas had already become a state. An Army contingent had come down to stop the Comanche flow of liquor, arms and guns. The Union was trying to sway the Texans to become a Union state, even though they were a part of the South.

Louis Cavour, a reporter out of Louisiana, was with a team of mule skinners coming up from Amarillo to the Panhandle area to establish communication lines. He was planning, once he got there, to join up with some buffalo hunters that were going toward Wyoming and write about their journey.

During this time the Senard farm, near a town called Leversville, was attacked by Commanche. The entire family was murdered. Louis followed a band of soldiers who were going to bring to justice some of the Comanche that were responsible for the raid. Louis Cavour was going with them to cover the story.

Louis was a square-built man of about thirty, dark-haired and bearded, and smoked a pipe of good tobacco. His belted pioneer pants were often a bit loose on him, easy to travel in.

Louis liked to drive the mules. A pipe stayed in his mouth whether it was lit or not. He liked to journey and explore. The men respected him. He was a man of his word.

Louis' small train of wagons was crossing the plains on a windswept day. The days were shorter now with less daylight to travel in, and the chill nipped at their bones. Some of the soldiers in the wagons were wounded from their skirmishes with the Comanche. Louis patched them up as well as he could but he was no doctor. The best he could do was pour some whiskey over the wounds, pull out a shaft or two and wrap them up with a torn-up shirt. Some of the men had mighty high fevers.

The pale sun on this cloudy day was half-set in the west when Louis spotted a band of Indians on foot, slowly walking north. None of them had horses. From what he could see, most were women and children. The men cocked their rifles just the same. There were no trees or hills around to hide an ambush, but they would be ready nonetheless.

Louis' wagon was in the lead. He trotted the mules up to the front of the walking band of Indians. As he passed them, he observed that they were a tattered group of skinny, downtrodden, ill-clothed people. They looked like they barely had the strength to go on, almost no strength to lift their heads as the dust his wagons kicked up filled the air.

When he reached the front of the traveling band, he reined in his six-mule team. The squaw in the lead stopped, lifted her head and walked directly toward his wagon.

Louis was shocked. She had piercing blue eyes. Even though she was noticeably thin and worn out, she was beautiful, the most beautiful Indian he had ever seen.

"Sir, do not harm my People. We are just a small band of mostly women and children trying to find safety. We have no home. We try to bother no one."

How curious, he thought. This squaw spoke with a Scotch-Irish accent, with even a bit of a French touch.

Louis looked around at her People. Their eyes were sunken in. He looked up again at Morning Glory but this time he suddenly became aware of a silver-haired brave standing behind her. The brave said nothing. He simply stood by her.

Louis cleared his throat of trail dust, took the pipe out of his mouth to speak and said, "My dear, I have no intention of shooting women and children. You all look like you have been through enough. So have we. I have some wounded men in my wagon."

"Perhaps I can help them," stated Morning Glory matter-of-factly. "But could you spare any food and water, perhaps just a little?"

"We will give you what we can," he started to say, but as he looked toward her again, he realized she was already half-way into the back of his wagon. The silver-haired brave stood quietly next to his People.

A few minutes later, Morning Glory jumped to the ground. "There are some herbs in this prairie that I believe can help your fevered men. If you will give me some time, I will gather them and prepare them."

"I'm afraid we don't have much time. Too many Comanche about. Your People can follow us. Maybe we can provide you with some protection. You can attend to the men in the wagon as we move on."

While the People were given rations of food and water, Morning Glory hurried onto the prairie to collect what herbs she could find in a short amount of time.

Two Moons could see that Louis Cavour was an honorable man. He allowed the People to travel under his protection. Morning Glory tended to the wounded men as best she could in a rocking, bone-jarring wagon. She would have preferred a fire to cook broths, teas and poultices, but she had to make do. The men appreciated a woman's touch. Louis' touch was none too gentle on an open wound.

After a while, Louis called her to sit with him at the front of the wagon. He wanted to know more of the plight of her People. He thought it would make a good story.

Morning Glory's English, with its touches of Scotch-Irish and French accents made a fascinating backdrop for her story. Her way of speaking, together with her beauty, spellbound him. Morning Glory told him about her life with Tom Shaye, how her tribe was massacred, and their journey to find peace.

Louis' head hung low as she bravely told him of their plight. "I shall write about your People in my journals. The whites shall know what man has done to his fellow man, be it red or be it white."

The group traveled together for many days. The women and small children took turns riding in the wagons. The women also helped tend to the wounded men and took over the cooking at the campfires.

Two Moons taught the men a few tricks about tracking. Two Moons was a man of few words, they found, but of much wisdom. They learned to appreciate his company.

Morning Glory often sat with Louis and talked to him for endless hours about sacred ways and honor. He took mental notes of everything she said.

The days became shorter and colder. There were few blankets, so the People huddled by the campfires at night, seeking shelter in each other's company.

Louis reined in his team just past a place he described as Four Corners. The striking red sunset served as a backdrop for a curious place of ancient cliff dwellings.

Morning Glory quickly jumped off the wagon. She started to walk about as if in a daze. She looked at Two Moons. "I know this place. I have seen it in my dreams, my visions. I can feel its very heartbeat. I have been here before. Someday this will be my home, a place where I can again roam." Two Moons nodded in knowingness.

Louis said nothing. In a way, he knew what she was saying. He was comfortable here. This felt like home to him also, but his mind asked how this could be. He felt that he had been here before but he knew that he had not.

They spent several days camped there, sheltered from the wind. Deer offered themselves to the People. The People thanked them and gave them grace. They all found renewed strength and were then able to go on.

They journeyed several days into Arizona. Louis yelled out, "Whoa, there. Whoa." He stopped, pulled the pipe from his mouth and collected his thoughts.

"My dear, this journey has been one of the highlights of my life. You gave me new insights to the red man's plight. You gave me joy being in your company. I learned more being with you and your People than I have in years of white man's school. Unfortunately, our paths must now split. I have to take these muleskinners north to Montana. Two Moons tells me you have to find your People to the west. You and your People shall become timeless in my journals. Someday, I hope our paths will bring us back together again."

Morning Glory smiled and simply said, "They will. Someday, sometime, they will, I promise you that." She jumped down from his wagon and shed a single tear. She would miss him dearly.

Morning Glory and her People journeyed for days in the desert. Two Moons was able to find water by having vision from the Eagle eye. He had asked the rock spirit to help him. He carried a stone with him that would talk to him and tell him where water was. He would go and scout it out. When he found it, he would signal with smoke and call the rest of the tribe. He was able to find underground springs.

He also had a tool with two leather straps and rocks at the end of them. As he scouted for water he would hold the stick in his hand. When he was close to water, the rocks would start to bounce off each other. They would make a clicking sound and the stick would start to vibrate.

For a while they tried to follow the Colorado River but they kept running into whites. They continued their journey away from the river trail, which meant they no longer had fish. It was difficult to find food in the desert. They were not accustomed to the plant life there. Animals were not plentiful. They ate rodents and desert life when they could catch them. The People were becoming sick and weak from their long journey and shortage of good food.

There were fewer than sixty People left. Each day seemed to claim another one. Many children could not make the journey and gave up their spirits. Many children no longer had parents. There was much sadness.

Two Moons and some of the braves left to hunt for food while the others rested. Morning Glory was alarmed when she spotted a dust-swirl far off in the desert. Someone was coming. Was it Two Moons, or trouble?

Suddenly, out of the dust, a white dog bolted forward. It was snarling and snapping at the People. Morning Glory knelt down and offered the back of her hand as a gesture. Slowly the dog approached and allowed her to pet it.

Through the dust she saw horses. Her heart began to pound. It was soldiers! There was no place for them to run. In the lead was an Indian scout.

He stopped the soldiers behind him and rode forward. He was a big man, about one hundred eighty pounds, six-foot one maybe, and dressed like no other. He wore a derby hat with two feathers sticking out. His brown boots had the heels cut off. His long hair was tied in a ponytail with a cloth. He wore army pants and a colorful shirt on which was an American flag! There was a patch over one eye.

Morning Glory stepped forward, waiting for the scout to address her, but he did not do so right away. His eyes locked into hers. He had to think for a minute. Where had he seen her before?

The scout jumped down from his appaloosa and dropped its reins to the ground. The pony knew not to move. He walked forward and called the dog back to his side.

"That dog has never taken to anyone but me before. Are you from the sky?" Jack did not know what language to speak to this one. He did not know her tribe so he reluctantly tried English.

"Yes," she simply whispered.

Jack was surprised to hear her reply in English.

"Are you from the Earth?"

"Yes."

"Are you from all Peoples?"

"Yes."

"You are the one I have been looking for. You are the woman of my dreams. I might have only one good eye, but I know what is in my mind. That is to help you find what you are looking for."

"So be it," she calmly replied.

"You are a woman of many dreams but of few words."

She said, "Yes."

"I am Taramenta, chief of the Papago Tribe. I scout for the Army. They call me Union Jack, or One-Eyed Jack. You I shall call Prairie Dog because I have found you wandering in the prairie. Your People do not look well. Where are you headed?"

"Do you know of a place with twin peaks that a dark cloud passes through?"

"I have heard of the place. I can take you there. First, let me bring you to my People. That place is far from here. Your People will never make it. Wait for me here. I will be back in three suns. Then I will take care of your People."

Jack walked back to the brigade of men who were waiting

impatiently on their horses. They did not understand what was being said between Jack and the squaw. They only knew that they had never seen Jack look so serious before.

"Sergeant," Jack addressed the leader, "I beg of you to leave these starving women and children some rations. They can hardly make it through another day without help. There are many sick. They need blankets to get through the night."

The men looked at each other, surprised. They were not accustomed to giving away their food to Indians, or being asked to. Jack had always provided for the men, bringing them to good hunting and water. Reluctantly, each man donated a can or two of his rations. The sergeant allowed Jack to go into the supply wagon for a few blankets.

Jack walked forward with the blankets and again said, "Do not leave this place without me. I will provide for you and your People, but you must wait for my return."

Morning Glory didn't know why, but she had full faith in this unusual man. She would wait.

Jack was going to lead these men through a place they called Scozzyland, looking for a rogue group of Arapaho. This small group of women and children posed no apparent threat to the well-armed cavalrymen.

During the next two days, Jack's mind was not with the cavalry. They searched in vain for a couple of days looking for the raiding band of Arapaho but they couldn't find them. He talked the sergeant into taking the men back to the fort. Jack then rapidly went back for Morning Glory.

Jack was in his late thirties. His wife had died, as had his two sons. He only had a daughter left. Disease and hunger had ravaged his village over the years, leaving only a small tribe. He was a lonely man. He saw that everything was changing. Jack knew that if they didn't bend to the ways of the white man, none of his People would survive. He compromised, using his crafty ways, staying friends with all.

Jack's People lived near a mission. The missioners taught him both Spanish and English. Because of his skill, he became valuable for the Army. He was a chief, so he could negotiate with the neighboring tribes. The cavalry needed him and rewarded him with food and supplies for his People. This is how he kept his tribe alive in the desert.

When Jack returned to Morning Glory's camp and reined his

horse in, he noticed about ten new braves. One of the braves had silver hair, but a young face!

Jack jumped down from his horse, dropped the reins to the ground to tie it and walked toward the silver-haired brave standing next to the blue-eyed woman. He stood before them. Neither said a word.

"These are the quietest People I have ever come across," he thought to himself.

Two Moons did not allow Jack to read his thoughts, but Jack could see that he was there to protect the blue-eyed one. Jack knew he would have to address him.

"I have come to take your People home with me. This blue-eyed woman was in my dreams. I know what I have to do. After I bring your People to my village, I will take you to where the crows fly, the eagles dare, and the peaks have a dark cloud above them. We will start at sunrise."

Two Moons knew some English but was not as fluent as Morning Glory. She translated for him. Two Moons then simply nodded in agreement.

Morning Glory went on to explain. "My People have endured much. They need a home. Ours is gone, destroyed by white man. We have come a long way. Some of my People are to meet us at those peaks. We must find the rest of my People. You are a good man. My brother and I approve. We know you will do what Spirit tells you to do."

Jack wondered how she knew her brother's thoughts, as he showed no response at all. But then, these were unusual People. So that is her brother, he thought. No wonder he stood guard at her side. A woman as beautiful as her needs to be guarded.

The People found the nights in the desert to be cold. They welcomed the blankets, but during the day the blankets became a burden to carry. They had no horses or dogs to ease their burden.

Jack's small village was in a sandy basin near a fort. During their travels they would often run into white men. Jack would spur his horse forward and meet with the men. Two Moons and Morning Glory would watch this man who acted in a strange way as he was approached by a white man.

He would invariably say, "Me like you." Then he would open up his coat, flash the flag he wore on his shirt and beat on his chest. "Me Christian." He would then whip out a black Bible from his back pocket and point to it.

Most people thought he was crazy. They would simply ride on. But Two Moons observed Jack, knowing he was smart as a fox. He also knew in his heart this man would protect his sister like no other. He was pleased: now his job would be a little easier.

Morning Glory always remained quiet when approached by the whites. Jack would always take over. The whites would ask him questions about who he was with. They would try to trick him. They thought he was just a dumb Indian.

Jack would cup his hand and run it slowly across the brim of his hat as he watched their eyes. He would tip his head to the left, allowing him to see out of his good right eye. He would look to the sky and talk about the Great Spirit.

"The Great Spirit is in the flag, you know," he would say.

He would always flash the flag on his shirt. "The Great Spirit carries the flag. I carry the flag on my back. I am part of you."

The whites would always shake their heads in confusion. They thought he was crazy.

Jack was not a handsome man like Dancing Eagle. He had an elongated leather-cracked face with a beak-like nose. He cocked his head all of the time because of his bad eye. Jack's face looked like a road map, from years in the hot desert sun. He was big and strong, though, with incredible physical endurance.

Morning Glory had traveled with Jack for days before she finally asked him, "Why do you wear boots? Why don't you wear moccasins?"

Jack smiled. She'd actually talked to him! He explained. "This is snake country. Boots better here. I carved snakes coming together on the inner side of both boots. This shows that I am brother to the snakes. Snakes don't bother me. They can see from my boots that I carry snake energy. My boots are brown, color of the earth. I cut off heel to be flat with the earth."

Morning Glory smiled. She was satisfied with his answer. She could understand any answer that came from spirit.

She observed that he had his left pant leg rolled up. Inside his boot he kept a large knife. She knew from her experience with Tom that men kept them there to pull out at a moment's notice. During the days they traveled, she also observed that he never missed his mark.

It took them seven risings of the sun to reach Jack's village. Travel was slow because Jack was the only one with a horse. Jack often let an old one ride while he led the animal, which he called

Thunderheart.

Morning Glory always had at least one or two children in her arms as they traveled. The little ones tired easily.

Jack leaned toward Morning Glory. "My village is over the next rise. It is a small village. Our People, too, had their share of troubles, but their home is your home."

Jack's dog ran ahead and alerted the other dogs in the village of the new arrival. Morning Glory noticed that the lodges were not tepees, but adobe buildings. It was not a pretty village like the Eagle tribe used to have. There were no trees, no grass, no birds, no river —just endless sand and cactus.

People began to peek out of their lodges to see what was going on as Morning Glory's People walked to the center of the village. There were maybe fifty or fewer lodges in the whole village. She assumed that meant maybe two hundred villagers.

A young girl came running out toward Jack.

"Taramenta, what have you to say? Who are all of these People?" she demanded to know.

Jack waited until more of his villagers gathered about. With a thundering voice of authority he announced, "I found these People starving in the desert. With them comes a special one, the blue-eyed one that I saw in my visions."

He reached out for Morning Glory, who was holding a screaming infant in her arms and holding another young child by the hand. Morning Glory could see anger rising in this one's face, so she looked down.

"Our People hardly have enough to eat now. How are we to feed all of these extra People?" she howled as she danced around like a bird.

Jack laughed. "This is why we call her Wonatoma, Desert Bird. You see, she dances around like a bird when she gets angry. She is daughter of my brother."

Jack answered his niece. "All People are of the land. I will provide. This I know I must do."

Sternly he then said to her, "I don't need two eyes to see the one who comes from the sky. I have been told through vision that this is the woman who will bring in the dream of true spirit to us."

Wonatoma stalked away. Morning Glory felt like hiding. Obviously, the girl was right; these People had trouble of their own. But her own People had no place to go. They were starving right now. She didn't know what else to do.

Over the next few weeks Jack often took Morning Glory to the fort with him. Forts were not new to Morning Glory. She knew how to address captains and colonels. She knew their language. She actually proved to be an asset to Jack.

The men at the fort liked Jack—especially the colonel. Jack would smoke all night long with the colonel and drink, then get up and do crazy dances. Jack could tell stories all night long. He liked to talk.

They were always exchanging presents. Jack had the tribal women make the colonel a big, warm blanket for his bed. Jack also carved the colonel a very nice pipe. In return, the colonel gave Jack a revolver, which proved to be highly useful.

Jack knew how to muster up wild horses for the cavalry. In return he was paid in blankets and food for his village. This is how he kept the village fed. The food sent to the village by the government rarely got there. When it did, it was usually spoiled.

If there was a sick cow in the fort, the colonel would use it as an excuse to give it to Jack.

When a mediator was needed for treaties and negotiations, Jack was called in. He was a chief and could speak many languages. That way he could both help out the Indian and keep his status with the white man.

Jack was also a leatherworker. Many times he would make saddles for the cavalry. He did many things to supply his People. He worked hard.

Morning Glory learned to respect him enormously for his diligent work in trying to keep peace between the red and white man and for supplying their needs.

She worked diligently too, as a healer between the tribes and even at the fort. When the fort's doctor could do no more, Morning Glory was called in.

One day the colonel tried to buy Morning Glory from Jack. He offered him many horses and much food.

Jack laughed. He said, "She belongs to no man. She is from the sky. She cannot be bought."

When the People of his tribe found out that he would not sell Morning Glory, they became upset. She was an outsider, she could have brought them food. But he would not sell her.

Shadow Dancer and his band of People had been moving around. He was chased from place to place because of his raiding and stealing for food. They wintered under twin peaks near the place called Taos.

Shadow Dancer was too young to be a wise chief. He would always roar out into the night, "Where is Dancing Eagle? He is supposed to be our tribal chief, not me."

"Soon, Two Moons or Dancing Eagle will catch up to us. Then I will be relieved of this burden," he would explain to Little Turtle Woman, whom he had come to marry.

Little Turtle Woman hated his raids and stealing. They would always fight about it. He would retaliate, "Should I leave our People to starve? What would you have me do?"

CHAPTER 36

Spring came. The Eagle tribe hardly noticed. Winter and spring were not as different in the desert as they were east of the big river. There was no snow to melt. Rains in the desert would bring flash flooding, the likes of which they had never seen, but they learned to watch for signs.

Trees were not present in this valley to announce by the opening of their buds the coming of spring. The birds did not greet them in the morning with their chatter. They missed life by the river's edge where they had bathed daily, watered their horses and washed their clothes. Here they had to deal with sand all of the time. Snakes were a daily hazard, having claimed the lives of two of the small children, who had never seen them before.

Their lips were always parched. Game was not plentiful. Jack's People had to show them how to deal with desert plants for food and with peyote for ceremony. They missed the shade of the bountiful trees of their valley. They missed their relatives. Life was an adjustment for all.

All during the winter, Morning Glory mourned the loss of her family and worried about her sons. She didn't know what happened to them, or even where they were now. Now that her People had found a place to call home (at least for the moment), she had to find her sons.

She knew Mary Worthington would be taking good care of them. Morning Glory did not know that Tom Shaye was dead. Life was hard for mixed-bloods. They had grown up with the white man's ways. They could read and write. Now it was time to be taught about spirit. Two Moons agreed.

Jack had been a lonely man. During the winter he fell deeply in love with Morning Glory. He could tell that her heart belonged to another, but just being with her brought him great joy. It was the first real joy that he had felt in many years. He had been so busy providing for his People that he forgot what it felt like to have joy within himself.

Jack had taken to drinking over the years. Morning Glory gave him a reason to give it up. Actually, she told him that she would simply not tolerate a drunk in her lodge. Either he had to stop or she would leave – simple as that. He stopped. It was good. He began to feel proud again.

Jack was not about to let Morning Glory travel all the way back east without him. He didn't want to lose her so he left his brother in charge of his village.

They all agreed to find the boys, bring them back, and on their return trip go to the twin peaks to look for Shadow Dancer and the rest of their People.

Reluctantly, the three left their People behind to embark on another long journey. Two Moons and Jack were both skilled in tracking and finding water. Jack knew more about desert skills, but they learned fast.

Jack had a special way with dogs. His white dog seemed to take a liking to Morning Glory. He let her keep the dog as her guard. The dog he was now training, he called Rattler. Rattler sniffed out snakes, which hide under rocks near water. If the dog found snakes, he also found water.

Jack seemed to be one in spirit with this dog. If Jack slept with one eye open, Rattler would too. Jack would always give the dog his better cuts of meat. When the dog tired, Jack would lay the dog across the back of his saddle.

Rattler always ran a mile or two ahead of them, scouting out the terrain. Jack could mentally communicate with Rattler. The dog became his eyes. Rattler would know when they should take a side path. Jack could feel it, then respond.

It took the three of them many weeks of traveling to get back east. Jack and Two Moons became the best of friends. Both of them were sharp and could sniff out trouble before they rode into it. The journey back was easier than the trip west, because this time they had horses and were not being chased.

All three of them could now speak English but they did their best to avoid encountering whites. In the event that they did, Jack would always go through his routine and head them away from Morning Glory.

They reached an area called Platte's Landing. Jack stayed behind with the horses. Morning Glory and Two Moons traded for a canoe and continued on to the fort.

They traveled at night to avoid being in the white man's sight. They walked softly, moved quietly and worked with the moonlight. Morning Glory always looked down when they crossed another's path. She didn't want anyone to see her blue eyes. She did not want to attract attention.

When they were close to the fort, they banked the canoe and hid it within the brush. For two days they hid among the trees, watching men go in and out of the fort. She could not just walk right in. She was the wife of Tom Shaye — there would be hell to pay. Two Moons would be immediately captured.

She hoped to catch a glimpse of her boys, but had no such luck. On the third day she caught a glimpse of an Indian scout she had once been friends with. She gave a birdcall he would be familiar with. He heard it, dropped his head and paused. She knew he had heard her. Then he went into the fort with the other men.

It was midsummer. The days were hot and sticky. The bugs buzzed past their heads as they hid within the tall grass. Ants crawled across their feet. Their supply of venison jerky had run out. Any berries that might be nearby were gone.

Late that evening, after the bugle announced retirement, she heard the fort gate squeak as it was partially opened. It alerted her. In the shadows, she saw a man coming through the night. He gave a signal. She returned it. He continued toward them.

It was old Rain Maker. He did a little shuffle as he whispered, "I thought you were dead!"

Morning Glory motioned for him to get down next to them in the brush. "The Creator did not have that in his plan. It is my sons that I come to seek. This is my brother Two Moons. He is here to help me bring them back to our People."

Two Moons nodded a greeting. Rain Maker understood. Words were not needed at such a time.

Rain Maker explained, "Mary Worthington has been taking care of them through the winter. They are well and growing tall like their father. When Tom was killed, his brother James came from the East to fetch them."

Morning Glory stiffened at his words.

Rain Maker said, "You did not know about Tom?"

Morning Glory could only shake her head.

"When Tom's body was brought back to the regiment, the cavalry revenged his death by destroying your village. They used his body as an excuse," Rain Maker concluded.

"Your boys are still here. James had some paperwork to handle, so they have not left yet. Seems James has some wealth back East."

Morning Glory became alarmed. She knew of Tom's brother and that he lived a long way from here. She'd never met him, but if he was anything like Tom, she would die before she would let her boys go with him.

"Rain Maker, I must find a way into the fort. Please help me," she pleaded.

Rain Maker thought for a while then smiled. "There is no time like the present. Our old friend Deer Slayer is guarding the gate tonight. I will go ahead and have him let you in. When I give the signal, come quietly forth."

A short time later, the signal came. Two Moons prayed to the Creator to make them invisible as they walked to the gate and quickly sneaked in.

There was a section in the fort where the mixed-bloods and scouts stayed. It was there that they hid for the night. Morning Glory was scared and restless. The night was long. She dared not sleep.

Morning Glory stayed near the window, observing who came to the well. As dawn came, men went back and forth to drink. She saw the skirt of a woman carrying a bucket. It was Mary, dear sweet Mary!

Morning Glory's heart began to pound. She crept toward the door. As Mary walked past, Morning Glory quietly called out to her.

"Mary! Tis me, Mary – Morning Glory!"

Mary stopped cold. Her heart began to quake! She thought she'd heard the voice of a ghost! She was afraid to turn around. She began to doubt that she'd heard anything.

In her Irish accent, Morning Glory went on. "Do not shake with fear, Mary. It truly is me, Morning Glory, in the flesh. But shush, do not disclose my identity. Meet me back here when the sun sets."

Mary nodded and did not even look her way. She was still scared and doubtful, yet elated that her dear friend was back. She still had not seen her face.

The day was truly long for Morning Glory and Two Moons.

Two Moons prayed to the Creator the whole day for protection and guidance. They continued to hide in the scouts' quarters. The soldiers did not often mix with the mixed-bloods and scouts. They rarely came to their quarters, especially during the day. Rain Maker brought in some food for them at midday then went off with a band of soldiers to a neighboring village.

Yellow Dog, a mixed-blood, explained to Morning Glory that he had seen James Shaye. "He is a big man like his brother but he does not carry his cruel eyes. I saw him with the commander. Heard he was trying to straighten out Tom's affairs. He tried to spend some time with your boys. They resisted him. They won't say a word to him, but James seems patient enough."

"Thank you, Yellow Dog," Morning Glory said. "I needed to know whom I would be dealing with."

All through the day, Mary dared not say anything to the boys about their mother being back. She still had not even seen Morning Glory's face. They might endanger her if they were to go looking for her.

It was a hot, sultry evening when Mary finally put the boys to bed. Commander Worthington went to play cards with the staff.

As soon as her husband left, Mary grabbed the leftover bread from the shelf, wrapped it in a towel and acted as though she were heading toward the well. When she was sure no one was around, she darted into the scouts' quarters. The door cracked open upon her approach. She slipped in.

Casually, the scouts stepped out onto the boardwalk and propped their feet up on some kegs, pretending to rest in the heat of the evening. This way they could give warning to Morning Glory if anyone were to approach.

The two women embraced tearfully. Mary pulled back and looked into her eyes. "It truly is you, child. I thought you were dead! I heard you were shot straight away!"

"I was at that, but it was not yet my time," Morning Glory said. "Mary, 'tis time you meet my brother, Two Moons. You have heard me talk of him so."

Mary curtsied to him. Two Moons nodded, not being familiar with such a greeting. He then continued to look out the window for danger.

"Child, you are a sight for sore eyes. Where have you been?"

Morning Glory tried to briefly explain how her village had been destroyed, McVain had tried to kill her, her family and friends had been murdered, and Dancing Eagle had disappeared from her life again.

Mary put her hands over her face and wept, knowing how much Morning Glory had endured during the last year. She put her hands on Morning Glory's shoulders and said, "Child, it is best that Dancing Eagle is no longer around. If he is still alive, he is a hunted man. He is the one who killed Tom!"

Two Moons' head sagged upon hearing Mary's words. It was not what he wanted to hear, but he was not surprised. Dancing Eagle had vowed many times to kill Tom Shaye, and he did.

Mary tried to lighten up the moment. "Your boys have grown like trees. They are getting too big to put over my knees."

"Mary, I must bring them back with me. They belong to me, not to white man's ways."

Mary tried to explain. "James is a good man, not like his brother Tom. Shortly, he is going to take them back to Pennsylvania, where he has a big farm and two children of his own."

Alarmed, Morning Glory said, "Pennsylvania! I do not know of Pennsylvania! Where is that?"

"To the east, many days to the east."

"No! They are of my heart. Two Moons and I take them with me. They belong to me, not James. You must help me. Please!"

Mary thought for a moment. "Of course I will. You are their mother. They belong with you, not a stranger."

"James is to depart in two days' time. You must leave tomorrow. When the sun reaches high noon, meet me two miles north of the fort. I will pretend that I am going to town for supplies and that the boys are to help me. I will not tell the boys of the plan for fear they might speak or even rebel. Nathanael feels that you have abandoned him. Thomas is in a rage. He does not want to be forced to go with James. They are not very happy right now. I will pack their things and meet you tomorrow, my dear friend."

Mary cupped her hand over Morning Glory's face. With a quivering voice, trying to fight back the tears, she said, "Will I ever see you again?"

Morning Glory hugged her. "Time seems to go on forever and ever. At some point in time, yes, we will meet again. You are an old friend. I do not know if it will be before the Eagle takes me away. But I promise you this: someday, sometime, we will have met again. I will never forget you. I will always be your friend."

Morning Glory took out her turquoise stone and pressed it into

Mary's hand. "When this stone comes back to me, we will have met again."

Morning Glory and Two Moons sneaked out of the fort that night, having consumed Mary's fresh bread. They did not want to push their luck any further and get caught. They found a grove of trees near a creek, not too far from the road out of the fort where they were to meet Mary.

Morning Glory did not sleep at all that night. She lay under the stars, watching them twinkle, while she wondered what her boys looked like and whether they would be happy living with her People. They would be whites amidst a village of Indians. Thomas Jr. probably would not like that very much. Of the three boys, he took after their father the most. He was rowdy, independent and rebellious. The two youngest more often would ask her ways of spirit.

In the morning, Two Moons and Morning Glory bathed and prepared themselves for the meeting. Both of them prayed to the Creator for guidance and help. Two Moons prepared a freshly caught fish, but Morning Glory was too nervous to eat more than a morsel. They enjoyed living beside a river again.

They hid among the trees, within sight of the road. They heard the beat of horses' hooves and the creaking of wagon wheels. Morning Glory's heart pounded. She felt faint. She was so nervous, she couldn't swallow. The wagon was now in sight through the dust that followed them. A hawk soared above them and gave out a shriek. They knew everything would be all right.

As the wagon approached, Two Moons ran into the trees to watch for any oncoming horses. Morning Glory stepped out into the road. Mary reined in the horses.

Three blond heads were bobbing in the back of the wagon. They started to look around to see why the wagon was stopped. Softly, with tears in her eyes, she walked toward them. "Kachant, Watna, Chata, I have returned for you."

"Mother!" little James softly said, his mouth falling open. "They thought you were dead, but I knew you weren't!"

He climbed out of the wagon and ran toward her. He got to her first and grabbed her around her waist. Morning Glory couldn't hold back her tears. Mary had to help little Nathanael out of the wagon. As he hit the ground, his little legs ran after his brother. He wrapped his arms around her legs. Thomas climbed out of the wagon and stood there, not showing any emotion. That was his way. She nodded to him and said, "Thomas, you look well. You will be taller than your father and handsomer too. I am proud of you."

"Where have you been?" little Nathanael demanded. "Why did you leave us?"

"It could not be helped, my sons. There was no other way. I came back for you as soon as I was able. I have come a long way. We have a long way to go. We go to be with my People. Will you all come with me?"

"Are you all alone, Mother? How did you get here?" Thomas wondered.

Morning Glory gave out a birdcall, the sound of a whippoorwill. Nathanael was surprised as he watched a silver-haired Indian come through the trees to stand behind Morning Glory. He walked up and stood by Morning Glory's side, quietly.

"This is my brother, Two Moons. I have often told you of him. He is now with me again and will help raise you. He will show you the ways of the Eagle and how to live with the land like no other man can. He is of my heart and my soul. He will always be there for you."

Little Nathanael could not take his eyes off this curious man. His face was young but his hair was old. His eyes were very unusual. Two Moons put out his hand. Nathanael somehow found himself moving toward him and touched his hand. Without realizing it, he was holding his uncle Two Moons' hand and standing by his side, but always looking up at him.

Young James said, "Yes, Mother, I will go with you. I do not want to go to Pennsylvania. I do not want to go east and be with people I don't know."

Morning Glory gently turned to Thomas. "Thomas, what of you? Will you go with me and the rest of your family, or with your uncle James?"

Thomas did not say a word for some time. Morning Glory and Two Moons did not push him. It was not their way. He had gone through a lot in his life. Now he had some big decisions to make. Thomas walked away for a while. They let him go.

Morning Glory picked up her Chata and held him tight. She took young James by the hand. "I have thought of you and prayed for you every day and every night. I was wounded and taken a long way from here to heal. I came back as soon as I could find a home for you to come back to. They have said they would welcome my sons there. It will be your new home."

Thomas came back and stood in front of his mother. "I will go with you. Uncle James is a farmer. I will be no sod-buster. I want to travel the rivers like my father and hunt and fish like my father. I'll never be a sod-buster. I will go with you."

Two Moons took their belongings from the wagon, swung them over his back and headed into the trees. It was his way of saying, "Time to go now."

Morning Glory and Mary Worthington gave each other one last hug. Mary went to each boy and hugged him goodbye tearfully. They had been like sons to her. She'd helped bring them into this world. She'd helped raise them. It tore her heart out to see them go and to lose her friend Morning Glory too.

Mary gave Morning Glory some money. "Here, this will help you to buy a canoe. You can travel much faster by water than foot. Maybe it will give you a little extra time to get a head start."

The newfound family started on their long journey home. They were an unlikely-looking family: an Indian woman with blue hair, blue eyes, and a Scotch-Irish accent, three blond sons and a silver-haired Indian brave!

They kept off the main roads, often traveling by night. When they reached the river crossing, Morning Glory saw a canoe for sale. Since she spoke English, she approached the man at the pier. He was a gruff, little old man. His toothless mouth endlessly gummed his pipe. Two Moons and the boys stayed on the bank.

"Sir, 'tis a boat that I seek. What do you charge?"

He spit out tobacco juice and turned around to reply to what he thought was a little Irish woman. Standing before him was a blue-eyed squaw. He looked around, thinking some other woman must have walked away. He looked up the bank and saw an Indian brave standing there beside three blond boys.

"What in sam hill is going on here? What's that Indian doin' with three white boys? Did he steal them? Are they captives?"

"Nay. Nay. They are just my sons. Their father, he was white, you know. That man be my brother. Now, 'tis a boat I seek. What say you for that one over there?"

"I don't trade with no Injuns. I've got enough pelts to my name."

"Tis cash I have. What be your price?"

He named his price. Morning Glory named hers. Tom had been a river man, and she was very familiar with canoes and also with dealing. He taught her well on that accord. They finally agreed. Two Moons and the boys came to the pier, loaded up and paddled south.

Quietly, Two Moons and young Thomas paddled down the river. Thomas knew how to handle a canoe well, having been taught by his father. Two Moons was pleased to have able assistance.

For the most part the canoe slipped quietly across the water. Two Moons and Morning Glory spoke little. They always knew what was on each other's minds. Thomas was a bit surly and never shared his feelings. Little Nathanael just liked to sit on Morning Glory's lap. James was somewhat on the quiet side, like his mother.

Mary nervously arrived back at the fort. Most of the men were out on maneuvers, so nobody really noticed that she had come back without the boys.

James Shaye usually had dinner with the Worthingtons every evening. He tried to use that time to get to know the boys, but it wasn't an easy task. They'd lost their parents. Now they would have to leave what they'd always called home, to go with a man they didn't know. He was trying to ease them into this, but spring was at hand and he had to get back to his family and farm. He couldn't stay away for the planting season.

James wasn't at all like his brother, Thomas Shaye. James was a quiet, nondrinking Christian. He was respectful to all. Mary actually liked him, but in her heart she felt the boys belonged with their mother.

At dinnertime, Commander Worthington came in and saw only three plates set on the table. James was sitting uncomfortably. When the commander found out what Mary had done, he went into a rage.

"Now, Commander, please settle down. Do not be so hard on your dear wife. She did what most women would do — bring a mother and her children together. I do not blame her for that. I will simply track them down. They couldn't have gone too far. After all, there are five of them."

"Mary has told me how special their mother is. I have half a mind to let them go with her. But I had always promised my brother I would take care of his children if anything ever happened to him. First thing in the morning, I will track them down."

At first dawn, James set out to find Morning Glory. The Commander had supplied James with a few men and a scout that knew the territory. They headed south.

Every time they saw somebody, they would ask him if he had seen a blue-eyed Indian woman with three blond boys. Eventually they came across the old, crusty man who had sold them the canoe. The old man spit out tobacco juice and pinched up his nose to hold up his spectacles. "Strangest family I ever saw, sure enough. They paid me cash and headed south. Knew how to handle a canoe well enough. Cut through the water purty as you please. Was out of my sight in no time."

James purchased a canoe and took a couple of men with him. He left the other men behind with the horses. They paddled rapidly, sleeping only a couple of hours that night.

The evening of the following night, they checked out a small campfire along the riverbank. He would have never noticed it had he not looked up to see a wildly blinking star. When he looked down, the fire caught his eye. Damnedest star I ever saw, he thought.

Quietly they snuck up on the little family. Morning Glory jumped up in panic. Two Moons simply remained seated on the log. He carried no arrows or bow, only a knife for camping and cleaning fish.

"Mother, this is Uncle James. He will not hurt you," said young James.

The elder James Shaye could not believe what was before his eyes. Tom Shaye had written that Morning Glory was beautiful, but he could not quite comprehend what he was seeing. She was far more than just a blue-eyed squaw. Now he understood why his brother had fought to his very death for this woman. She carried an aristocratic elegance despite her buckskin dress. A power and presence emanated from her being.

"Why are you here, sir?" Morning Glory inquired in her Irish accent.

James Shaye was speechless for a couple of minutes, then he caught himself staring. "Uh . . . why, these boys have the Shaye name. I promised Tom I would raise them if anything happened to him. I always keep my promises."

Morning Glory stood before him defiantly and said without blinking an eye, "As long as these boys are of the land, they are mine, not yours!"

James started to stammer, "Legally, Tom left them to me. He

left a will. It must be honored by law."

Two Moons quietly got up from his seat and walked over. "There is only the law of the Creator," Two Moons simply stated. "These boys have a mission beyond your own. These boys have to go to the mountains with me. I am their uncle, as you are. But the boys have chosen to go with their mother, not a stranger."

The whole while little Nathanael kept clinging to Morning Glory. Young James stood by her side. Thomas stood off to the side, holding his hand over his pocketknife but not saying a word.

Two Moons kept adding small logs and twigs to the fire as they talked through the night. The air around them seemed deathly still, and nothing disturbed them. Periodically, James would look to the sky and notice that blinking light above them.

Morning Glory diligently explained to James what her life with Tom had been like. She told him how he'd kidnapped her from the arms of the man she loved and how her tribe was eventually destroyed by Tom's men. James' head hung in shame and sympathy.

Morning Glory stood up and started to pace. "It is time my boys learn the true way of the land and live amongst my People, who will show them true spirit."

James was a Christian and was not fully aware of the Indian ways of nature but he understood virtue and righteousness. He could fully see that Two Moons and Morning Glory were of a spiritual nature, and the boys would be brought up honoring some form of godliness.

James could also see that the boys were not interested in being with him. In fact, Thomas Jr. stated in no uncertain terms that he would simply run away before he would be a sod-buster, plain and simple. He could see that the lad had his father's nature and would most likely do just that.

Throughout the night, Uncle James kept catching himself staring at what he termed "a bonnie lass." "If she were mine, I would treat her like a princess," he caught himself saying.

Soon it neared dawn. The sun's rays flickered through the trees. James watched Two Moons and Morning Glory rise and walk toward the river. Quietly he followed behind them but stopped short of being seen by them.

As the sun's rays began to shoot forth, Morning Glory and Two Moons raised their arms to the sky, facing east. The rays would shoot out between the clouds and seemingly touch their hands. They would glow. He saw her raven-black hair turn an aqua hue and her skin turn a golden bronze. She then turned around. Her blue eyes shined beyond her. James was stunned. Her eyes looked straight at him, but yet he knew that her spirit was beyond him. He felt a sudden desperation to not leave her side.

Quietly she and Two Moons walked back to camp, passing straight by him. He swallowed hard and sat down to think. The boys were now up in the camp. The fire was being built. Breakfast was at hand, and Morning Glory came to get him.

As James sat and sipped the herbal tea Morning Glory had prepared, he spoke. "I still want to do right by the boys. Morning Glory, you are welcome to come with the boys and live with me back east. I shall always take care of you. You are my sister-in-law. You are family. I will give the boys an education and always provide for you. I am a wealthy man. You will want for nothing until your dying days. Come back with me."

It took but a minute for Morning Glory to reply. "Everything in my being calls me west of here, not east. My People must all go west. It is our destiny. I cannot go with you."

James was heartbroken. He wanted her so. He kept looking at her and could not believe the insanity his brother must have carried in him, to treat her like he did. James watched her move about the fire, swiftly preparing things. He watched her hair gleam in the sunlight. He loved her unusual Indian-Irish accent and her quick, to-the-point replies.

She talked straight from the heart. There was no denying that. He knew that he had to go back to his wife and children. If he hadn't already had a family, nothing could have pulled him away. He would have followed her to wherever she wanted to go and even live among the Indians if he had to.

James came to a decision. "Morning Glory, I will let you take the boys to your People but only if you promise to keep in touch with me. You must always let me know how everyone is doing and if they need anything at all. You must let me know. I know you will always keep your promise. If you promise me that, I will let the boys go freely and not try to take them back."

Morning Glory smiled with relief. "You are a good man, James Shaye. I am glad to see that in the Shaye bloodline there is some kindness to pass down to my sons. I would be proud to remember you in my heart. I will keep you informed of the boys, as I can read and write. If you ever need anything from me, let me know. Agreed?"

"Agreed." James Shaye packed his belongings and made ready to leave. As he started to walk toward his canoe, he stopped and turned one more time. "Tom has an inheritance from our father that he has never accepted. I will keep it for your boys. When they need it, tell them to contact me. I can put them through school or set them up in business. For now, I will give you some cash to help you get back to your People. It will buy you food and blankets, maybe even horses if you need them. Spend it well and in good health. May God bless you."

Morning Glory hugged him. He rode out, not turning back. He did not want her to see the tear in his eye.

CHAPTER 37

Morning Glory, Two Moons and the three boys journeyed until they rejoined with Jack and the horses. The boys rode double with them as they journeyed back.

As they traveled, Jack always spurred his horse ahead when they saw a white man coming. He would flash his flag and whip out his Bible. "Me Christians," he would always say. "I am part of land. I am part of you." He always headed off trouble that way; he was devoted to protecting Morning Glory.

They were now an even more unlikely group of People. Not only did they have a blue-eyed Indian squaw with an Irish accent, three blond-haired boys and a silver-haired brave, they also had a crazy-acting Indian wearing a derby hat, feathers and an American flag! They tried not to attract attention, but the only way they could avoid it was to stay off the beaten path and to travel at night.

Two Moons seemed to have incredible night vision. The dogs always scouted ahead, so they ran into little trouble. The journey was a long one, though. They were all tired.

As they journeyed through the night, there was always an incredibly close blinking star wherever they went. They didn't know if the star was following them or if they were following the star, but they never felt alone.

The dogs would always scout out water, or Two Moons would find it with the stones. Food seemed to come their way, as Jack was an incredible tracker and hunter. The Creator provided, and they were grateful, always giving thanks.

On their route back, they again passed through Mesa Verde. Jack's dog, Rattler, had been bitten by a snake the day before. They had tended to the dog best they could, but it was still very sick. Jack was extremely upset, as this dog was very special to him. He made Rattler a bed near a cave entrance and put him in the shade.

Morning Glory had put a poultice on the dog's wound and sat near its head. As she looked around the cave, she happened to see the sun's rays flicker off a brilliant clear stone. She went to pick it up and brought it back near Rattler's bed. She put Rattler's head on her lap as she examined the stone.

As she rotated the stone to look at it in the sunlight, the rays were bouncing off Rattler. She began to chant in prayer. Not very long after that, Rattler suddenly jumped up, licking her face and barking!

What happened? she wondered. That very morning the dog had been near death. They'd held very little hope for it. It seemed after she chanted with the stone, the dog regained life. A gift from the Creator!

Two Moons and Jack examined the stone. Jack said, "This stone is especially for you. It is like another eye. You are to wear it like an eye." Two Moons nodded in agreement.

Jack said, "I will make you a crown out of silver. It is as though you have worn a crown before. I see it in my eye. I know how to work with silver. I know what to do. The jewel will be set in the middle of a headband. It will rest across your brow and hook around your head."

Morning Glory sat under a tree, holding the stone in her hand. Her vision showed her going into a misty land, right through an invisible opening. Time seemed to stand still in this land. There was peace. She knew she had been there before. She knew how to get in and out of their doors. She saw People on the other side. Some even looked familiar to her. She told them she would be back.

It was time to find Shadow Dancer and his People. Two Moons prayed to the Eagle to give him vision, to show him where his People were.

He saw them between two peaks, in a land with much sun but not much food. They were weary and sick. He saw Shadow Dancer in a bit of a fix. He felt that they must go and find them now.

Jack knew of the place. He had never been there but he knew how to get there. It was to the north, a place they called Taos.

This was a lot of traveling for the boys, but they reveled in it. Every inch of the way, Two Moons taught them of spirit and showed them how to be one with the land. Morning Glory showed them herbs and ways of healing. She taught them how to ask spirit to come through their hands. She taught them how to have spirit show them which herb to use for the purpose at hand.

Jack grew to love Morning Glory more through every moment of each day. He only wanted to be with her. Nothing else mattered to him anymore. Two Moons saw this to be true. Jack now felt that he knew what to do.

Morning Glory learned to respect Jack as a very strong individual. He would show her how he danced to spirit and teach her his ways. She marveled at the different methods he had, yet they worked for him. She wanted to learn more and more. He taught her Spanish and the language of his People. She taught him some of her language. Their whole journey was one of teaching and learning among the six of them.

Occasionally they would find a friendly village along the way that would let them stay. Two Moons and Jack would talk with the council. Morning Glory did healing work whenever she was needed.

With each village they came across, they asked about a lost tribe. More often than not, they heard of a tribe that roamed, without a place to call home, whose leader was a hunted one. He stole cattle and horses from the whites. The whites were after them, so the other tribes would not let them stay. They brought trouble wherever they roamed. Two Moons and Morning Glory were becoming increasingly concerned: they knew how their brother could be!

They prayed to the Eagle. The Eagle led the way. They found Shadow Dancer's People hidden in a cave. Shadow Dancer had done well in hiding them.

Two Moons gave his signal so they would not be attacked. Shadow Dancer stepped out, knowing his brother's call. He was ecstatic! It had been a long, long time.

Morning Glory walked up to him and patiently stood until he noticed her. As Shadow Dancer embraced Two Moons, he felt her presence and looked up.

"Morning Glory! You were so badly wounded! I didn't know if you had survived!" They embraced as tears ran down her face. Shadow Dancer was a rascal, but she truly loved him. It felt so good to see her brother again.

Behind her stood three blond boys. Shadow Dancer peeked behind her and looked in wonder. "They are yours?" he asked.

She nodded and pulled them in front of her. He stared at them in amazement. They stared back, not saying a word, either. They had learned from their mother and Two Moons to always think before they talked, to examine the situation fully before expressing an emotion. They did not show their emotion at all. They allowed no one to read their minds.

"Powerful little braves you have there, sister. If they be yours, I'm sure they are of the Eagle eye and will be friends at my side. I see it in their eyes. They have your eyes."

The little one especially entranced Shadow Dancer. He carried in his eyes the depths of the sea and walked with nobility.

Morning Glory noticed his gaze. "He is my Chata — Nathanael," said Morning Glory. She then introduced young James and Thomas. Thomas, as usual, stood off to the side. Chata stood by his uncle, as they had become instant friends.

Turtle Woman stepped out and stood beside Shadow Dancer.

Shadow Dancer put his arm around her shoulder. "She is now my woman," he proudly stated.

"Yes, I had to take him for a husband. What else could I do?" she said in mock exasperation.

Morning Glory and Two Moons laughed out loud. Life would never be boring for Turtle Woman, living with Shadow Dancer.

The People started coming out of the caves. Before them stood Morning Glory and Two Moons. With Morning Glory stood her three white-eyes; not everyone there was happy to see the boys. Their father had brought destruction to their village! They didn't know what to think of them. But they were of the princess and they stood by Two Moons' side.

"Let no one of this tribe harm these blue-eyes," commanded Shadow Dancer. "They are of the Eagle and of our princess. You treat them with respect or you answer to me." He pounded his chest.

Those who knew Shadow Dancer knew well of his love for his sister. They did not doubt his words.

Two Moons brought Jack forth and addressed the People. "This is Taramenta, chief of the Papago tribe in the land where the firebird flies. He has taken in the rest of our People; they are with his People in the desert. He has honored our People and given them a home. We will take you back with us. You will then have a place to call home."

The People began to whisper to each other concerning this new arrangement. They had some questions, which Jack went about answering for the People.

While Jack was making friends with the Eagle tribe, Two Moons pulled Shadow Dancer to the side. "Brother, I have heard of the trouble you have brought upon the land. Is this an honorable way for our People to live?"

"Two Moons, this land is not like our home. Food is not plentiful. We have to travel far and wide to hunt. Our People were sick, tired and wounded. Am I to allow them to starve? Would that be more dignified? No . . . . I am a warrior. My People will not lie down to die like tired old dogs. I had to provide in the only way I could."

Two Moons shook his head in disgust. "Brother of mine, if you were only of spirit, the Creator would have provided. But no, you had to run about like a wild one. Come. Come back with us. You will be provided for by the government."

Two Moons explained to Shadow Dancer, "On our way back, we must stop at a place of the ancients, a place our ancient People once called home. There is something there that I must do before we go back to the land of the firebird."

The People were very tired of journeying but they still needed a home. Now that Shadow Dancer was back with the princess, they thought they had more of a chance. They would also be rejoined with the rest of their tribe. That would be welcomed.

In the morning Jack parted temporarily with the Eagle Tribe. He decided to go ahead to his own People. He had been gone too long and worried about their well-being. They were on government land, and food was supposed to be provided, but rarely was it on time or very good. He had his ways of providing for them.

Jack did not want to leave Morning Glory behind but he knew she was in good hands with her brothers. Shadow Dancer had about fifty People with him. The group would travel much slower than he would going alone. He had to go ahead to warn his People that there were more coming. That would be a problem too. The fort would have to be notified. Provisions would have to be increased.

Jack ambled over to Morning Glory. One of his feet had a slight limp to it because it had been crushed when a supply wagon he was driving tipped over on him. He took off his feathered derby and fingered the rim as he solemnly stated, "You are my Desert Moon. I will be anxiously awaiting your return. For now, we both have responsibilities to our People. Take care, woman, for you are of my heart."

Morning Glory embraced him then stepped back to watch him ride Thunderheart from her view. He was a good man, always providing. Jack left the white dog with Morning Glory and rode off with Rattler in the lead.

The remnants of the Eagle Clan journeyed for many days before they arrived at the mesa. They sought shelter within the cliff dwellings and rested their weary bones.

Two Moons took to walking off in the moonlight. The People could hear him talking with the wolves. When he returned, he never spoke of what he saw.

Morning Glory was kept busy working among the sick. A man had burned his hands so they brought him to her. She shook his hands and put them in his hair. She poured water upon his head and chanted. The People watched in wonder as sparks of lightning flew all about him! He could not stand. He fell to the ground. He couldn't pull his hands away from his hair. He shook and quaked and fell asleep like a baby. When he awoke, his hands had no scars!

Morning Glory was known to do these things. "I am to work with my energies only," she explained. "The Great Spirit tells me what to do, what to say, where to go, who to be with. I must be obedient. I alone am nothing. I only allow the Great Spirit to flow through me, as all should do!"

In the moonlight, when most of the People slept, Two Moons, Morning Glory and Shadow Dancer slipped out of camp and went to a special cave. Two Moons held a staff in each hand – a staff of life and a staff of will – in which he focused power. Morning Glory held a carved stone in her right hand and held the left hand out to pull in energies as she closed her eyes and focused. Side by side the two of them stood. The wall simply opened up!

Shadow Dancer guarded the entrance. Two Moons and Morning Glory walked into the cave as though they had been there a hundred times before. Through the night they packed artifacts onto the horses.

As the sun's rays rose in the morning, it heated the rocks with its generous heat. Morning Glory and Two Moons were ready to journey and stood beside the packhorses.

"Two Moons," Short Leg inquired, "what have you in those packs?"

Two Moons was never long on words. "We have lights to take

to the fire mountain to give to the Great Eagle." Then he simply grabbed the rope on the lead packhorse and started the journey. The People had to quickly gather their things and catch up to him.

This was the final leg of their journey. They were heading to Jack's village. As they journeyed, they only saw desert sand, unrelenting sun, no shade, and cactus.

"Two Moons," Shadow Dancer yelled, "what kind of place will this be? Are we to eat off the sand? Will there be no trees to shade us from the sun? How are we to get food?"

Two Moons would not look into his brother's face. He simply replied, "You will be provided for."

"By who, Two Moons? The white-eyes? Are they going to feed us? I doubt it. Since when do the white-eyes do anything they said they would do?"

Two Moons stopped walking and turned to his brother. "These are troubled times, my brother. For a while, humble yourself. It is our People we must think of, not our foolish pride."

When they arrived at Jack's village, Jack had his People prepare some lodges for the new arrivals. His People were not pleased with the new burdens that were arriving, but they did what Jack told them to do. It would take the Eagle Clan some adjusting to learn to live in the desert, but right now they were just weary.

The haggard remnants of the Eagle Clan journeyed to the center of the village. Jack's People peeked out of their adobe lodges. They were a shorter, stockier People than the Eagle Clan. They had rounder faces and darker skin.

The village had a small well, rather than a river flowing by. There were cactus instead of trees, but the cactus were as big as trees. The village had few horses. There was no grass to feed them. This was to be their new home.

The People Morning Glory had brought there the previous year ran from their lodges to greet the rest of the Eagle Clan. They rejoiced in seeing more of their own kind but were saddened when they found out who hadn't survived.

With both surviving parties finally brought together, there were only about seventy People left of the Eagle Clan. They were mostly women and children.

Satisfied that the People were settled into their new lodges, Morning Glory and Two Moons continued on their journey to the fire mountain and hid the ancient artifacts. Spirit told them it would be for another time, another place. The Great Spirit would see to it that these items were protected until it was time to use them again. They did not question. They only followed spirit.

They both were shown visions of things flying in the sky, People in different clothes and other visions that made no sense to them. Another world, perhaps another land. They did not know.

Morning Glory and Two Moons quietly rode back to Jack's village. Morning Glory knew Two Moons would be leaving soon. She also knew he would take her two oldest boys with him. Chata would join them later. Two Moons was their uncle, and as was their custom, it was his place to teach them the ways of manhood and spirit. He would journey with them to the sacred places in the mountains. Two Moons would teach them as no other could. She would miss the boys, but their journey into spirit was more important.

Morning Glory also knew they would be more comfortable traveling with Two Moons. Her blond boys would be uncomfortable living in an isolated Indian village. They had grown up with the whites at the fort. Also, the People from her tribe would never truly forget that Tom Shaye was their father.

With the money that James Shaye had provided, she purchased two horses from the fort for her boys. With the ability she had to communicate with Two Moons, her heart would always know where they were and if they were well. Bravely she kissed them and Two Moons goodbye, not really knowing when they would return.

Chata often accompanied Morning Glory when she was called to help with a healing. She wanted him to learn all aspects of healing, and he quietly observed her. They too had a special relationship. Words were not often needed.

Jack remained devoted to her. He was a skilled man. He made her a tiara of silver and inserted the stone she had found in Mesa Verde. As she traveled from village to village to both help the sick and learn of their ways, it became her calling card.

Morning Glory, in her quiet way, would often simply observe Jack. He was not a handsome man, but he always had a certain cockeyed smile. Half of his lip would curl and the other half would frown. He never really fully laughed. If he was happy, his lip would curl and a few of his teeth would show.

Morning Glory didn't care what he looked like. It was only his spirit that counted to her. That was all she really saw anyway. He provided for her every need, yet she still always had Dancing Eagle on her mind. No one would ever share her heart as he did. A piece of her was always missing. She never mentioned his name to Jack, but Jack knew. He knew he would never fully have her heart. He was just happy to be with her.

Morning Glory wanted to live out the rest of her life in anonymity. Because her eyes would often attract undue attention, she did much of her work at night. Often, if she heard of a sick one, she would leave herbs at that one's lodge door. They would be found in the morning.

Because of her night work, she was given the name Desert Moon. Nobody knew she was once called Morning Star or the Glory of the Morning. Only those who knew her from before would remember that.

She would correct them: "I am Desert Moon!"

CHAPTER 38

Dancing Eagle was a hunted man, for the murder of Thomas Shaye. He changed his name to Windchimer and headed southwest, looking for his lost tribe.

Whenever he came across a village, he would ask if they had seen a band of Indians traveling with a silver-haired leader, a blue-eyed princess or three straw-haired boys. He was always directed south or west.

Dancing Eagle grew weary and lonely in his travels. He had lost contact with the Eagle long ago. Only the lost spirits would talk to him but they gave him conflicting information. The spirits kept him busy, kept him alive, but always sent him traveling in different directions.

"Where does the Eagle fly?" he would scream to the sky.

His horse grew thin and weary. There was little grass to eat in this desert land. He had trouble finding food for himself. Hunting was not good. Water was sparse. There were no currents of river filled with fish.

Every place he traveled seemed to have its own war going on. Grays were fighting Blues. Indians were fighting whites. Whites were stealing cattle from whites. Men fought for land. He could find no peace or sense anywhere.

Soldiers were about. At first he tried to hide, but this land had few trees. He could only sit out in the breeze and pretend to be one with the land.

His horse became lame. It could go on no longer. Dancing Eagle's lips were parched, cracked and bleeding. He didn't have the strength to continue.

Some soldiers rode up to him. He was too weary to care

whether he lived or died. He sat there and did not try to hide. The Indian scout from the brigade jumped down from his sorrel gelding, handed the reins to the man next to him and slowly walked toward Windchimer. He was a short, stocky brave wearing Indian-style leggings and a blue cavalry shirt. He wore a cavalry hat with a feather in it.

Windchimer did not bother to get to his feet. The scout squatted down beside him and softly said, "Brother, why do you sit here alone in the desert sand?"

Windchimer shrugged his shoulders and with no emotion left in him said, "Because I am alone and no longer have my land. My People are gone. I am weary. There is no food wherever I go, so I might just as well sit here."

The Indian scout sat on the ground facing Windchimer and looked straight into his eyes. He saw the eyes of a gifted one, but with a dying spirit.

"Ride with us. We will give you food and supplies. You can be our eyes. One of our soldiers has been felled by an arrow. You can ride his horse and rest your pathetic pony."

Windchimer thought for a while. The soldiers sat impatiently on their horses in the hot sun. He again shrugged his shoulders, unexpectedly stood up, and leaped onto the riderless horse. "I might as well ride with you. I have no place else to go."

Weeks went by. Many moons passed through the sky. They would ask him to find water amd he would. They would ask him to find a certain band of Indians and he would. In exchange they gave him food, supplies and a horse to ride.

While he traveled, he asked every band of Indians he came across whether they had seen his People. He got a lot of shrugged shoulders, a lot of false hopes and no real promises.

Each day was endless. Each day was the same. Another winter passed. He became numb to the world. His heart barely kept a beat. His life had no real purpose.

He often asked himself, Why did I let her go? Anything would have been better than this endless waste of soul. She had a purpose. She had a plan. If only he hadn't been such a fool and had opened his heart up to her sons. At least he would have love.

He walked the land, looking for something, searching for fulfillment. He wanted a boy, a son. He had never received one. He wanted someone to talk to, to relate all the wisdom he knew. He had so much to tell, stories that dwelled in the darkness of his own mind, of how the sun rises and shines and how the moon with its beam would come back to be seen by all men's eyes.

He would have told the boy of the flight of the bird, the deer that was not heard, the buffalo as it roamed, the badger in its home. He would have told how the Great Lakes existed and the rivers flowed, and how a great hunt would let his spirit go.

Oh, how he searched for one woman of one time, to release the memories of his own mind and bear him a son.

But no. It was not to go that way. It went to another, the white man. He got the three. Windchimer seeked only one, and that man got three!

Was it of his true being that this had to happen to him? He had nothing to carry on his own life. Why did he not sow his heart with the purity of its own form? He said that he was born on this ground, this land that he loved. He had to give it to a son, so the sun from above could then free his spirit also, for once you give all the wisdom that you know, your heart and soul are free to go into the happy hunting ground. He had nobody to relate to.

He now knew that he must once again set out to search for his People, for the woman of his soul and for her sons, to tell them that he wished them joy also.

Now he was a man without a face, without a race. He had to go. He had to go. . . .

When Dancing Eagle was about to marry Morning Glory, Two Moons had given him a stone that was gold with a blue radiance to it. "If we should ever get separated in the trials to come, use this stone. It is a directional," Two Moons said as he handed it to him.

Windchimer recalled that at the time he only had one thing on his mind, and that was Morning Glory. It never occurred to him to ask more about the stone or how to use it. He just wasn't thinking about it at the time. In fact, he thought it an odd present for a wedding — but then, it was from Two Moons.

As Windchimer traveled across the land looking for his People, he remembered the stone and took it out of his pouch. He sat by the firelight and rotated it between his two palms. He was deep in thought as he twirled it about, with questions in his mind. Suddenly he realized that the answers seemed to be coming from the stone. There was a spirit in that stone!

"Where have my People gone?" he asked the stone.

"To where two peaks lie with a dark cloud hanging over them," it replied.

He did not know where this was. He roamed from tribe to tribe, from place to place, asking where the two peaks were. There were many twin peaks. He would have to try them all. He was a man without a home.

As he roamed from tribe to tribe, he would often sit in council. As he talked, he would roll the stone in his hands. Answers would come.

"He carried spirit!" they would say.

Windchimer was now the spirit of the name he carried. Whenever he sat in council or before a fire, he would finger the windbone necklace that Morning Glory had given him on their wedding night. He could always hear the wind chime through time. It always reminded him of her. His life now traveled with the wind.

The Eagle didn't come to him anymore. He could no longer carry the name of the Eagle, only the wind.

Windchimer would give prophecy to people in his travels. He told one chief that soon his light would be put out, meaning that his son would die. The son died.

Windchimer saw misery and pain in his travels. Everywhere he went, white man was sure to follow. The Indian was losing face wherever he roamed. In his visions he saw a village burning.

He screamed out, "The arms of the fatherless have been broken!"

As he traveled, he came upon the village from his vision. The braves had been killed. Children were orphaned. He led the survivors to another location out west, by a body of water, then continued on his travels.

Before council fires in the villages he journeyed to, he would speak fast and furiously. "I am like the fire out of your mouth that will absorb your being. It will take you as you see me," he would shout out.

Many would gather to hear him talk. There were times they didn't understand what he was talking about, but they sensed it was from spirit.

Windchimer would never stay in one place for very long. He was searching for his People. Occasionally he would be told that the blue-eyed princess had passed through. He would always seem to just miss them.

He would shout, "A black cloud always comes and takes her away from me!"

One elder said to Windchimer at a council fire, "Why are you so upset over the loss of a woman? We have many in our village. Take one."

Windchimer sighed deeply and hung his head for a while to compose himself. In a humble voice, very quietly, in front of many who had gathered to join him, he solemnly told his story.

> A long time ago, where my People had once lived, there arose from the water a woman who was guided by the stars. She was to be a princess among the tribes and bring all the red men back to the roots of the land and the Great Spirit.
>
> She walked among our People, proud and strong. She proved to our People that she was a promised one who could bring peace and harmony to the land of our fathers.
>
> Stories were told of how the Eagle had brought her from the sky and deposited her within our tribe. We were so proud the Eagle had chosen our tribe for her arrival.
>
> When it was time for her to be my bride, a great white serpent swept her away, bringing grief to our People.
>
> She returned years later, having lived among the white spirits, to resume her place within our tribe. Upon her escape, the wrath of the white man pursued our People.
>
> We had accepted the decision of the Great Spirit to separate our People from our homeland. I see the princess from the stars walking among the other tribes, teaching them the wisdom of our youth. We have not lost her forever, for our brothers of the plains will share, as we have, her beauty, wisdom and courage, for a future time.
>
> If you see this maiden, you will know that what we once had was indeed a gift from the stars, and that we have sacrificed much so others could experience her glory.
>
> Wherever she goes, you will know her, for she has gathered among her the animals of the Earth. We as spirits will follow the spirit of our homeland, no matter where we are.
>
> So praise her name and thank the stars for bringing one so precious to us.

Windchimer buried his head between his hands and said, "Ask me no more."

The council could feel his pain. Slowly, one by one, they got up and left him to sit alone by the fire.

CHAPTER 39

Windchimer saw several winters come and go as he traveled through this desert land. Much of his hair was streaked with the silver of wisdom. Part of an arrow shaft from the attack on the village was still in his left shoulder, and the shoulder frequently bothered him when he tried to raise his bow for hunting. His left side would often pain him, especially when he remembered the pain of his People. He never learned to love the desert but he roamed it endlessly, searching—constantly searching. He never accepted any village as his home. He was all alone.

His eyes were not as good as they used to be. The desert sun almost seemed to have burned them.

One evening as the sun started to turn red just before it set, Windchimer built a fire on the desert and fanned its flame until it leapt brightly. A curious-looking brave on an appaloosa horse appeared in the distance, riding toward him. Running ahead of the horse was a pug-nosed dog that the brave called Rattler.

As the rider approached, Windchimer thought, What a strange-looking brave—he doesn't seem to know if he is red or white! A feather hung from his derby hat. He had on white man's boots, but with snakes carved into them. And he was wearing a red, white and blue flag on his jacket!

The Indian gave him a crooked smile, showing a couple of missing teeth. "I am Taramenta, Chief of the Papago. The Army calls me Union Jack," he said with a sly smile as he pointed to his flag. He pointed to the black patch on his left eye. "White man call me One-Eyed Jack. Lost my eye scouting Apaches for the Cavalry."

Jack jumped down from his pony and rubbed his sore leg. He noticed that the brave before him was taller and leaner than most of the braves in this part of the country. He also noticed that the feather he wore was the feather of an eagle and that he dressed quite differently from the Indians of this area.

Windchimer greeted him with some hesitation. "I am Windchimer. You may join me by my fire." Jack noted the tongue to be the one used by Morning Glory and Two Moons.

From a distance Windchimer suddenly heard a commotion coming from behind a rock, much growling and thrashing about. A moment later, Jack's dog trotted out carrying a rattlesnake with its head bitten off!

Jack laughed, patted the dog and started to prepare the snake for dinner, giving the first morsel to the dog, in praise of its effort. He offered some to Windchimer.

"I see you wear an eagle feather," remarked Windchimer.

Jack's knife, with its bite of snake meat, stopped momentarily in midair. "There were some People in my village who wore them. I found the People in the desert a while back. This feather was a gift from them." Jack then smiled by curling the corner of one lip and continued his dinner.

Windchimer had to stop himself from sitting bolt upright. His heart began to pound in anticipation, and he decided to choose his words very carefully. For all his pleasant demeanor, Jack was a stranger to him, and he did not know his connections with the whites whose clothing he wore. He did not want to mention the name Dancing Eagle. He was still, after all, a hunted man for the killing of Tom Shaye.

With a quiet voice, looking down, Windchimer said, "I used to know a silver-haired one, a quiet brave. He was their leader. He often traveled with their princess. They have no home. They were a lost tribe."

Jack swallowed hard but tried not to show his alarm. He had heard of one called Dancing Eagle who was a past love of his Desert Moon. Could this be the man? Did this man come to take her away from him? Two Moons had told him of the heartbreak that she once had. Morning Glory never spoke of him. He knew the loss brought her much pain.

Jack had to think. His first thought was always to protect the blue-eyed one. His next thought was that she had told him that she never wanted anyone to know who she once was.

Jack had noticed that although the eyes of the brave before him were piercing, they were filled with loneliness and pain. Until

Morning Glory had come into his life, Jack had also known that kind of loneliness and pain. He could not bear to lose her and take on that pain again.

Slowly, while he continued to eat, Jack volunteered, "The silver-haired one left three moons ago. He took some of his People north, to the great mountain. I do not know where that is."

Windchimer jumped up and began to pace anxiously. "What of the princess?"

Jack would not look him directly in the eyes. He could see this man had searched far and wide for her. "I know of no princess. No one in that tribe ever called herself a princess."

In Jack's mind this was true. Not once had Morning Glory ever told him that she was a princess. It suddenly came to him that that title had only brought destruction to her and her People. It was something of the past. Jack did not like to lie; it was not part of his nature. But this wasn't a lie.

Windchimer still paced wildly. "Morning Glory? Was there one called Glory of the Morning? Was she with them?" he asked nervously.

"There was no woman who called herself by that name." Jack continued to eat without looking up.

Windchimer's shoulders drooped. He became despondent and had to ride. Again he had come close to finding his People but he was always a step behind. He walked over to his pony and jumped onto its bony back. "Thanks for the meat."

Jack called out, "There is a woman from your tribe who stayed behind. I shall tell her that you passed through. What did you call yourself again?"

"Call me Windchimer. I follow the wind."

When Jack got back to his village, he found his Glory at the fire, stirring beans in a big pot.

"I met a brave out in the desert. He wore an eagle feather and spoke your tongue."

Morning Glory's heart skipped a beat. Her palms became sweaty. "What was his name?" She was almost afraid to ask.

"He called himself Windchimer. Didn't have much to say."

Morning Glory continued to stir the beans and quietly said, "I know of no Windchimer . . . but then, I lost track of the life of the village when I was with Tom Shaye."

Morning Glory was almost relieved that it was not Dancing Eagle. She was with Jack now. She didn't know what she would do if Dancing Eagle came looking for her. Oh, how that man walked in her soul.

CHAPTER 40

Windchimer continued to wander, continued to search for Morning Glory and his People. No matter what he did, he just couldn't connect with them. The curse the Raven had laid upon his soul seemed to hold him in its grasp.

Everywhere he went in the desert plains, he saw loss of spirit, isolation and pain. People constantly reminded him of his own pain. He couldn't take it anymore.

Upon his knees, in the sand, he thrust his fist toward the endless sky and shouted out in vain, "I am brother to the wolves and companion to the owls!"

For days and days he wandered on. The sun parched his lips. The nights were cold. He felt that he was journeying round and round, as if there were no end. A moon had come; the moon had gone. Still he could not find the way to go.

One day his horse could go on no more. Its knees crumpled and it sank to the sand, dead. Far from any village, Dancing Eagle staggered across the endless desert floor. Finally, his knees buckled beneath him and he found his face in the sand. Only the wind was at hand, the wind that ever chimed.

He lifted his head up from the sand. His parched lips were cracked. His tongue was so large that he could not swallow. For a brief moment he thought he saw the White Buffalo People. His breaths continued to rasp in and out and in again. Were they coming to take him? No — it was not to be. The Creator would not take him home.

"Why not? Why not me?" he screamed into the land. "I don't want to be here anymore. I have nothing to live for. Take me. Take me . . . ."

He was so dry, tears would not even well in his eyes. His heart began to beat irregularly. He lost consciousness. When he awoke, it was nighttime.

Dancing Eagle struggled to sit up. There was no sound, no moon in the sky. He was in a void. No spirits talked to him. There were no thoughts in his head.

"What? Am I dead?"

But it was still not to be.

"O Creator, O Great Spirit, what have I done? Am I not from the Sun? Have I forgotten you?" Part of his mind said, Apparently I must have, for when I remember that I am with the Creator, I am never truly alone. The thought caught at his breath. "If I had held you in my heart, none of this would have happened from the start. We were told to move our tribe. We did not listen. We were told the princess would have great sons, but I thought they could only be from me. You never forgot me, but I forgot you."

With that, he saw something moving toward him in the night, soundlessly. He blinked his eyes. There before him stood a white buffalo! A shot of light hit him straight in the eyes, blinding him. He fell down and lost all sense of time. When he awoke it was sunrise. His hair showed even more streaks of silver!

An eagle flew over his head, squawked three times, tipped its wing and flew northwest. He knew that he was to head that way too.

He knew that he now connected again to the Great Spirit and that he was to help the Indians keep spirit. In his lifetime he had faced all things: hate, death, anger and greed. None of them brought him spirit. He had fought bravely for the land and for love, but it only brought him more pain and misery.

It was now that he began to realize that, yes, Morning Glory's sons were of the land, for there was a new plan. Not everything was of the red. Not everything was of the white. All hues were to come together again. The rainbow was at hand and with it came the pot of gold - not the gold of metal, but a golden hue. Oh, but he had been so bold, to think that the Creator didn't know what to do!

CHAPTER 41

Shadow Dancer became very restless in his new desert home. He did not like it there. Time after time, when supplies came to the village, the flour was full of bugs. The meat was spoiled. Time after time he would ride to the fort to complain. He was always told that an Indian agent would be sent to straighten out the matter.

"But what are my People supposed to eat until then?" he would shout. "I shall hunt like the true warrior that I am. My People will be provided for. It is my duty."

"You are not to leave that land, or you will be hunted down like the savage that you are," the agent would hiss at him.

Shadow Dancer went into a rage. In the past he had stolen cattle and horses from the white man, and they hadn't been able to catch him with the goods. Shadow Dancer was pretty crafty, but he was also angry.

Before his brother left, Two Moons had tried to talk to him about being one with spirit, allowing spirit to guide him.

"Don't talk to me about spirit, Two Moons," he had said. "Spirit is not putting meat in my People's bellies."

"But it could, if only you'd . . ."

Shadow Dancer had stalked away. He was in no mood to listen. It made no sense to him. He could only see that the white man was taking everything away. They were his enemy. He would make them pay.

The Army had Union Jack stalk a band of renegade Indians led by an Apache named Dog's Head. They were teamed up with a group of Comanches and Mexicans. The band stole horses and burned houses. The Cavalry had been out in the desert for a long time when Jack led them to an area called Clint's Well. Because he saved many men by finding water, they named a town after him. They called it Happy Jack.

Dog's Head was pretty crafty. Often he would go across the border and make raids. The Army wanted Jack to go across the border too, but he said, "No. Dog's Head is too crafty." The real reason he would not go was because he did not want to leave Morning Glory alone for too long. He felt responsible for her safety.

The Cavalry made a raid on the renegade Indians. The battle was desperate and many men lost their lives. During the raid Morning Glory had a vision that she was going to lose Jack. Jack felt her presence with him.

When Jack returned to the village, Morning Glory was very upset. He promised her he would go on no more missions. Jack had always said, "If ever there was a reason to live, it is Morning Glory." And he was true to his word.

He knew she had a mission and would have to travel from tribe to tribe. Now he could be with her and be her guide. He would show his love in that way.

Three seasons earlier, Two Moons had begun a journey north with the boys to look for the great mountain. They traveled many moons to the home of the Sioux, where Two Moons made friends with powerful leaders named Red Cloud and Iron Hand.

Long ago Schalute had told him that the People to the north were descended from the same ancestors as their People. Schalute had also made a journey to the north to be in council with the Sioux and to hunt and trade. Because the council from the Sioux nation had been impressed by Schalute's powerful, wise presence, his son Two Moons was made welcome also.

At last Two Moons felt the need to return to his People. He looked forward to Morning Glory seeing her sons again and he felt that Shadow Dancer was in trouble.

The boys had grown tremendously since they left the village. They walked with the spirit of their People and shared some of Two Moons' wisdom. They also walked with the spirit of the white man. Their hearts pulled them in both directions, causing them turmoil.

As the rays of the setting sun began to turn red in the west, three horses trotted into the village. The women looked up from their cooking fires, as did Morning Glory. Morning Glory dropped her stirring stick, wiped her hands on her skirt and ran toward the dust of the horses. As the boys dropped to the ground from their ponies, she gathered them together in a huddle and hugged them as one. She then stood back to admire their growth, and her smile showed she was pleased. Two Moons had quietly slipped away. She knew they would speak later, alone.

They all shared the evening meal together. Two Moons allowed the boys to chatter and share their adventures with their mother. When the boys slept soundly in their lodge, Morning Glory sought out Two Moons and found him sitting on a large rock on the outskirts of the village, facing the moon, his hair and skin shining from its rays. He always looked so mystical and calm.

She quietly sat down beside him, wrapping a blanket around their shoulders to keep out the night chill. "My sister," Two Moons addressed her, "the Sioux to the north have given their word that their lodges are open to our People if we choose to come. They are a powerful nation with much spirit. The plains are filled with buffalo. Food is abundant. Someday our People may want to seek refuge with their ancestral cousins."

Morning Glory listened. She would wait until spirit guided her before she would uproot her People again. They had been through too much already.

Two Moons and the boys stayed in the village for a season, then Two Moons knew he had to go on. Spirit called him to the mountains. Morning Glory also knew she had work to do among the villages so she again allowed Two Moons to take her boys. This time Chata went too. She would miss him terribly.

The Papagos were having an even harder time these days. Because Jack was no longer scouting for the Army, he was not readily able to get supplies as he used to. The People in the village knew Morning Glory was responsible for this, and many of the original inhabitants found it difficult to be pleasant with her.

By and by, a new Indian agent was assigned to their area. His name was William O'Toole and he was an object of scorn and derision. He wore spectacles, a dark suit and a flat, broad-rimmed hat. His dark clothes were always dusty from the desert sand. He was from the East and hated living in the desert.

Morning Glory watched him ride his horse. It amazed her that he didn't fall off daily. He never seemed to master the art of moving with the horse or sitting straight up. He crouched over, hanging on to the horn of the saddle. His stirrups were hiked up and he bounced so much that it seemed blisters must have been a daily affair. Often, his hat would fly off. He would have to dismount to fetch it, then struggle with the horse, trying to remount, as it circled about him. The horse always held its head up high, hoping to avoid the pull on the bit. O'Toole always seemed to be holding himself on the horse by hanging on the poor beast's mouth. She pitied the poor animal daily.

O'Toole had a habit of selling off reservation supplies for his own personal profit. When Shadow Dancer realized this, he became even more enraged. He continued to rustle cattle to feed his People. And because he had become a hunted man, he no longer lived in the village. The rangers were always looking for him. This distressed Morning Glory.

Food was becoming more and more scarce. Jack had heard that there was gold in Colorado. If they could find gold, he could use it to feed his People again. He talked it over with Morning Glory. She agreed to go with him, because under the circumstances they had been forced into, there was no hope left in the village. Once again, Jack's brother would be in charge during his absence.

Jack and Morning Glory headed out riding their two equipped horses, Jack on his appaloosa and Morning Glory on her bay mare. They had a pack mule loaded with supplies, and his dog, Rattler, in the lead.

Morning Glory and Jack settled in a peaceful valley called South Park, in the mountains of Colorado. Because winters were severe, with sometimes over three hundred inches of snow, Jack built a small, one-room cabin, in a small, protected valley, near a stream. A tepee would not hold up under three hundred inches of snow a season.

There was plenty of game to hunt and fish in the river. It wasn't long before Jack found gold in the rushing current. Each time he found a few flakes or nuggets, he would hide them in a safe place. Morning Glory did not even ask where he put them. She placed no value on those gold flakes. She didn't like them, except inasmuch as they promised food for the People. If it had not been for that, she would have scorned the gold altogether. They could not eat it, they could not warm themselves at night with it, but to have gold in their possession, people killed for it.

Morning Glory thought often of her People, Two Moons, and her sons. The boys were now grown and were out on their own. True to her word, Morning Glory had written to James Shaye from time to time, and now Nathanael was going to law school. His uncle James had given him the money for that. Thomas was all the way out to the western ocean; James had given him money to buy a boat. Young James was a scout for the Mormons, bringing people into Utah. Her boys had spread across the land, as she had known they would. Two Moons knew where to find them if he had to.

Morning Glory still moved with the natural, regal bearing that was always part of her, and retained her subtle beauty. She still maintained her slender stature and her quiet voice. Now, wisps of silver wisdom streaked her long blue hair.

For the most part, Jack and Morning Glory kept to themselves. There were few Indians panning for gold. Most of the miners were white. The whites didn't bother them much because more than once Morning Glory had helped heal the miners when they were injured or sick. Doctors were nonexistent there. Women were few and far between. Morning Glory never turned down a plea for help. Word got around, and the whites left them alone.

The air carried the frosty message that winter was soon to come. Golden leaves cascaded from the trees. The winds became increasingly colder.

One night Jack stood by the fire in their tiny cabin and stroked her beautiful hair. Solemnly he said to her, "Before you came to me, I had a dream that I was to guard you and be your protector. In my dream a golden-haired man came to me. He told me to sing praise to you and keep you warm during the winter nights, keep all love in your sight. He told me that you would come. Then you came one day and swept my heart away. I would ride my horse and talk to the stars and say, 'Of course. Of course, this is what is supposed to be, a course in my own destiny.'

"If you are as sly as the fox, you can succeed in a world of hate and greed. But you are from a loving heart and it is for that very reason that you succeed.

"Oh, loving eye, what is it from the sky that they want from you? They tell me to be your protector. What am I to have given to this world if I cannot give it to you? Oh, loving eye, I adore your face, your stature, your grace. I adore the life of you. Oh, loving eye, to be with you is to be free.

"In my dreams last night, I saw myself being taken away and given the gift of new life. But what happens to you, my love, the one I found in this desert as a flower? What happens to you? Will you now go on and become the peace of a dove?

"I haven't given you much, but what I have given you is love.

Of that you are deserving. The Earth has needed you.

"A gentle breeze sweeps all away. It sweeps away now into the seas of all harmonies."

Morning Glory sat quietly in awe. Jack had never expressed his thoughts or feelings at such length before. He had always served her and provided well for her and her People. She knew he loved her dearly, but he had never expressed his love in words before.

Morning Glory stood, turned quickly and embraced him. She could find no words. She simply held him for a long, long time.

Jack told nobody of his find. Too many men had died because they talked about their good luck. If you showed a few flakes here and there, you'd be all right, because almost everybody there found at least that. But if you had a big find, you did best to keep your mouth shut.

The great snows of winter were about to set in. They would need supplies to get them through. One morning Jack and Morning Glory rode down the mountain and into town to the general store. Indians were not usually welcomed there, but as long they could pay, they could get supplies. Jack and Morning Glory both spoke English, which helped pave the way. Jack often acted so ridiculous about being Christian that people would just shrug their shoulders when they saw him. They thought of him as no threat.

At the general store, two miners approached Jack. Lucius had a three-day beard and a couple of teeth missing. His teeth were brown from chewing tobacco. Tobacco stains covered his sleeves, as he routinely wiped the juice from the corner of his mouth. His pants, held up by suspenders, were two sizes too big on him. He wore high boots for river panning.

Ben was taller than Lucius and a bit younger. He had a foul mouth and a bad temper. He had no time for courtesy. A long rifle was always at his side. He sported a mustache, and his dark, greasy hair hung to his shoulders. He wore a broad-rimmed hat that carried a couple of bullet holes and lots of dust. As he walked on the wooden porch of the store toward Jack and Morning Glory, he dragged his heels noisily.

"Jack, old Union Jack, what in tarnation are you doin' all the way down here, you old coot?" Ben said as if they were best friends.

Jack knew these two were up to no good. The last he had seen them, they were conniving to get by on the desert by cheating and lying. He played his routine. "Me part land. Me go where people go. No problem."

They both slapped Jack on the back and bade him adieu.

"That sly old fox," Lucius said when the two were out of earshot. "I heard they paid him well for all the scouting he did. Heard they paid him in cash, too. He could find anything under the sun. Bet he even found gold up there — lots of it. Let's follow him, see where he's goin'. I bet he's got a stash up that mountain."

Heavy snow clouds had been gathering throughout the morning, and the early afternoon sun could no longer be seen. Large flakes of snow began to fall. Jack and Morning Glory headed for home before the going got too hard for the horses.

Ben and Lucius saw Jack and Morning Glory ride toward the mountain pass. They stayed out of sight and waited a bit. They knew all they had to do was follow the tracks in the snow up the mountain.

The tracks led Ben and Lucius right to their little cabin. They hid in the woods and bided their time. The snow stopped, the clouds parted and the night was lit by moonlight. Smoke poured from the chimney.

The pair shivered through the night, waiting for the right moment. As the sun rose, they could hear the cabin door creak open. Jack carried his rifle. He was going hunting for fresh meat. He wanted to bring in another buck before the deep snows set in.

As Jack headed in the opposite direction in the bright sunlight, Lucius swatted Ben on the arm to gain his attention. "Perfect. Jack is gone. Wouldn't want to mess with him. He's a fightin' man, knows his way with a rifle and knife. He left his woman behind, though. She would know. We can get out of her where the stash is."

Morning Glory was cooking over the fire in the fireplace. Suddenly the door burst open. Two men with cold eyes stood before her. Her blood turned cold. They were so bold. She knew this was trouble!

Lucius spit out his chaw upon her floor.

"Where's the stash, squaw? We know you and Jack have one. Just fork it over and we will leave you alone. There's plenty more of that stuff around here. You can just get more. Come on, honey, don't give us no trouble."

Morning Glory's heart pounded. She could hardly speak. "I know of no stash. He tell me not what he do."

Ben stepped forward and with the back of his hand knocked her across the room. Glory stumbled to her feet, blood trickling from the corner of her mouth.

"Don't waste your time, Ben," Lucius told him. "I know how to get through to these Indians. They believe that you feel spirit from the souls of your feet. All we have to do is burn her feet. She'll talk plenty fast."

They dragged her outside and Lucius held her as she struggled while Ben tied her to a tree. They gathered wood and straw and began to build a large fire at her feet. When she kicked away the wood, they tied her feet together.

Morning Glory closed her eyes and prayed to the Creator to help her as the mound of twigs and branches grew. She couldn't understand why she couldn't be left alone. She'd never bothered anybody. She and Jack were just trying to survive. Lucius put a match to the outer edges of the wood and smoke puffed into the air.

Stalking the buck he had spotted earlier, Jack felt that something was wrong back at the cabin. He had begun to head back when he saw smoke. Fire! he thought and ran back as fast as his legs could carry him. Before he reached the brow of the final hill, he ducked down and looked over.

He saw Morning Glory tied to a tree, with the fire about to reach her. Two men were standing in front of her, laughing. They were actually laughing! He went wild, cocked his rifle and shot. One man fell. The other man looked up, saw him and ran into the trees.

Jack barreled down the hill and kicked the fire away from Glory. Tears were running down her cheeks. She did not fear death, but fire, yes! Dropping his rifle to the ground, he untied her, hugged her tight, picked up the rifle and was about to pull her into the safety of the cabin when he heard a rifle cock behind him.

"Put the rifle down, Jack, or I'll shoot her!"

Jack dropped the rifle and spun around.

"Old Lucius, you desert rat. Always knew you were scum," Jack seethed.

Lucius circled around Morning Glory and grabbed her from behind, one arm across her throat, the rifle to her head.

"Where's the stash, Jack? I'm not foolin' around. You've got till I count to three, or I'll blow her brains clear through."

Jack knew that Lucius wasn't likely to let either one of them live. With one sweep he reached for the knife in his boot. A shot rang out—Jack fell lifeless to the ground.

Morning Glory screamed, an incredible scream that roared

through the mountains, echoed back and forth and reverberated back to them. She dropped to her knees and threw herself over his body. She surely would have given her life before she would let another die for her. Not Jack! Oh, not Jack . . .

The neighbors' dogs over the hill began to bark. Cold, brittle branches could be heard snapping back as someone was rushing through the trees. Lucius took off toward the river, jumped into Jack's homemade canoe and traveled the rapids downstream.

Jim Wolf, a half-Indian friend of Jack's, ran toward Morning Glory where she still bent over Jack's body. They were to hunt together this morning. When Jack hadn't met him halfway, Jim had started toward their site and heard the crack of rifles.

"What have they done? Not Jack," Jim said, shaking his head.

Jim knew the Indian way. Morning Glory had to have some time to grieve for Jack. She had to sing him home with her chants.

Morning Glory rocked back and forth with Jack in her arms until his body started to stiffen. Then she knew his spirit had left.

Her mind went back to the time so many years ago when this crazy, heart-driven man rode up to her in wonderment.

"You are the one I have been looking for," he'd said. "You are the one I am to provide for and keep in my heart."

And so he did, like no other man could. Now they had taken him away too.

Morning Glory cut off her hair with Jack's knife. She took off the necklace that she wore, tied her hair with it and put it in his hands, which she had crossed over his heart. Jim Wolf helped Morning Glory dig a grave. Jack was buried with his flag, his Bible and his eagle feather. He was truly a man of the land. He had worked hard to bring peace to his People. He was a man like no other. She wanted so much to bring Jack back to his People; he was their chief. But it was not possible; it was too far. They buried him by a tree, near the stream, upon this mountain with its soaring hawks and eagles.

Jim Wolf encouraged Morning Glory to leave quickly. A white man had been killed, and the white man's law would soon come. He didn't want her to face the wrath of the white man's law.

She wanted to stay by Jack's grave and mourn him for days, but she couldn't even do that. Numbly, she packed her few belongings. Jim Wolf and Morning Glory packed their horses with provisions and their belongings and headed back toward the village in the desert. The days were now becoming cold in the mountains and the nights even colder. It was a gray, overcast day, with snow clouds hanging low over the mountain peaks when they left.

Morning Glory was in so much emotional pain that she didn't feel the cold and biting wind as their horses plodded through the deep snow of the mountain passes.

Morning Glory rode a buckskin mare, which she dearly loved. Jack's dog and her dog trotted alongside them. Jim Wolf had a bay gelding that was beginning to show age. Its breathing became labored in these high mountain passes. They could not travel very fast, for fear that the horses would lose their footing, but they pressed on. Oftentimes the snow was so deep that they had to put the dogs on the backs of their horses and carry them.

Morning Glory's eyes peered through the blanket that she kept over her head and shoulders. Jim simply bowed the rim of his hat down when the wind gusted and kept the fur collar on his old coat turned up around his ears. Jim mourned Jack's loss too. Jack had been his closest friend in these mountains. It was a long ride home.

When Morning Glory returned to the village with her hair cut off, they knew their chief was dead. As she and Jim rode solemnly into the center of the village, the women began to wail.

The People of the village had hopeless looks upon their faces. She saw even more desolation than when she had left. Their eyes were sunken and their expressions were hollow. Their spirits were gone. What had happened?

A council meeting was called. Morning Glory was instructed to speak. She told them of Jack's bravery and how she wished she had been the one the Eagle had taken away, not Jack.

Desert Bird then boldly spoke before the council.

"This woman took our chief from us. In his absence many of our People have starved because we no longer received enough supplies," she explained as she began to shuffle with rage.

"This woman, who is not even from our village, has brought us extra mouths to feed. We cannot even feed our own. She must leave. She has only brought destruction to our People and death to our village. Her People should leave our village now."

Morning Glory's heart was heavy. She held her head in shame. What this woman was saying in anger had truth to it, but what was she to do with her People? Jack had tried to provide for all. Now he was gone.

Morning Glory was in shock. She would, of course, leave first thing in the morning and take her People with her. She would head north. Two Moons had told her they would be welcomed there.

The People from the village, in their desolation, had forgotten all that Morning Glory and Two Moons had done for them, the sick they had healed, the wisdom they had brought. Now they spoke from their empty stomachs. She understood. Without Jack, there was no purpose for her to be there.

Morning Glory addressed the council humbly. Then she asked desperately, "Has anyone heard from Two Moons or Shadow Dancer?"

Members of the council hung their heads in shame. Gray Feather spoke through the few teeth he had left in his mouth. "Shadow Dancer has been arrested by local authorities. He was accused of killing our Indian agent, O'Toole. He was seen at a saloon near the fort fighting with O'Toole over missing supplies. The next day O'Toole was found dead. They blamed Shadow Dancer. They will probably hang him!"

Morning Glory shot to her feet. Her heart pounded mercilessly in her chest. "Does Two Moons know?"

Gray Feather again answered. "Two Moons went north to find your Chata, who has been studying the white man's law and is almost done with school. Two Moons feels that he is Shadow Dancer's only chance in the white man's court. He knows the law and he looks white."

"Where did they take Shadow Dancer?" Morning Glory asked in a voice that was barely audible.

"He will have a big trial; they will make an example of him. We do not expect to see him ever again. White man will not let him win."

"I don't know what to do. I need to take my People north. I need to see my brother one last time. How can I do both?"

Jack's brother rose and walked toward Morning Glory, putting his arm around her shoulder. "You are only one woman. You cannot help your brother now but you can help your People. Two Moons will do what he can for Shadow Dancer. You do what you can for the rest of your People. You do not want to be involved with the white man's law now. There's nothing you can do. They wouldn't let a squaw into court anyway. Take care of your People."

Morning Glory nodded numbly. She didn't know how much more pain her heart could bear. It never seemed to end.

CHAPTER 42

Shadow Dancer had been held under heavy guard. Officers from surrounding forts were ordered to attend the trial. The officers were then to bring word back to the villages they supervised, telling them what happens to Indians who kill agents.

Nathanael had grown to be a tall, extremely handsome young man. With his blond hair and blue eyes he could almost pass for a white man. The shape of his nose and his copper skin were the only giveaways. He had almost finished law school. His uncle James had kept his promise and provided him with a white man's education. And Two Moons had taught him the Indian way of nature. He was an impressive man.

Two Moons was allowed to visit Shadow Dancer only once before the trial. When he walked into Shadow Dancer's cell, he was heavy of heart. Shadow Dancer sat on a straw-covered floor, his hands and feet in heavy chains.

Shadow Dancer pulled himself heavily to his feet and dragged his way toward his brother.

"Two Moons, oh Two Moons, you have come to help me. Tell them, Two Moons! Tell them I did not do this thing."

Two Moons hung his head in despair. "I warned you of your path long ago. You carry the fire of our father. I tell you now, this is the same. I saw this in my father's eyes. I see it in yours now. Shadow Dancer, you have paved your own path. There were many witnesses, my brother. This could be your end."

Shadow Dancer pleaded with his brother, "No! I don't want to go this way. Protect me now. Take my life. That's the best way. You take my life. Father would want it that way. Don't let them take it. Don't let them . . . . Don't turn me over to them. You know it will be my end."

Two Moons embraced him. "You know I cannot do that. I cannot kill my own brother." He turned and looked over his shoulder past the bars and the guard. "There is another here who loves you to the end." He signaled to the guard, who rose from his stool and opened the cell door. Two Moons walked out. Turtle Woman walked in.

Turtle Woman embraced Shadow Dancer, sobbing. Shadow Dancer fought back his own tears and pulled back to see her face one last time.

"Go now and forget me. I am from the past. The Eagle shall return upon my death, giving my People freedom again."

On a sweltering summer day, young Nathanael tried his best to defend Shadow Dancer. He explained that the People were starving. He told how O'Toole had taken their supplies for his own profit. They didn't believe him. He explained how Shadow Dancer's People were a lost tribe without a home. The whites didn't care.

Nathanael gave evidence showing that an Indian from another tribe was paid by the whites to kill O'Toole. He showed that O'Toole was not only stealing food but also buying up Indian land with the money from his theft. The whites did not care. Shadow Dancer was an Indian. A white man was dead. The final decree was that Shadow Dancer was to hang at first light.

In his cell that night, Shadow Dancer sang his death song. His chants were carried by the whispering wind throughout the fort.

During the night his deceased relatives came to him one by one to give him praise. They said, "You will be with us soon, so hold your head high."

Then came Schalute, looking at him sternly. "You have now disgraced my name!"

"But Father, you fought the white ones. You said that this is the way it was to be!"

Schalute shook his head and said, "I didn't want you to hang from a tree! You should have gone out in honor."

Shadow Dancer said, "Father, forgive me. I have caused you so much trouble and so much pain, so much agony in your name."

A drum beat a stern tattoo. Soldiers entered his cell. With his hands in chains, Shadow Dancer was led toward an old tree with a heavy, overhanging branch from which a rope hung down.

As the small group passed Two Moons in the courtyard,

Shadow Dancer turned to him one last time. "Kill me now," he pleaded. "Don't let me die this way!" Two Moons bowed his head in shame. He couldn't.

Marshall Bill Wendt was the agent who had brought Shadow Dancer in. The drums rolled. Shadow Dancer was put on a sorrel gelding, and Wendt placed the rope around his neck. The gelding was struck on its haunches and bolted forward. Wendt laughed as Shadow Dancer's neck snapped.

Turtle Woman screamed out a curse: "When the spirit seeks the eyes of one, the love-lost summon has begun. The crime for which my man had to pay will find its way back to you!" She was grabbed by the soldiers and pushed away.

Two Moons came to her side and took her into his arms as she sobbed. They went together to cut Shadow Dancer down from the tree.

It has been said that Marshall Wendt was later shot in the back of the head by unknown assailants in the streets of Laredo, after winning at an all-night poker game at a saloon called the Hangman's Noose.

Two Moons and Turtle Woman buried Shadow Dancer and sang his spirit back home. They then headed north to Red Cloud's village. Word had been sent to them that Morning Glory and their People were headed that way.

Nathanael stayed on. The white man wanted to take even more land away for the railroad. He would fight it and represent the red man from now on. His mother's blood beat in his heart.

Turtle Woman died during their journey north. Her heart was broken. She could no longer go on.

CHAPTER 43

Two Moons traveled alone and arrived at Red Cloud's village before Morning Glory arrived with their People.

Two Moons spoke before the council fire that night.

"Mighty Red Cloud, I speak to you and your council this night. My sister and the remnants of my People are heading this way seeking shelter. They are mostly women and children, a few braves. That is all that is left of my People. Would you welcome them to your lodges?"

Red Cloud spoke. "Our village is large. Our People are strong. Our braves are proud hunters. Your People would not be a burden to us. We would be honored."

Two Moons nodded his head once in agreement.

Red Cloud continued. "I understand that your sister with blue eyes came from the sky."

Two Moons did not reply.

"I heard that she has the markings of the blue star!"

Still he made no sign.

"I heard that she came the same year as a fireball shooting across the sky. Surely she must be a special one!"

Two Moons took a deep breath and again stood quietly. He looked down. There was an uneasiness within the council; they were not sure what to make of his silence. Then, in a quiet voice, he spoke stern and solemn words. "My sister does not wish to be truly known. It makes her job so much harder. Because of her blue eyes, she cannot wear a disguise. Because of her beauty, the men all want her to be their prize. Because of that, many have died.

"She is not here to be one man's squaw, but when she walks about, that is every man's talk. I must protect her and honor her and her three blond sons with blue eyes!"

The council was surprised. Schalute's princess had sons from white-eyes! How could this be?

"She was taken from our arms and our hearts by the man who destroyed our village. Because of his obsession with her, many men died. Now she feels that she must hide."

Two Moons paused. The council circle watched him soberly as they waited for his next words. "What my father, Schalute, did not realize, was that the future lies within these sons of the white-eyes. It is written in the stars. In order for us to survive we must learn to live with the white-eyes." He went on:

> Morning Glory produced three white sons to show the white man the true spirit of the Indian way. Who better to make changes than the three sons — so that the red can live with the white? Who better than they to go into the white man's world and teach the true feeling of spirit that finds honor in the red man? The white must teach the white . . . not just through the black robe but through true totality of spirit. That is why the Creator saw fit to have our princess produce sons of the sun through the white-eyes. The red in them will cleanse the land through the fire and flame they represent. The white in them will reach the white. These boys will spread across the land with their mother's spirit in their blood.
>
> Do we dare to question the ways of the Creator? Do we think that the Creator does not have a plan greater than our own? All are brothers from the Creator.
>
> First we must teach spirit to the white man. It will be a slow process, but the boys that Morning Glory brought forth are part of the plan.
>
> I must ask the council, before I bring her in, to honor us by not talking of her at the council fires of others. She is not to be known yet. It only brings trouble. She asks to be allowed to live in your lodges but without any special attention. She will quietly walk and heal among your People. In return, she only asks that she not be known. Do you agree?

Red Cloud spoke with authority. "We will make our decision when your sister arrives. First I must look into her eyes and then I will know."

Two Moons nodded and excused himself from the council fire. He walked into the night, his hair glowing under the moon, and disappeared from view over the hill. He was not seen for three more days and nights. When he returned to the village, Morning Glory and her band of People were arriving.

Morning Glory simply looked at Two Moons, too weary to run up and embrace him, too sick at heart to show any emotion.

Two Moons looked upon her thin, weary frame. He had never seen her so thin before. Her face was drawn, and dark circles lay under her eyes. Her moccasins had worn through. Her feet were bound in rags, as were those of the rest of her band of People. As they walked into the village, his heart went out to them all.

Within her band of People was the face of a young brave that bothered him even more. Black Wolf, the son of the Raven, had grown to manhood. He had been with Shadow Dancer's band, but since the misplaced band had merged with the rest of the clan, he was now among Morning Glory's People. Black Wolf had the eyes of the Raven. Two Moons was concerned.

Those who lived in the village came to the village circle. Morning Glory's band had been expected for days, and they were prepared for them. The village women walked up to the People, embraced them and took them off one by one to join them in their lodges for shelter and food.

Morning Glory was left standing alone with Two Moons. Red Cloud's daughter approached her, carrying the gift of a white doeskin dress decorated with much beading and fringe.

Red Cloud's daughter, Nia, was younger than Morning Glory and much shorter in stature and she beamed with a beautiful, compassionate smile. Morning Glory immediately felt a bond with her and couldn't help smiling back. Nia brought her to a lodge that Red Cloud had prepared especially in her honor. A basket of berries, cooked meat and cornmeal awaited her. As Nia was about to leave Morning Glory to rest and eat, she turned on her heel and said, "You shall be a Sun Flower in our village. You are a flower that grows under the light of the sky."

Morning Glory fell to her knees and buried her head in her hands. In a cloud of weariness, she allowed herself to mourn the loss of Jack, who had died protecting her. She mourned the loss of her brother Shadow Dancer. She mourned the loss of Dancing Eagle, who had never left her heart in all these years. She mourned the loss of her family members and her entire village. When would it end? Would there be no peace or harmony upon the land again?

She was almost too tired to eat but she forced herself to pick at the food. She closed her eyes and brought Dancing Eagle to her mind. Where was he now? What had his life been like all these years? Did he think of her, as she thought of him? She lay down on the soft bearskin rug and drifted off into memory.

On the day after the arrival of Morning Glory and her People, the beat of the drum announced the gathering of the council. Two Moons sat within the lodge as sage and sweetgrass cleansed all within the structure. Prayers were offered to the six directions. Red Cloud spoke.

"Two Moons, we of the council request that you now bring your sister before us. You asked silence of our People for her protection. To ask silence of an entire village is asking a great deal, for if one of our People were to break that silence, there would be a penalty to pay, perhaps even death.

"The council would have to enforce the ruling. We of the council must know that your sister is truly exceptional before we enforce the law of silence. We must be sure of her worth first."

Two Moons spoke not but stepped outside of the tepee and reentered with his sister. She was greeted at the entrance by one offering her a cleansing of sage and sweetgrass, which she readily accepted, pulling the smoke toward her and asking the Creator for his blessing.

Two Moons quietly sat down, while she stepped into the middle of the circle, courteously looking down. Glory stood before the council wearing the white doeskin dress. A single eagle feather stood straight up at the back of her head, held in place by a beaded headband.

She stood before them, taller than most of the women, more regal than any they had seen before. She was finely built and very slender. Her long black hair was almost blue and worn in long braids.

Red Cloud stepped toward her. He reached out with his hand and gently lifted her face. When she looked into his eyes, his hands began to tremble. Even though years before he had heard from Schalute of the beauty of her spirit and the gentleness of her heart, he was not prepared for what he saw. Spirit flew straight from her eyes. She truly could wear no disguise. He could only cup his hand and hold the side of her face.

Red Cloud found it difficult to talk. With a raspy voice he said, "Woman, you are truly from the stars. This will be your home. We will protect you. Your presence will never be known, I promise you that. You and your brother honor our village. Our lodges will be your home forever."

Red Cloud turned to the council and said, "Is this not so? Do I speak for everyone before this council fire?"

All before him acknowledged his decision, especially the medicine man, who could see a buffalo woman before him, although he did not speak of it at this time.

Morning Glory turned to the council and softly spoke. "I am honored to be in your village. My People have needed a home for a long, long time. I will try to serve your village by whatever means the Creator will allow.

"I thank you for the law of silence. If it is not faithfully observed, death could well follow, as it has so many times before. If anyone comes to the village and asks of the blue-eyed one, I do not exist. The one called Glory of the Morning no longer exists. This I ask, for the safety of your People."

The council members all agreed. They knew that among other Indian villages, she would be sought as a prize. They knew that her beauty would be sought also by white men's eyes. Her presence in the village must be kept secret for the protection of the People.

Those who had accompanied Morning Glory happily settled within the comforts of Red Cloud's village. Two Moons and Morning Glory worked diligently within the village. Two Moons was noted for his ability to negotiate with the white man. He could speak English and settle many disagreements with amazing deftness. He became a liaison among the villages on the plains. Morning Glory quickly became known for her healing ability.

No one in the village called them by their original names. Two Moons was often called Walking Straight. Morning Glory was often called Sun Flower. However, both of them were known by many names. Wherever they went they would answer by a different name so their presence would not become known.

Many white men would come through the plains of the Dakotas, often in wagons with white, billowy clouds on them. Two Moons would often ride alone and hide within the trees, watching these cumbersome, ungiving, stiff boxes being pulled over land, causing the boxes to bounce from side to side or up and down. He wondered at the discomfort of the people inside them, peeking out, holding on so as not to bounce out.

He wondered why they carried so much with them instead of

allowing the Creator to provide for them as they journeyed. It seemed that they made it harder for themselves.

He also watched from the hills as the whites would come in numbers and slaughter their sacred buffalo by the hundreds, leaving the life-giving carcasses to rot under the sun and feed the flies. He watched them kill the young calves too so that they could not grow and produce more. He watched them kill the prime breeding females so that they could never replace themselves by giving birth to more. He could not understand what they were thinking of. He knew that when you disrespect what the Creator has provided for you, it will be taken away.

As the seasons came and left, the buffalo were killed with such mass destruction that they could not replace themselves. Entire herds were destroyed, debasing both the sacred animals and the sanctity of the land upon which they grazed. What few were left were scattered at great distances. The People did not have enough hides to make their clothing or their tepees, or enough meat to smoke to last through the winter snows.

Sun Dog, the medicine man, fasted for four days and nights and went into the sacred hills for vision. He was an old one. His father and grandfather before him had also been gifted medicine men. It was in his blood. His concern now was that food for the People was becoming scarce. He prayed to the Creator for help.

On the fourth day Sun Dog sat upon his blanket on the side of a high hill. Lightning struck repeatedly into the hills surrounding him, but he did not move from his blanket. He no longer felt the thirst that parched his throat. The sky blackened around him. Winds whipped his thin gray hair across his face. He did not move.

Suddenly the winds stopped. He could see something white coming toward him from a distance. At first his vision was hazy. He blinked his eyes and pushed his hair away from his face. He saw a buffalo. The buffalo was being led by a woman in a white buckskin dress. As the vision drew nearer, he could see the woman's face: it was Morning Glory. She turned away from him and pointed as more buffalo appeared. Then she turned back to him, smiled, bowed her head in respect and disappeared. Before him stood three buffalo, grazing peacefully near his blanket. Sun Dog thanked the Creator for such a clear sign, gathered up his blanket and returned to the village.

A council meeting was called. Sun Dog spoke before them. He felt truly blessed, for he had seen who Morning Glory truly was.

Because of the law of silence, he could not fully expose what his vision meant to him. He knew he had to protect her. As the others watched him, he chose his words carefully.

Sun Dog spoke softly. His voice was still raspy from his fast. His thin body was stiff with age. It was difficult for him to sit entirely straight but he sat this day with some pride, for he knew what he had seen.

"My brothers, our prayers have been answered. The Creator has shown me that we have one among us who can call the buffalo forth. She has blessed us with her presence. We have blessed her with our silence. She is our Flower from the Sun!"

Two Moons sat in silence, as usual. He rarely offered advice unless asked. He almost never talked of his sister.

"Two Moons," Red Cloud asked, turning to him, "is this so? Do we have a buffalo woman in our midst?"

Two Moons took his time to speak. "My sister is but a messenger of the Creator. If the Creator wishes to grant a blessing, my sister is a messenger of His blessings. She can provide only what the Creator allows. She is of service to the Great Spirit."

"Two Moons," Red Cloud said with resolve, "bring your sister before this council fire. We will ask her to bless our village in a new way. If she consents, we will have a ceremony tomorrow at first light."

Two Moons quietly rose and left the lodge. Within a short time he returned with his sister. She stood before the council and waited to be addressed.

Red Cloud spoke. Whenever he was in her presence, his usual boisterous voice became a gentle whisper. "Sun Dog's vision for the feeding of our People showed you as a buffalo woman, able to call the buffalo for the benefit of our People. Will you help us feed our People?"

Morning Glory stood motionless for a while. She wanted to express herself properly. "If the Creator has chosen me to call the buffalo, then I will do my best. I will do as He directs me."

Red Cloud said, "With the beat of the drums, we shall have a ceremony to call in the buffalo. We shall do the buffalo dance as our Flower from the Sun calls to them with a voice only the buffalo can hear."

The beat of the drums called the People to the village circle. A fire was built within the circle. The smell of sage from the desert, which Morning Glory brought with her as a gift to the council, permeated the air. The rhythm of the dance was picked up by the dancers, who wore horned buffalo heads and capes of buffalo hides.

Morning Glory sat within the circle. The drumming took her into an altered state of consciousness. She was unaware of the multitude of People around her. She chanted to the Creator for His help in finding the buffalo. When she saw them in her vision, she called to them to be of service, to allow themselves to help mankind. She asked them to come forth and be seen.

In her vision she saw a small herd separating from a larger herd. The smaller herd grew to about seventy-five head. None of the herd contained young ones or breeding stock. They were the ones that were ready to depart this plane.

"Come closer, precious ones, so my People can find you. We promise to honor you and give you grace. We will not waste or disgrace any part of your being. You will be of service to the Creator."

She saw them wander over the hills and plains of their sacred land, heading in the direction of their village. They stopped. Morning Glory rose from her position. The drums ceased. The dancers looked her way.

She looked with composure toward a band of braves. Her voice was clear. "You may get your mounts and put your quivers on your back. Our sacred buffalo will be a half-day's ride north of here, behind a cliff, near the water's edge. They will be there by the next sunrise." She bowed her head and quietly walked away.

When the sun had risen and set three times, a large band of braves returned, whooping and hollering. Their ponies' backs were burdened with meat and hides. The dogs were barking. The women were proud. They had food and hides to help them get by. A ceremony of thanks would be offered that night.

As the seasons came and went, Red Cloud truly fell in love with Morning Glory. He already had a wife but he would have taken on another if she consented.

Morning Glory had said, "I cannot belong to any man, although I am truly honored. There seems to be a curse on me that brings pain and death to every man that takes me for a wife. From this point on, I live only to serve the Creator. If I do that, the curse will not follow me."

Red Cloud honored her with many presents. Often they would sit and talk by the riverside, her favorite place to be. They would talk of the coming of the white man, the changing of the land, and spirit.

He was surprised at her wisdom and knowledge. He knew of no other woman who had traveled the lands as she had, who knew so many languages, who could read and write the white man's language, and who could heal. Both she and Two Moons served in many ways. They always did it quietly so as not to bring attention to themselves. It was the only way they could work without bringing harm to anyone.

Two Moons was often welcomed into the council meetings within the Sioux nation. He became good friends with Iron Hand, as he traveled from village to village. He always worked to bring peace between the Indian and the white man. He knew it was the only way, if any were to survive. He also knew there would be many trials and tribulations.

CHAPTER 44

Dancing Eagle, now known as Windchimer, continued to travel across the land looking for Morning Glory and his People.

He still carried with him the two hollowed-out bones from the shoulder of a buffalo that had been gifted to him by Morning Glory on their wedding night. When Windchimer would climb a peak and stand facing the wind, the wind would howl through the bones, causing them to shake. He would do an ecstacy dance, moving his spirit upward. He had powerful medicine with these bones.

If someone from a village came to him with a problem, he would go into a dance, whirling, twirling, saying, "All of your problems go to the wind. I release all to the wind!"

One of his greatest joys was to sit by the fires at night and tell stories. He would start out by leaning back, fingering and twirling his special stone. At first the words would come softly. The listeners around the fire would lean forward to hear him. Louder and louder the words would start to dance in their heads — words of wisdom, reminiscences from the past. He talked to the wind so the spirit could then talk to him. Spirit would sit as a friend at his campfire.

He would tell stories of a past life, and histories of his childhood, so the children would learn. "The Indian spirit doesn't have to die," he told them. "If you carry the frame of the stories within the eye and always pass them on, this will keep us, the race, alive."

In his stories he embedded a seed of thought about the races together, so that the future might become a glorious plant from a seed in the past. Very true to his nature. He was directed by spirit to do this.

His stories told the tales of the suns and the moons in the sky. The listeners would sit transfixed. Then spirit would wait and listen as they in turn would tell tales of woe, hate and despair. After that, Windchimer would tell them a story of love and joy, beauty and harmony. The children would sing and dance and say all things are free because that is the way life is.

This night he closed his eyes and spoke of times past; he told of visions as they flashed before his eyes. Windchimer had a golden tongue. The People did not always understand what he was saying, but he would entrance them, young and old alike. The words would just flow.

> With these eyes I have seen the spirit from the skies, hovering in these trees, these skies, these deeds, these lodges, these things. I say, I know because I and the Creator are one!
>
> As I have spoken from the Sun, I have spoken before on these very lands to the tribe that mellowed in the meadow days. The forest was alive with game. The birds would fly hither and come and sing in the trees. We would all praise the spirit for fulfilling our needs.
>
> The mighty council would sit, twelve brave men, and make decisions and judgments. With the heart they would speak. We would formulate a new way of making a day.
>
> The tribal hunt was a celebration. Campfires bright, lit by the night. Talk of love, forlorn in the night. Starry night, beautiful heavens that glowed. The braves would ask what made that so.
>
> The wise old man sat there and shook his head. "Don't you know the spirit is not dead? Spirit produces these things, all the stars and lights you see. That spirit is pure form that comes from my eyes to see."

Windchimer was wise beyond his days. When he would speak this way, the People would listen to the rhythm of his words, understanding with their hearts.

The children came near. He would say, "What do you fear? Little ones, come to me. Sit. I shall teach thee. Come. Come, everyone. I talk. I speak. I talk through spirit. Can you see? I am the one who knows the spiritual light. Come to me, day and night. Come. I beat the drum. Come, be as one."

They would gather and sit near, like a grandfather whose spirit would hear. He would roll his head. His eyes would shine.

"Spirit, spirit, love of mine. Speak through me so I can tell these children what to see in thine eyes."

With a roll of thunder and a sharp clap, the sky would open. Spirit would shake its mighty wings and say, "Now, this man has seen." The children would sit back and say, "Ah, heavens above. The sky is open. It gives love."

Spirit would take its form and sit next to the man. Hand in hand, they would say that no one rules the land.

"O spirit, from thy deepened heart, come back and make a new start upon this land, for we are all part of everything."

When he fell silent, the children would beg him, "Tell us more, Windchimer. We do not want to go."

He told the story of the great bear who walked and talked and sniffed the air but whose claws were of the gentlest touch.

> Bear was a friend of man, and he came down the mountain one day to tell the story of what he had seen and of the spirits that played on the peaks.
>
> The Indian chiefs all sat in a circle and listened to the great bear, listened to the sound of his garbled voice, the truth that was of his choice and the words that were true to his being. The great bear would tell what he had seen.
>
> Bear told the chiefs in the circle that he had been looking for the great beehive on the side of a high mountain. As he hunted he looked upward beyond the trees where dancing lights had begun to tease the afternoon sun. The lights grew brighter and swept through the trees as the air would flow. The great bear wanted to know with his nose what was happening there.
>
> He lumbered up the side of the hill and when he reached the top he saw that everything was still. The stars of the night did blink, and the bear's eyes would turn from red to pink. He would sniff the sweetness in the pure air. He knew that something spiritual was there.
>
> Then he saw three beings circling, beings that knew of animal, plant and mineral forms, each speaking the sounds they knew so well. The bear knew these beings were all spirit, born anew.
>
> Of their golden hair and their tall stature, the bear was

not fearful, for of love they were adorned.

They spoke to the bear and said, "Bear, the one that can hear in the cave of the air, go down and tell the others what you have seen here."

The three did a circular dance. Their fingers would touch. The light would enhance their abilities. The fire was swept across the land. The energies they used were of the hand.

The bear knew when he saw these three. In the trees the birds would sweep and come forth. All of the animal kingdom started to climb the hill to see the dance that was so still.

In the air, the clouds didn't move. One large cloud was in view. Of this, the bear didn't know; but he knew that it was true. Of the light source it was.

These three beings were able to communicate form to all the animals that were being reborn into an earthly plane. They said, "Call us by name. We are back now to save thee."

The bear said, "Save thee from what? Now you live in a forest that is not. An illusional frame of the mind cast name." The bear would not tell man the same. All the animals then could call his name: Lord of Light.

The bear was an illusional form. Spirit would seep out and seek to know more. These three minds would come together as one. The bear would see the Central Sun. The bear knew that from that day forward he would be protected forevermore.

All the animals chattered that night. They said they had seen such a sight! As these three had danced and played in the light, they also wanted to be.

The bear came down with a message from the hill to give the People that were still ill a new plan. That is not to hurt the land, but to enjoy and taste the love and fruits of all. There is enough to go around, so there has to be no more fall.

The bear knew, as the kingdom did too, that the mighty Earth was pure and a golden hue would surround it soon. The airs would clear. The sky would form. The sun would shine. The moon would glow. The stars would want to be part of Earth now, as the bear was.

> Message to be given to the lower life forms to bring spirit up, never to be afraid, for the spirit and the light that was on the hill that day.
>
> Now the bear knew what to say, where to go, and the love and the truth that will always show. He has to give this to man. He goes down now and tells him of the land, how to use things properly, and to follow his hand, because he can show them the way. The bear knew of the day of the lights.

Windchimer finished his story and looked at the faces around him. They looked puzzled. He had given them a lot to think about, a lot to figure out. If he'd made it too easy, they wouldn't stop to think. He dismissed the children and walked out into the night.

Years had passed, and still he had not found anyone from his tribe. Memories of Morning Glory were always comforting to him. He would reminisce about the time when they were together. This carried him through a lot of turbulent times in his mind. Often, when he went through difficult days and nights, thoughts of her sustained him. He would call Glory and say, "Glory, you have to be with me in spirit today. I am having a terrible time."

He would remember scenes, such as the time when they were together at the creek. They'd jumped together down into the water and swam for about a quarter of a mile. Then they stopped and floated and did a ritual turtle dance in the water. They went in circles, round and round. He dived down and brought up a stone he had found. He said that if she would wear it, it would look pretty on her. He splashed her face and they began to laugh.

Even as an old man, he remembered all the good times they had and the glories of being together. Those times were so precious. He would always keep her in that frame of existence. He dedicated his life, every day, to her. No matter where he was, he put his spirit forward to protect her from strife, saying, "Give me the burden. Let her have the peace."

He would salute the sun and give her a dance. Then, in vision, he would know she was at peace. The rest of the day would be all right because he knew she was all right.

His torment was that he could never be with her. He never tried to find somebody else to take her place. He knew no one could replace her. It was a comfort just having known her. Together their light burned bright. After they took her, the flame no longer burned.

He made a point of remembering that when you awaken in the morning, you should produce love in yourself; in that way you will remember that when a part of your love is taken from you, as Glory was from him, you can continue to make more love within. As long as love still burns brightly in your heart, you can live through the darkest turmoil and death. He tried to remember that.

Windchimer often went by himself into the mountains. One day he was sitting by a stream when two braves came to him. The chief had sent for him because his woman was having a difficult childbirth.

Windchimer by this time was advanced in his years. He had much white hair. He carried a staff with him because he had an old wound that often acted up on him.

He called this wound the Snake. One foot would burn and the pain would start to come up his leg from his foot. He saw a snake coiling around his foot and leg, up to the kneecap. The snake would rest right there. When this happened he would stop what he was doing, uncoil the snake, put it on the ground and brush it away. The pain would be gone again. He did this before he got up to go to the chief's wife.

When he arrived at the village he could hear the woman screaming. Two old women, who moved slowly with their thick hips and short legs, held her hands. He asked them to leave. Windchimer placed his hands on her forehead as he talked softly, calming her down. He took her spirit out. She went into a trance. Her mouth dropped open. Nearby was a bowl of fruits and berries. He directed the spirit to go there and feed itself for nourishment.

The child was then delivered peacefully. He held the child above his head and said, "This is a lighted one."

He cleaned the baby and handed it to the chief. Then he called the spirit to come back into the mother peacefully.

His journeys took him across all of the land. Everywhere he went, he asked about his People, about his princess, the silver-haired one, and about the blond-haired, blue-eyed boys. He thought if he could find one of the boys, he would be able to direct him to Morning Glory. It was not meant to be. Something always blocked his path. Something always led them away just before he got there.

When Morning Glory and Dancing Eagle were married, they had vowed not to leave this world without each other. Now he was getting old. He tried desperately to find her, to fulfill his promise.

He continued to search because a piece of his soul was missing without her. He felt he could not go back to the Sun without her, so he kept his weary bones going, on and on, carrying stories from tribe to tribe. One story that was especially close to his heart was that of the Great Healer.

The youngsters gathered about the fire. Windchimer sat his weary bones on a log and held on to his staff. His white hair flew wildly about in the wind. A blanket kept the wind off his back. He pulled it tighter about him. He sat quietly and looked at the eager young faces surrounding him.

> I am going to tell you about a white man who walked the lands, going from village to village, healing the People. The man was a blue-eyed one. With a touch of his hand, a look from his eye and a few words of wisdom, he was able to heal. No one ever stood in his path, as he carried an essence and power about him. Where he walked, they made the way pure.
>
> He arcs his fingers. He curls his thumb. The power and force come one by one. Through every finger, of every force, he knows what to do.
>
> The touch of his hand on the forehead of his loved one gives peace and harmony, and the healing has begun. He's home.
>
> He has the mark of the dove. He wears buckskin clothes, long blond hair, pure blue eyes. He has got the stare. The sea is his tranquility. The eyes produce fertility.
>
> He walks, but there is no trace. He talks, but of a dying race. He salutes the morning sun. He sits by the glory of the moon as one.
>
> His spirit goes from place to place. Of the land-locked People that took to the shores, he helped them with the hope that was lost in the stars.
>
> He has come back to redefine the truth of the eternal plain, to walk again, to call the Indian name. Of all the times, the songs that were sung, the man was of the Indian tongue.
>
> Preachers would come from mountain to prairie to view this man, not to be his query. He knew of a voice in the forest that beckoned him so, and across the plains his body would go.

> The image of the spirit he possessed would come back to give other men the true test of their time. Indian braves would whoop and holler because the son of the Sun was there upon the hour of their needs.

As usual, the children sat there quietly, trying to figure out the true meaning of his story.

One little girl then popped up and said, "Windchimer, you are always alone. Have you never had a love to call your own?"

Windchimer was taken aback. How dare this little girl ask such a personal question of his heart! He was about to tell her so but as he looked up he saw Morning Glory's spirit standing serenely behind her.

A tear formed in his eye. He quickly wiped it away. He thought for a moment, to find a way that he could bear to tell her the story of his love. He took a deep breath and started to speak.

> Snowbird would fly with a golden wing. Snowbird always came to the joy of singing. Snowbird would always be the friend around. Snowbird always found the ground. Snowbird would always be of the mountaintops. Snowbird would always be the word that would never stop. Snowbird was the word.
>
> Where spirit flew and the bird would be, Snowbird was there to only see. The eyes that it was of reality, would always bring back her forth. Her frame of her time of her name, Snowbird was. Snowbird was the connectional light. Snowbird was the guiding flight. Snowbird was its own resonance of due. Snowbird was the golden hue of life.
>
> Snowbird came in the form of a woman frame. A maiden they said they called by name. Snowbird was her image and presence of form. Snowbird was what man adored.
>
> Many men came and praised her name: "I can give gifts of game." Snowbird would say, "Yes, I know, but I am from the spirit so."
>
> "That is why we want you. We want you to know that our spirit too grows with thee." Snowbird said, "Not this way, you see."
>
> Then one day a man would come, big structure, many

guns. Said, "This one they call the Snowbird frame, I'll take her and put her in a cage in my name."

Stole her away from the tribe where she belonged and took her back without a song. The bird then could not speak. The spirit was not free to seek its own.

Other spirits would listen to the bird and its chirping ways; said something was stolen from the mountains this day. From the valley and the creeks and the plains that we know, Snowbird was gone forever so.

"Track them," they said. "We will find him, and he is dead."

Snowbird said, "No, please. It is only what has to be. Stay the distance and set me free."

"How can we do that, if you won't let us come? Spirit now is all one. The Great Eagle has spread its wings. You, Snowbird, please fly again in your youth!"

"I can't, because I have to bear the three, the three little birds that will sing in the breeze. In the tree, in the mountain they find, there is of another, of a lost time."

"Snowbird, what are you saying to us? You have given up what is and was?"

"No. I am saying I must find in my heart a time when I can make a new start. When white and red and black and blue spread the mountain of the hue and come back and form a new view, the Great Eagle flies in my name, for I am the Snowbird. I am the same."

From the starlight came the Morning, the Glory of the chirping of the bird that was, it came forth upon the golden view. "I am the Snowbird."

Snowbird said, "I will always walk and talk with my People, you know, but with the white I must go. With them I will find a new path, a new peace, and with that I will bring a new breeze. Then we can all walk as sons and daughters of the land. The Snowbird will lay its golden hand upon us all, again . . . again."

The children sat there stunned, not knowing what he was talking about. With that he got up and walked away. Windchimer had sat by the fire, telling the children about Morning Glory, but he couldn't bear to use her name. He finally realized what had happened to his love. His realization came in a pure form. The snow is driven as a pure form of heart.

He had once said, "When the chirping of the bird comes into the breeze to see the one they call Snow at ease, the bird you see, and the two eyes that are the female form that forms within her, brings back the word, the whisper so, upon the winds they know to go and follow Snowbird home."

She was just part of a plan, but she brought in the new age of man, the age of the white-eye. She saw in a vision, before she was born, that the white-eye was going to take away her home.

She had said, "I will bring the home a new day. I will bring upon the prairie, and they will say they heard the Snowbird that came from the mountain of its due."

They said, "Snowbird was all of you. It is you People, you the fire that is in the eye that comes back from the great sky and brings Glory back to the Earth!"

Every day he would do a dance of praise for her. He asked the elements to keep protection over her. He would see her in vision every so often and contact her. He knew when she was well. He also knew when she was hurt. He picked up all of the emotions from the dirt.

He would lie on the ground, swivel around, find wherever she was and tell her it was all right, wherever she was and whatever her plight. He would rock her and cradle her, ever so. The tender sweep of his hand across her hair would be there so she would always know he was with her. That is the way he came to her.

She would know. He would cuddle her in his arms like a little child. He would whisper sweet things to her all the while.

His love was brighter than when they were together. It was more powerful and steadfast. The image of the two of them when they were together was very powerful. He knew that. It didn't have to be physical. He knew they were one in spirit. That was all that mattered to him. It was all that mattered . . . .

That is life! he told himself. That is love!

CHAPTER 45

Morning Glory sat upon a hill, watching the skies. In her view, between the sun and herself, was the Eagle. It landed in a tree nearby.

She had noted that here in the western part of the country, the eagle carried a golden hue. She sat staring at it. The eagle gave out a squall, shifted its weight, twitched its tail and looked right back at her.

"What is it that makes my heart beat so when I look at your majesty?" she said to her friend, the golden eagle. "Why does watching your flight put a tear in my eye? What energy you carry! Is it that each one of the eagles carries a spirit of my People? When you go away, are you carrying one of my People away? Well, bird, what have you to say?"

Again the eagle twitched its tail, let air bring grace to its wings and settled down once more.

"It is of spirit I am! I can sail higher and farther than any other. Your People are of the Eagle. They came from the Sun. As long as my spirit can fly free, your People are free. If I am disgraced, so are they. When I can no longer fly, your People will die! So set me free to sail the sky. I am in the Creator's eye! My wings beat with the flow of love. Love will set me free. I salute thee. Come fly with me!"

And so she did. For that moment in time, she closed her eyes and became one with the Eagle. Her heart began to beat to a different drum. She became the Eagle eye and soared through the sky and shared its heavens. As she glided she felt the air as though it were a gentle breeze. The land was barely in view.

She landed on a mountain peak, wings slightly outstretched to catch the wind spirit. The sun was so near. With the eye of the Eagle everything was in clear view, even the reflections in the dew.

On the mountain peak, her vision became far-reaching and wide. She then knew that the eagle had moved on because her People could not survive where they were. Her People cannot survive if the eagle is not alive. They must always live with the eagle. The eagle knew what to do.

She woke up lying on the ground, her arms outstretched. The sun shined in her eyes. As she began to rise, the sun glinted off the golden reflection of a true prize. The eagle had dropped her a feather.

How many of my People will survive? The eagles were going away. They do not want to stay. How will my People be?

Her vision then went to her sons. She saw them with their blue eyes, standing side by side. Over them she saw two eagles. One was the black and white eagle of her original homeland. The other was the eagle of the golden hue. Both of the eagles knew what to do.

Her sons carried the spirit of the Eagle, whether it was black and white or of the golden hue. They had the blood of the white, the blood of the red, the hair of gold, the skin of copper, the eyes of blue. Everything was of the rainbow! Everything truly was one.

Her sons would carry the spirit of oneness through. Like the Eagle, they knew what to do. They were the bridge. Their children's blood would carry the knowledge of their heritage through to their children's children.

One day that knowledge would be known again. The Eagle will return and all will go home.

CHAPTER 46

Many seasons had passed. Morning Glory quietly continued to heal within the Sioux nation. She also worked with the children, sharing whatever knowledge they would accept. Some referred to her as Woman from the Whispering Sand. Others called her Womona, the Widow Woman. The name Glory of the Morning was unknown to them.

When Glory traveled from tribe to tribe to heal, Red Cloud provided an escort for her. She was respected and honored.

In her travels she often heard reference to Thunder Mountain. There was a white man who lived in the hills who used dynamite to do his mining. The Indians were afraid to go there, because they feared that if they were killed by a dynamite explosion, their spirits would be shattered for all of eternity. This man became known as a man who carried much medicine. Because of this power, Red Cloud and Iron Hand paid him a visit. It took courage on their part to do this, but because they respected his powers, they honored him and even became his friends.

Corey Walker was his name. His beard was black, as was his hair. He was average in stature, with strong shoulders from the work he did. His eyes were piercing. His soul was fiery. He often wore a plaid flannel shirt. A pick and ax were never far from his hand. He was an Irish radical who had fled to America to escape death in Ireland. He hid in the mountains and, like the Indians, stayed clear of the white man. Because of that, he and the Indians had something in common.

Corey was no fool. He knew that if he stayed friends with the Indians, the white man would stay away. He was, after all, in Indian territory. He often gifted the Indians.

One day in the springtime, Corey went hunting for fresh game. He had a campfire going, cooking freshly caught fish for dinner. A bear caught scent of the fish and came lurking about. Corey had only one chance to fire off a shot. It hit the bear but only wounded it. The angered bear charged and tore him to pieces. Corey fell unconscious.

The next day, Sioux braves found him in the woods and brought him back to his cabin. Word was sent to Red Cloud that the man from Thunder Mountain was near death.

Red Cloud honored Corey's medicine and liked his courage. When the chief had visited him recently with his braves, Corey was outnumbered by twenty to one but stood his ground, showing no fear. The Indians honored that. He was a brave warrior in their eyes, one who should die with honor.

Morning Glory was summoned. A couple of braves escorted her to his cabin. She walked through the door of his dark cabin, barely able to see his body on the bed for lack of light through the dirty windows. She felt his head. It was burning with fever. He was sweating profusely, moaning and muttering something about his people in Ireland.

Quickly she found a rag in the corner of his cabin, dunked it into the dirty water that was left over in his wash basin and washed his two windows so that the Creator's light could come through. Now that she could see, she knew what to do. First she brought in water from the stream, then she made a fire. Into the fire she put herbs to change the air in the cabin and to bring in spirit. Then she brought the water to a boil. She made him a brew of herbs to drink so he would sleep heavily. She had much work to do on his wounds. He had lost much blood and his muscles were torn. Patches of his skin had been ripped away. He could be saved only through the Creator's Grace.

She put more herbs into the boiled water and used this to cleanse his wounds. She boiled some cloth in which to bathe and bandage him. While things were brewing, she kept offering him more to drink. It was bitter and he did not like it.

"Corey," she whispered as she ran her hands through the dark ringlets of his hair, "you must drink this or you will endure much pain."

Corey could hear her voice in the distance, but his fever ravaged his thinking. Trusting no one, especially strangers, he would not allow himself to go to sleep.

"Do what you have to, lassie, but I prefer to stay awake."

She brought the bucket of medicine water to his cot and proceeded to bathe his many wounds. They were deep and angry and some still bled. She had a salve with her that she put on some of the cuts after she cleansed them. He grimaced as she touched him, but still he would not take the brew. She was as gentle as she could be, but there was no getting around his pain.

Some of the cuts were so deep that skin and muscle were hanging loose. "Corey," she said, taking his head between her hands, "I have to sew your flesh back together. There is no other way. You are torn too badly for salves alone. Drink the brew – it will make you sleepy."

Corey looked over to the cabin doorway where two painted warriors stood. "No, lassie. I'll just stay awake. If I die, it will be with my eyes open."

She did not want to do this. She remembered how she'd caused Dancing Eagle so much pain when she took the arrowhead out of his festered shoulder. There had been nothing with which to put Dancing Eagle to sleep then. She had learned more skills now, had more medicines to work with, but this man would not trust her to use them.

She did not want to dishonor him by binding him so that he could not twist and turn – but if he moved, she could injure him badly. He obviously did not want to be touched by the braves in the doorway.

"Corey, 'tis a hard thing I have to do. You cannot be movin' about when I do this. Why make it so hard for yourself? Are all Irishmen so bullheaded?"

Corey suddenly became awake. His vision had been blurred by his fever, and what little of the brew he drank had made him a bit woozy. His eyes had been closed as he grimaced through the cleaning of the wounds. Now his eyes shot open as he realized he was hearing an Irish accent from an Indian squaw! For the first time, he actually looked at her.

The woman whose face he looked into had blue eyes! She was beautiful! And she spoke his language!

"Lassie, I thought they were sendin' me an Indian woman! What are you? You kind of look Indian, but like no Indian I've ever seen before! Who are you?"

"I'm Womona. I do what I can, that is all. The question is, What am I going to do with you? You are not being cooperative. I can't leave you this way, but I have much to do yet with your wounds."

"Just do what you have to do, woman, but I stay awake. That is how I stayed alive this long."

Morning Glory sighed. "Irishmen are all the same. There is no changin' them. Have it your way then, but if you move about on me, I will have those two braves hold you down."

Oh, great, he thought. *There* is an audience. He had earned respect from the Indians because of his medicine and his courage. If he were to cry out in pain and they had to hold him down, word would get around. He would lose face in the eyes of the powerful chiefs.

He put his hands above his head and grabbed the headboard of his bed.

"Just do it, lass. Just do it."

Glory used a porcupine quill and hair from her horse's mane to reconnect the torn muscle tissue and then, finally, sewed together the skin that covered it. Corey was a tough one. He grimaced and made his knuckles turn white, but he held his own as she skillfully sewed him back together.

Between sewing each wound, she bathed his head, gave him sips of the brew — very watered down so he wouldn't notice — and let him catch his breath.

There was one last wound that wouldn't stop bleeding. She had put poultices on it and left it for last, but still the blood welled out.

Corey was exhausted from the loss of blood and all he had gone through. He just wanted this to be all over and for the braves to go away. He shut his eyes for a moment, then he felt her put her hands over the wound. It felt good. He heard her quietly chant a mysterious song. He did not know the words but he felt as if he were floating out of his body.

When he looked down he saw a serene and beautiful Indian woman with her hands upon his chest. Light flowed about her, a golden light. It filled the room as though a thousand candles were alight.

He drifted back into his body. Where she held her hands, there was a wonderful warmth. Colors filled his head. He felt incredible peace and strength come back into his body. He didn't want the sensation to stop. He felt as if he were in a place of no time, no space.

He looked at the wound that previously had been oozing his warm blood. It had sealed up. It was then that he realized his strength had become renewed.

"Lassie, what did you do? Who are you? I've not seen the like."

"Tis the Creator at work. That is all."

Morning Glory went to the braves and requested they bring back some wood, water and food. Then she asked them to go back to their village. She would stay here until the man was healed. They complied.

Morning Glory poured some broth into Corey for strength, and he slumped into an exhausted stupor. His body had been bandaged and his wounds sealed. Now he needed to rest until morning.

Throughout the rest of the evening, she swept out the cabin, washed his bloodied clothes, made soup and washed his dirty dishes. Periodically throughout the night, she applied poultices to some of his wounds so the infection would leave.

At sunrise the next day she went out, as usual, to greet the sun and wade into the river to cleanse herself. She brought back water and picked some fresh herbs for medicine on the way back. She brought back with her some budding flowers to make the cabin bright. Some of them she braided into her hair. It made her smell sweet.

When Corey awoke later that morning, a fire burned brightly in the fireplace. The cabin carried the sweet, pungent odor of sage. The room was filled with glorious light — the windows had never been washed before. There were flowers on the table — and sitting beside him was Glory of the Morning.

He was stiff and sore and still very weak. Morning Glory lifted his head so he could drink from the bowl she held for him. She said nothing but got up and stoked the fire, putting a pot of water over it to boil.

Corey continued to look around his cabin. He had never seen it so clean before. The table had been scrubbed. A clean shirt hung on the hook. Nothing was thrown about, and the room smelled sweet from the flowers.

As she stood beside the fire, the blue in her hair glimmered in the morning sun. She turned to look at him, and the blue shot from her eyes. It took his breath away.

"You are an angel in disguise," he whispered to himself.

"May I look at your wounds now in the sunlight? I need to clean them and put more poultices on them," she softly said.

Morning Glory pulled his covers down and lifted the poultices and bandages off. His body looked like a patchwork quilt, but the bleeding had stopped and the fiery red had gone away.

She put her hand to his head to see if he still burned with fever. He put his hand over hers and held it there tenderly. It had been a long time since he had a woman by his side. He had forgotten how good it felt.

For the first time, she got to look directly into his eyes, into his soul. Her heart skipped a beat. Something about this man reminded her of Dancing Eagle. Perhaps it was the fire in his soul, the spirit he possessed.

The pain in her heart from missing Dancing Eagle had never left her. Her heart also bled for the loss of Jack. Jack had meant so much to so many People, and he lost his life trying to save hers. She had buried herself in her work and in her People; it was all she had left. But this man, Corey of Thunder Mountain, was a white man, and an Irish one at that. Why was her heart beating so?

Corey fell in and out of sleep over the next few days, each day getting stronger — and more verbal. He had the golden tongue of an Irishman.

As the days went by, Corey started coming out of his shell. With him was a beautiful woman who could speak his language. He shared with her the sorrow that he held for the family lost to him in Ireland. She told him how the whites had destroyed her own family.

As Corey realized that they both were hunted by a world that didn't understand the true nature of heart, he healed not only in body but in spirit. He saw in her not the bitterness that he held, but a tenderness for all living things, human, animal, and reaching out to include even the plants.

Without restraint he fell incredibly in love with her. Each day he would hold her in his arms as they sat before the firelight.

Morning Glory was torn. She felt strongly that she needed to get back to her People, but the happiness that she felt in Corey's arms held her back from her responsibility.

As the days turned into weeks, Corey's wounds healed. Once again he was the proud, virile and independent man he used to be. Now it was time for him to bring fresh meat back to the cabin. He didn't want to leave, but they had to eat.

He had been gone for two days when three braves appeared at the cabin. Red Cloud had sent them for her. Morning Glory walked out to greet them and was startled by the curt words of one of the braves.

"Woman, what are you doing so long with white man? Do you not know your place is with your People?"

Morning Glory became indignant. "I belong to no man. What I do matters only to me."

"Then if you do not think of your People, perhaps you will think of your brother. Two Moons has been taken by the whites. They need you to talk to an enemy of the People. They call him General Custer."

Morning Glory's heart sank. She knew of this man. He was not to be trusted. He was not a friend of the Indian nation.

"Give me a little time to gather my things. I will go and talk to this man," she said staunchly to the braves.

When she walked into the cabin she could hardly shut the door behind her to hide the fact that she was doubled over in pain. She held her gut and put a hand over her face to fight back the tears.

Once again she would have to leave a man she loved. Once again her People's lives were endangered. She had to bring them to safety before all of them perished. Nothing else mattered now. Her desires did not matter now. Her life never had been and never would be her own. Her People had to come first.

Morning Glory reached into her pouch and took out two stones, one blue, the other green. Corey used to say these stones reminded him of the blue sky of her eyes and the green of her world. They reminded him of her.

She once said, "When I leave, these stones will be yours, so you can remember me."

Alarmed, he'd said, "But I love you. You wouldn't leave me, would you?"

She only replied by looking down, knowing she would not be allowed to stay with any one man ever again.

She left the stones on the table, next to the flowers she had put into a small pot that morning. Quickly she wrapped up her few belongings, wiped the tears from her eyes and stoically walked out the door, never to look back again.

As the sun started to set behind the sacred hills, Corey returned with a buck on the travois hitched to his horse. He called out to her, but she did not greet him at the door. Perhaps she was down at the river. He ran toward the river, but an uneasiness hit him. Something was different. Things did not feel the same here anymore.

Frantically he ran up to the cabin and flung the door open. His eyes were drawn to the two stones on the table.

"No!" he screamed. He called out her name. He ran into the forest, through the trees, calling her. He ran back to the cabin, but all of her things were gone. So was his heart.

He knew he would always search for his heart, which was with her and only her; for love is a strong bond. No man can break it, living or dead. His spirit would always be bonded to her.

CHAPTER 47

The three braves brought Morning Glory directly to General Custer. When they arrived, soldiers stopped them to inquire what they were doing there.

Morning Glory replied in perfect English, but with an Irish accent, "I am Glory of the Morning of the Eagle Clan, and I am here to talk to General Custer regarding the release of my brother Two Moons."

The soldier said, "Wait here. I will notify the general of your request."

The soldier knocked on Custer's door, opened it and walked into the smoky, log-walled room. He saluted and stood at attention. "General Custer, sir, there is an Indian woman here who wishes to speak to you."

Custer took the cigar butt out of his mouth as he almost choked on it with rage. "Tarnation, soldier, I have no time to talk to squaws!"

"I think you'd better talk to this one, sir. She carries much power within the Indian nation, and word has it she's under Red Cloud's protection. She's lived in several forts and she's known many generals in her time." The soldier went on. "This woman knows many prestigious people, both red and white."

"All right, then. Send the squaw in, but this better be worth my time, or I'll have your damn stripes."

General Custer had his back to the door, shuffling through a pile of paper. He was in a room with straight, hard walls and rigid furniture.

"I beg your pardon, sir. I wish to speak to thee about my brother Two Moons."

Custer spun around on his heel. He'd expected to see some dirty little squaw with a scout as an interpreter. Instead he saw a blue-eyed woman who spoke beautifully. It caught him off-guard. She stood poised and confident, yet she was soft-spoken.

"My brother, sir, is a peaceful man. He has never killed another, yet you hold him prisoner. You hold him for no real reason except that he is Indian. I wish to take him back with me."

Custer was shocked at her bluntness. "Your brother has caused much trouble with his meddling in our affairs. All he wants to do is talk, and I'm through with talking. I am going to do what I came here to do. Your brother has been getting in the way."

Custer could see that she was not going to be put off so easily. He could also see why she had so much influence. There was a power in her presence, and the quietness about her was disarming.

Custer paced back and forth. Never before had he had to deal with a woman. He found this puzzling. He didn't know why she upset him so. She hardly said a word, yet he felt he had to answer her request.

The general took the cigar out of his mouth to talk and gestured with it to emphasize his words. "I'll tell you what. If you promise to get Two Moons away from here, I'll take your word and let him go. I hear he has much influence among the tribal chiefs, and I'm through with his meddling.

"I know that Two moons and your People are from another part of the country. How the two of you got so much power within the Sioux nation is beyond me. Leave. Leave this troubled land."

Morning Glory lowered her eyes for a moment then raised her head. "My People have made their lodges with the Sioux; therefore, we are now Sioux."

Custer became angered. "Then you will die with the Sioux," he said coldly.

Morning Glory could have no more death among her People, whom she had been sent to protect. She would leave as he had warned her to do. She also had to save Two Moons. It was not yet his time to die.

Morning Glory's head popped up. "General Custer, release my brother. My People will travel to less troubled lands."

Custer replied shortly, "Go, then. Take your brother with you and don't look back. There will be nothing left for you here."

Morning Glory was escorted to the guardhouse where Two Moons was being detained. As Two Moons walked out, something caught his eye. Around the corner, with his head down, talking to some scouts, was Black Wolf!

"Do not look now, Morning Glory," Two Moons whispered, "but we have been betrayed. The curse of the Raven is yet upon us with her own blood. After Shadow Dancer's band rejoined us, Tall Trees revealed a secret that Red Hawk had gone to his death with. The Raven's son was sired by Thomas Shaye! Red Hawk only told Tall Trees, as they were best friends. Tall Trees' wife was barren and yearned for a child, so they raised Black Wolf. They later regretted that decision, as the boy turned on them many times."

Terror struck her heart. Now she knew why Black Wolf had haunted her, why he always stared at her. He was the half-brother of her sons.

The sun was directly overhead when Two Moons and Morning Glory arrived back at the village. They gathered up their People for a final meeting. There were fewer than forty of their original People left. The sun was high in the sky on this hot day, leaving no shadow. Morning Glory stood before them with her head bowed until all her People had arrived. She then stood straight and bold and began to speak of their new predicament.

"Once again the Eagle has left us. Yet there is a valley of eagles that I know of. It is an ancient land of our ancestors. I will take those of you there who care to follow me. There must be a remnant left of our People to take care of that sacred spot, for one day our spirits will all gather again at that spot. We cannot all die in the senseless fight with the white man. Come with me. I will teach you how to transcend the land. Our People have in their memory the way to get to the Central Sun from which we came. Those of you who wish to follow me, meet me here at the rising of the sun. We will make our final journey."

As she walked away, the People were left speechless. Most of them were women. There were only a few braves. Many of the women had taken Sioux braves as husbands and did not want to leave them; this was understandable. Some of them were just too old to journey once again. If they were to die, this was as good a place as any.

Morning Glory went to Red Cloud and thanked him again for taking in her People and keeping her name unmentioned in the council meetings among the tribes. Red Cloud feared for his own People without her. It was she who called the buffalo to them. He begged her to stay. She of course could not.

She went to Nia, her dearest friend, and hugged her until she thought her heart would break. Morning Glory said, "You know, there is no end. You will always be my friend. Some day we will meet again."

It was springtime when the tiny remnant of the Eagle Clan departed. Only the families of Little Beaver, Lame Deer, Black Otter, Silent Wind, Tall Trees, and the half-white Black Wolf and his white wife joined her.

During the journey south to the desert land, where many say the phoenix shall rise, Black Wolf tried to claim leadership of the clan. "My mother was a prophet," he would exclaim. "I have powerful gifts. My father was chief. I am his heir."

Tall Trees could hold his secret no longer. "You are not the son of a chief. You are the son of the man who destroyed our village. Red Hawk told me before his death. He went to his grave with your birth upon his lips. My woman needed a child, so we held your secret."

Tall Trees' wife grabbed his arm and tried to stop him from telling the rest of the clan. Tall Trees pulled away and shouted before the People, "But your true blood is coming through."

The People looked at each other in shock. He took so much after his mother, and the desert sun had baked his skin dark; they did not notice the white. He had never been a popular man, always surly and looking for a fight, but he was powerful.

Black Wolf looked around and saw that everyone eyed him suspiciously. He turned to his wife and said, "Woman, we go now. I can no longer live with the blood of those who have murdered both my mother and my father. Someone will have to pay. I will see to that."

A sharp pain hit Morning Glory in the heart. It sickened her inside. She knew something was going to happen.

Two Moons wanted to go with Morning Glory, but spirit told him that he could not. He felt the need to search one last time for the boys. He was concerned for their safety, and he was not sure why. Once again Morning Glory's heart was torn in two — but as before, they knew that they could never really be parted. They would always be as one, no matter where they roamed.

In Morning Glory's head were visions and ancient memories of a protected place where they could live within the shadows of a sturdy cliff dwelling, near a running river, which would supply fish. There was a pool that had an underground river. Where it surfaced, the water was warm, even in the winter. The People could bathe and heal themselves. The water could irrigate their crops in this arid land. It was a sacred place where spirits who were pure could come and go from this earthly prison. Some called the place Montezuma.

By early fall they arrived at this secluded place near the central part of Arizona. They built themselves dwellings out of poles, sticks and mud. These would keep them cool in the summer and warm in the winter.

A chill was in the air when Morning Glory called her People to a meeting within the circle of the village. The circle, bordered by large rocks to sit on, was cleared of any small rocks in the middle. Sage was burned and passed around. A fire periodically spit flames as the wind stoked it.

The People felt a seriousness about the night. Morning Glory was very somber. She had gone on a vision quest for four days and returned the day before. Since that time she had kept to herself and not talked among the villagers.

As she sat within the light of the fire, it was as though they could see through her. Waves of translucency came as she started to softly talk. The People had to strain to hear her. Her voice seemed to drift off.

"My People," Morning Glory said with her hands folded in her lap, "soon I must return to the place I came from. My time with you is near an end for now."

Morning Glory stood up and softly walked the circle, looking into each one's eyes for just a moment. "I promise you this. When the land upon which we walk and live and give our blood is about to renew itself, I will return to this very spot. Part of my spirit will stay here to protect this sacred ground. I will come back to reclaim that part of me that I leave with you until our spirits are rejoined. The love I have for you will guide me here, for you will never be forgotten. You all will be in my heart and in my soul. You will know when that time is at hand.

CHAPTER 48

In honor of her friend, Nia had planted many sunflowers on a high mound in a grassy meadow. The meadow was by a river that wound around a mountainshed.

Nia, over the following weeks, missed Morning Glory terribly. In her despair she took a long walk toward the meadow that she had planted with sunflowers three moons ago to honor her friend.

She walked around the mountainshed into the meadow and couldn't believe her eyes. Nia had planted flowers on a mound. Now the ground around the flowers had produced other flowers to make a beautiful field and garden. The mountainshed speaks water and brings water down. Flowers bloomed even from the water. As she marveled, mist from the mountain rain came down also, in front of her misty eyes, and sprinkled the flowers with a golden light.

Since that day, that field has produced many other fields of flowers that stay there forever. The Indians said that Sun Flower never left their land. Her spirit stays there to sow the seeds and forever sing with the breeze. They will never forget that morning star.

CHAPTER 49

Two Moons went west to find Chata/Nathanael. There was knowledge that he still had to bring to him. Tribal artifacts had to be moved to a safe place where the white man would not bring them disgrace. These artifacts had to be hidden for another time, another place. Nathanael would have to be the one. He knew spirit. He knew grace. It was the reason Morning Glory brought him to this place.

Two Moons was one lone, old man on a pony, quietly heading to California. No one seemed to notice him as he quietly rode by. He seemed to occupy no time or place. He was not bothered, as long as he followed the way of the Eagle eye.

In the town of Yreka, northwest of Mt. Shasta, Two Moons found his nephew. Nathanael had found a stranded wagon train in the mountains during a winter storm. He knew the land and was able to bring them to Yreka. He helped them settle the town of Yreka, creating a spiritual haven for the stranded people. Nathanael turned into a handsome lad with his mother's eyes. People seemed to flock around him wherever he went.

Nathanael had a small law office in town. He was running for political office, but was disliked by some because of his support for Indian rights. Two Moons slipped into town quietly one foggy night, calling at Nathanael's door with his birdcall.

He opened the door and Two Moons slipped in. They embraced. It had been a long time since they had seen each other.

"Uncle," Nathanael said in surprise, "what brings you here? Is Mother all right?"

Two Moons walked up to the window and closed the curtains. He dressed simply, wearing no feathers in town so as not to attract attention. Turning, he said, "She's fine, son. It is your brothers that concern me. You didn't know it, but you have a half-brother. He has the controlling ambition of your father and the black heart of his mother, the Raven."

"The Raven!" Nathanael had to pull up a chair and sit down.

"He knows that Tom Shaye's sons have been financially provided for through your uncle James. I fear that he plans to eliminate his half-brothers and lay claim to his unwritten inheritance. He has already failed at trying to gain power, so now he wants money and revenge for the deaths of his parents. James is in Mexico; he is safe for the moment. It is Thomas that I'm concerned for."

Nathanael got up, paced across the floor of his log cabin and looked out the window. "First thing in the morning, I will book passage on a ship and we will sail south to his port. I too feel very uneasy now."

Nighttime was starting to come faster now. Morning Glory was grateful they were south this time of year. Winters were harsh in the north, and her People had become weary on their long journey to a new homeland.

There was an uneasiness within her soul that she could not figure out. During the night, just before the sun began to light up the eastern sky, she left her bed to walk under the stars. She felt an explosion in her head, a pain in her heart, and looked up to see a star fall from the sky.

Her knees gave out from under her, and her body fell to the earth. As the rays of the sun gently embraced her in the morning, she opened her eyes.

"O Creator, not my son. Not my son, oh please, anything but my son. Let me be wrong. He is not even here for me to sing him back home."

With her face to the ground, she clenched the earth and shed a mother's tears onto the Mother, each having known so much pain. She now knew she could not stay upon this earthly plane much longer. It would soon be time for her to go.

It was a foggy, misty, chilly morning when Nathanael and Two Moons arrived at Thomas' port of call. Thomas' business of hauling cargo had been financed through his uncle James from the money his father had left behind. He carried goods back and forth between San Diego and San Jose. His ship, the Morning Star, was not in port, but there was a curious amount of debris washing upon the shore; lots of wood, pieces of metal.

Nathanael buttoned up his jacket against the morning chill, put his hands into his pants pockets and walked up to a scavenger on the beach. He was an unshaven old man with a toothless smile and a bottle sticking out of the back pocket of a baggy pair of brown pants. The old man was stuffing the inside of his jacket pockets with the finds on the shore.

"Friend, would you happen to know when the Morning Star pulled out of port?"

The old man didn't bother to look up, just bent down to pick up a piece of metal that he thought might be a coin. He picked up the bent metal and threw it back down as he stood up.

"Guess ye haven't heard. Must not be from around these parts, or ye would have heard. Couple of mornings ago, just as the sun began to rise, there was an explosion I never heard the likes of." The old man stopped to pull the bottle out of his pocket and take a swig, wiping his mouth on his shirt sleeve. He popped the cork back in, this time putting it into his coat pocket to make it more accessible.

Nathanael grabbed him by the lapel and shook him. "Old man, what are you saying? Tell me." Two Moons stood quietly by with his head down, fearing the worst.

The old man pushed Nathanael off and put his hands in the air to pacify him. "Easy now, lad. No reason to get violent. What's got you all fired up?"

"Nevermind, old man, just tell me what happened." Nathanael was about to grab him again.

"All right, all right, just back off now. Damnedest thing the town's ever seen, in daylight, too. Those bandits were bold, yes sir. Damnest thing. They must have had a whole cargo of dynamite, they did. Could hear it for miles. Not much to salvage. Everything on shore was just bits and pieces."

Nathanael threw his hands in the air and was about to tear his hair out. "Old man, what are you talking about? Did you see the Morning Star or not?"

The old man took another swig of whiskey, corked it, wiped his mouth dry and said, "That's what I've been telling you. Those bandits were the boldest. Came right into port, they did. First there were a few shots fired off, back and forth. People began to see what the ruckus was all about, then you could hear the explosion. Debris flew all across the bay. It's still washing up. You can see that. No survivors — all taken by the sea."

Nathanael's heart stopped. A lump formed in his throat. He could hardly talk. In a whisper, he asked, "Did anybody see who did it?"

The old man started to walk away but stopped and said, "Yeah. Someone saw that ship turn about and sail off. Heard someone say they saw the name of the ship. I think it was the Raven."

Two Moons just kept shaking his head. He was two days too late. Two Moons had come by horse; Black Wolf must have come by train. He knew Morning Glory must have felt it; no need to send word to her. He could already feel her pain. But even worse, he could feel evil around him still. Chills went up his spine. The hair stood up on the back of his neck.

Nathanael stood to face the sea. Jabbing his fists into the air, he shouted, "Black Wolf, you black-hearted bastard, you shall pay for this. By the blood of our father, you shall die for this."

Two Moons felt the vibration of footsteps behind them on the dock. He turned to see who was coming. "Chata — look out!"

Black Wolf sailed through the air, knife in hand, knocking Nathanael face-down into the sand. Before Nathanael could turn, Black Wolf grazed the back of his neck. It started to bleed profusely.

Nathanael knew how to handle knife fighters. He was taught well by his father. With a knee to Black Wolf's crotch and a left-handed swing to knock the knife arm back, Nathanael reached inside his coat for his gun. A shot rang out, and Black Wolf slumped across Nathanael's chest.

Nathanael cast him off into the sand and pulled away in repulsion. He had shot Black Wolf's face away and was covered with his blood. Nathanael could not run fast enough to wash himself in the ocean.

Two Moons knew that at this point it didn't matter. Black Wolf died disfigured, so he would come back disfigured. Thomas and Nathanael both shed blood upon the shore, so someday they would have to return to the shore to reclaim the part of the spirit they left here. Violence never settles anything; it just makes violence go on.

Two Moons spent the next few weeks talking to Chata. He told him of his true mission in life, to be guardian and protector of ancient secrets and to bring white man and red man together. Two

Moons explained to him that neither of them would live to see the end result of such an immense and wide-reaching mission, but through them the seeds were being laid.

Two Moons knew his time was coming near and that his mission was almost over. Chata had to be shown where everything was hidden. Before Two Moons departed, they had to get back to the original place of the Eagle Clan.

Winter set in and ice formed in the bay. Ships could not get out of the harbor. Two Moons asked, "When will the boat be ready? Is it time to go home?"

"You have to wait, Uncle. Ice is blocking the bay."

"I can't wait anymore. I have got to go home. I will find an overland route."

"No, Uncle. The mountains are all closed. It is a terrible winter. You have to wait, Uncle. You can't go."

Chata slept in the Red Squall Hotel, but Two Moons had to sleep in the barn. Indians weren't allowed in the hotels.

Chata had a box full of money, money that he had received from his other uncle, James Shaye. He paid for everything with this money.

Two Moons spent the cold weeks telling the young man stories of how he used to fly with the Great Eagle and how he could land on top of things, peek around, set up home, watch over the land, see the bear coming from the mountains, the fish jumping in the streams, the deer eating the bark off the tree, the wildcat stalking for its morning breakfast, and the peaceful valley where the People roamed.

Two Moons continually dreamed about being home. He didn't want to be away from it any longer. He had traveled many, many miles. His legs were tired and his bones hurt. He didn't wear his feathers anymore. They had traveled to Puget Sound, and the people there didn't like Indians.

Spring came. They took a steamer down the Sacramento River into Sacramento. From that point on, they traveled by stagecoach and buckboard. The boy didn't want him to go, but Two Moons had no liking for the sea.

In St. Louis they took a riverboat north. When high hills and deep valleys started to appear, they knew they were near their old home, near the place the white man called Galena. They walked the rest of the way.

During his last days, Two Moons just stayed there. No one

bothered him. Some of the locals thought he was crazy, as he would just sleep out under the trees. Chata spent some of his time in town, trading with the locals and being consulted in legal matters by the mining company. Periodically he would go to the hills and find his uncle.

Two Moons still made medicine. Every time somebody was sick, he would knock at their door and leave medicine for them. There were only a few Indians left in the area, but they all appreciated this.

When Two Moons knew his time was at hand, he took Chata to the cave, beneath the waterfall, which he had previously sealed with rocks and brush. Chata removed the rocks and helped his uncle walk through the stones. He then followed his uncle into the cave. There on a rocky shelf, intact, lay the leather bags which he and Glory of the Morning had filled so long ago. Safe within them were the sacred artifacts that spirit had led them to, sealed securely with vines.

Two Moons showed him their sacred artifacts and said, "It is your mission to see that these are kept safe. It is for the survival of the human race. When you return home to your sacred land, take these things with you for the new race of man."

Chata looked at the artifacts with some puzzlement. He did not fully understand what they really were. He knew that someday, however, they would be very important. Two Moons would not explain to him their meaning or use. He only said that it was meant for another time, another place. Chata took this mission very seriously. Two Moons would not have dragged him across the country for a menial task. Respectfully, they walked out of the cave, dodging the cascade of water.

Two Moons stood by a tree that had fallen to the ground and become hollow. He looked within this log to see if the soul had left. He could not find the fruit of life that this tree had borne at one time. The life light that had been there was gone.

Now he saw himself, as he sat on this tree and pondered, as a log. He saw himself also becoming an empty spirit that had no reason to be, but was a quiet thing to sit upon, to remember, through memory.

As all things come into a life form existence and climb to the mighty skies and reach their branches to the highest, they thank the ground and they thank the highest spirit for their new life and form. Around this log he saw them, little new trees starting to sprout.

He said, "This will be my life when I leave this hallowed ground. I shall go to the Great Spirit and come back as a newfound form.

"As I leave now my body, placed upon this ground, hopefully the life form of this earth will give that new growth the life form it needs to be strong again like the mighty tree, and not hollow, as my heart feels.

"As the Great Sun bears down upon me now, I feel my withered bones wanting to depart, to become now the hallowed earth as they once were, and my dust to the dust, and my ash to the ash. I shall rise again like the great bird and sing the praise of the Sun and the spirit to the day that I was."

Two Moons turned toward the blurry-eyed Chata and softly said, "Shed no tear for me. As the cry goes to the sky, the love reflects back to you. Don't waste your time crying, but see it in your heart to make a new start, for all life begins again. The rains are the tears in the sky!"

With that he spoke his last words and listened to his heart, for the last time, beat. He fell to his knees and his body leaned against the tree. Spirit departed for all to see, into the sky.

Chata spread a great robe over his body and buried him in the chamber. Out of respect for his mother, he loved his uncle and buried him as a father.

CHAPTER 50

Windchimer's bones had grown very weary. He had spent many years searching for Morning Glory, but to no avail. His special stone would have to be left behind for one of her sons. He had promised her they would go back to the Sun together, not apart. His heart was weary from this burden he bore. He was in total despair. He felt he was going to fail in his promise to her. He had made a sacred pledge to her and had to keep his word. That was all he had left.

His old body and rattled bones would sit there at night all alone and ask where his Morning, his Glory was now. She would come in a shroud, in a cloud and sweep across his view. He would say, "Morning, I love you!"

Then he would rest those weary days, to stand the test of another day. What kept him alive, they would always say, was Morning Glory!

In his golden days he took a woman — he called her Prairie View. His eyes were failing him, so she led him through.

"When I die, woman, take off my moccasins and cover me with a buffalo hide. Take this stone and keep looking for the golden-haired one. This stone cannot be left behind. Do that for me, woman. You have been good to me."

Windchimer knew his time was near an end. He began to prepare himself. He purified himself for spirit. He prepared a sweatlodge and went in with his aching bones.

He asked the Great Spirit to take him. He no longer wanted to continue this life. He had searched the land from east to west, from south to north, but never found her. He was old, weary and lonely.

Once again he called out her name. In a vision, across the

steaming rocks, he saw her. His hand reached out to her. He felt a tear fall from his eye as he saw Morning Glory standing close by.

His heart pounded and a lump formed in his throat. His hand was still reaching out to her as he admitted, "Our hearts have never been separated. I was of a bolder time, a brave and a warrior. My name spread across the land — the one who had the Eagle's hand. The cloud would always be my semblance of a tool; but you see, I was the fool. My love is brighter now, even brighter than when we were together. I had to spend all this time clearing myself to be with you. I had to learn to clear every day of my life. I was in constant turmoil, constant pain. Now I am ready to be with you!"

As the vision of her faded, he heard her say, "You and me. Together. At last."

He realized his hand was still reaching out to the place where she stood. He let it drop into his lap. At last he felt peace. At last he felt love in his heart. Now he could go on. He struggled to get up and opened the flap. A cold chill whipped through this day. The drum sat there, as if to play the song of the Eagle.

Slowly he walked back to his little shelter on the shore, slipped into his hole and hibernated no more. Life came swift and death came near. He could still hear the rumbling of the water and the call of the deer.

But he had had his day when he walked with the Eagle that way, flew to the sky and saw the eye, part of the sun, and became one.

The river that flowed had a crimson glow to it. He was in a time of a lonely state of mind. Friends had all left. Dear departed ones were gone. All he had left was a memory in his mind to play this song again from his heart of when he made the first start of his life.

He thought, I never regretted a moment of my days, though I had to wash a lot of tears away, for I lived, as I learned how to do. The Great Spirit showed me through the times and the troubles we all have to transcend to find the life that is a friend on the other side.

With that he hung his head and simply died.

CHAPTER 51

Morning Glory stood on a cliff, looking over the horizon. As her thoughts came back to her, she realized there was a tear in her eye. Her hand had been reaching out.

There was a quiet, misty haze over the valley as she looked beyond. It was the haze of another dimension, another time. She stood in its doorway, one foot in, one foot out, wondering which way to go today.

Poised on the rock cliff, head held high, hands down at her side, she listened to the message in the breeze. Glory's heart began to beat to a different drum, one that seemed to come from the Central Sun. It pounded like a herd of thundering buffalo, faster, faster, until she could hardly breathe.

Below her, at the base of the cliff, was a mirrored pool. While she gazed into the pool, her image became translucent. She turned around to look one last time at the few remaining People of her beloved tribe. They started to fade from view as a brilliant light overtook her.

Her hands reached up over her head as she dove into her reflection. She floated through eternal time, as if she had fallen through an open door.

Tunnels of light zipped past her, colors swirled around, as she became eternal again. When she reached a point where everything was of a golden hue, she stopped traveling. Her heart quickened as she saw the face of the one she loved.

Dancing Eagle stood before her. They joined hands and became one, carrying each other's heart toward the Sun. They had finally come together again as they had promised.

Spirits of the Eagle Clan were left behind by the Glory of the

Morning to watch over the land and the treasures she left for another time.

There they stay to this very day, walking in and out of dimensional doorways, waiting for her return to finish up what they have to do.

The story has never ended. Glory's surviving sons traveled across the land, each marrying and producing their own offspring, to implant in the bloodlines the memory of what is to be.

Two of the boys took hundreds of people across the lands in wagon trains to sacred areas. They healed. They led. They showed spirit.

The oldest boy had sailed the seas in search of all eternity, bringing artifacts to and fro. He navigated his ship by the Morning Star.

This chain of events took place one hundred forty-four years ago. It takes the human emotion one hundred forty-four years of light to reconstruct itself to a new form of thought. Light is love, and one hundred forty-four years is the cycle. It is the return of the being, the spirit's quest.

EPILOGUE

Oftentimes it is difficult to truly put things on paper that are of the heart. My heart pounds with the love of the People. Through the centuries, the blood of the Ancient Ones has fed the veins of the Earth. Mother Earth's veins are now beating at a faster rate, beating to a rhythm that calls many of us home.

Native Americans have long been aware that Montezuma's Well in central Arizona is a place of emergence. At the time of emergence, the People went in different directions. They were the ancient Medicine Wheel People. Having settled in different lands and having different ancestries, they are the Rainbow Warriors.

When they emerged, they had to leave behind many of their tools so they would not be misused during troubled times. They knew that someday they would have to return to this place. Through many incarnations, they had forgotten where they came from and who they truly are.

Before the groups took off in different directions across the land, each group had at least one person who was in charge of regathering them. Encoded within their DNA was a sign, a signal, of when it was time to remember, of when it was time to prepare to go back to their true home.

This book is one of the signals that it is time. I am one of the People in charge of alerting a specific soul group that now is the time to start remembering.

Each soul group will resonate back to certain areas of the world, to the places from which they emerged. The ones who resonate to Montezuma's Well and to the Four Corners area will be the ones who resonate to *The Legend of the Eagle Clan.*

Montezuma's Well and Montezuma's Castle have long been

overlooked, as they were meant to be. At one time the area was among the most sacred spots on the planet. It has remained relatively undisturbed, as it is a protected area, protected first by the spirits and now, interestingly enough, by the government, all in proper order.

The signs that the time is now have been distinctly given. The Condor of the south has flown with the Eagle of the north. Russia has changed its symbol from the Hammer and Sickle to the Eagle. On August 20, 1994, Janesville, Wisconsin was blessed with the birth of a white female buffalo calf named Miracle.

All of us at some point in time must return to our place of origin. Like the salmon, we must return to our run to find our way home.

Traditionally, Native Americans pass their legends on orally. That is how they preserve their culture and history. However, the Eagle Clan was annihilated. There was no one left to pass it on. Now it is being remembered, for the spirits have returned one last time to tell their story.

When the Eagle gives out its call, a sound will be heard. The sky will turn a purple hue. Those who have kept their spirits pure will again be able to hear the Eagle upon its return. They will know it is time to go home.

Listen for the call!

IT IS WRITTEN IN THE WIND

BOOK MARKET ORDER FORM

BOOKS PUBLISHED BY LIGHT TECHNOLOGY PUBLISHING

Title	Author	Price	No. Copies	Total
ACUPRESSURE FOR SOUL	*Fallon*	$11.95		$
ALIEN PRESENCE	*Ananda*	$19.95		$
BEHOLD A PALE HORSE	*Cooper*	$25.00		$
CHANNELLING: Evolutionary Exercises	*Vywamus/Burns*	$9.95		$
COLOR MEDICINE	*Klotsche*	$11.95		$
COMPLETE ASCENSION MANUAL	*Stone*	$14.95		$
I AM VICTORY	*Busse*	$10.95		$
EXPLORER RACE	*Shapiro*	$24.95		$
FOREVER YOUNG	*Clark*	$9.95		$
GOLDEN PATH	*Ryden*	$11.95		$
LIVING RAINBOWS	*Bain*	$14.95		$
MAHATMA I & II	*Grattan*	$19.95		$
NEW AGE PRIMER		$11.95		$
PRINCIPLES TO REMEMBER	*Maile*	$11.95		$
PRISONERS OF EARTH	*Starr*	$11.95		$
SHINING THE LIGHT		$12.95		$
SEDONA VORTEX GUIDE BOOK		$14.95		$
SHADOW OF S.F. PEAKS	*Bader*	$9.95		$
SOUL REMEMBERS	*Warter*	$12.00		$
SOULS, EVOLUTION and the FATHER	*Fanning*	$12.95		$
STORY OF THE PEOPLE	*Rota*	$11.95		$
THIS WORLD AND NEXT ONE	*"Aiello"*	$9.95		$
Wesley H. Bateman				
RODS OF AMON RA–I		$49.95		$
DRAGONS AND CHARIOTS		$9.95		$
KNOWLEDGE from the STARS		$11.95		$
Lynn Buess				
CHILDREN OF LIGHT . . .		$8.95		$
NUMEROLOGY: Nuances		$12.65		$
NUMEROLOGY for the NEW AGE		$9.85		$
Dorothy Roeder				
CRYSTAL CO-CREATORS		$14.95		$
NEXT DIMENSION IS LOVE		$11.95		$
REACH FOR US		$13.00		$
Vywamus/Janet Mcclure				
AHA! THE REALIZATION BOOK		$11.95		$
LIGHT TECHNIQUES		$11.95		$
SANAT KUMARA		$11.95		$
SCOPES OF DIMENSIONS		$11.95		$
THE SOURCE ADVENTURE		$11.95		$

BOOKS PRINTED OR MARKETED BY LIGHT TECHNOLOGY PUBLISHING

Title	Author	Price	No. Copies	Total
ASCENSION HANDBOOK	*Stubbs*	$11.95		$
DEDICATED TO SOUL	*Vosacek*	$9.95		$
E.T. 101 INSTRUCTION MANUAL	*Mission Control/Luppi*	$12.95		$
EXPLORING LIFE'S . . .	*Harder*	$15.95		$
HOOPS ACROSS AMERICA	*Sarki*	$12.95		$
"I'M OK . . ."	*Golden Star Alliance*	$6.00		$
LIFE ON CUTTING EDGE	*Rachelle*	$14.95		$
OUR COSMIC ANCESTORS	*Chatelaine*	$9.95		$
OUT OF BODY EXPLORATION	*Mulvin*	$8.95		$
REIKI	*Mitchell*	$14.95		$
SOUL RECOVERY/EXTRACTION	*Waya*	$9.95		$
TALKS WITH JONATHON	*Miller*	$14.95		$
TAPESTRY OF LIGHT	*Drew*	$11.95		$
THE ARMSTRONG REPORT	*Armstrong*	$11.95		$
Elwood Babbitt				
PERFECT HEALTH		$15.95		$
VOICES OF SPIRIT		$13.00		$
Richard Dannelley				
SEDONA POWER SPOT/GUIDE		$9.95		$
SEDONA UFO CONNECTION		$11.95		$
Tom Dongo: Mysteries of Sedona				
MYSTERIES OF SEDONA—Book I		$6.95		$
ALIEN TIDE—Book II		$7.95		$
QUEST—Book III		$8.95		$
UNSEEN BEINGS . . .		$9.95		$
Preston B. Nichols with Peter Moon				
MONTAUK PROJECT		$15.95		$
MONTAUK REVISITED		$19.95		$
Lyssa Royal and Keith Priest				
PREPARING FOR CONTACT		$12.95		$
PRISM OF LYRA		$11.95		$
VISITORS FROM WITHIN		$12.95		$

ASCENSION MEDITATION TAPES

Title	Set	Price	No. Copies	Total
Vywamus/Barbara Burns				
THE QUANTUM MECHANICAL YOU	(Set of 4)	$40.00		
Brian Grattan				
EASTER SEMINAR RESURRECTION—1994	(Set of 7)	$59.95		
YHWH/Arthur Fanning				
ON BECOMING		$10.00		
HEALING MEDITATIONS/ KNOWING SELF		$10.00		
MANIFESTATION & ALIGNMENT WITH POLES		$10.00		

BOOKSTORE DISCOUNTS HONORED

SEND ☐ CHECK OR ☐ MONEY ORDER
(U.S. FUNDS ONLY) PAYABLE TO:
LIGHT TECHNOLOGY PUBLISHING
P.O. BOX 1526 • SEDONA • AZ 86339
(602) 282-6523 FAX: (602) 282-4130

NAME/COMPANY ____________________

ADDRESS ____________________

CITY/STATE/ZIP ____________________

PHONE ____________ CONTACT ____________

SUBTOTAL: $ ______

SALES TAX: $ ______
(7.5% – AZ residents only)

SHIPPING/HANDLING: $ ______
($3 Min.; 10% of orders over $30)

CANADA S/H: $ ______
(20% of order)

TOTAL AMOUNT ENCLOSED: $ ______

All prices in US$. Higher in Canada and Europe.

CANADA: Cherev Canada, Inc. 1(800) 263-2408 FAX (519) 986-3103 • ENGLAND/EUROPE: Windrush Press Ltd. 0608 652012/652025 FAX 0608